CW00347501

AUSTIN - HEAL

MK. 2 and MK. 3
SERIES BJ7 and BJ8
MECHANICAL AND BODY
SERVICE PARTS LIST

	Commencing Car No.	Finishing Car No.
BJ7 Mk. 2	17551	25314
BJ8 Mk. 3	25315	43026

	Commencing Engine No.	Finishing Engine No.
BJ7 Mk. 2	29F/101	29F/6188
	29FF/101	29FF/164
BJ8 Mk. 3	29K/101	29K/17636
	29KF/101	29KF/223
	29KFA/224	29KFA/399

	Commencing Body No.	Finishing Body No.
BJ7 Mk. 2	17424	70760
BJ8 Mk. 3	70761	87903

PUBLICATION NO. AKD 3523 ISSUE 6 AND AKD 3524 ISSUE 5

British Leyland Motor Corporation Limited
BMC Service division
C O W L E Y · O X F O R D · E N G L A N D

Telephone	-	-	-	-	-	-	-	-	Oxford 78941
Telegrams	-	-	-	-	-	-	BMCSERV. Telex. Oxford
Telex	-	-	-	-	-	-	BMCSERV. Oxford 83145/6/7
Cables	-	-	-	-	BMCSERV. Telex. Oxford. England
Codes	-	-	-	-	Bentley's, Bentley's Second Phrase, A.B.C.
				(5th and 6th Editions), Western Union and Private

Austin-Healey 3000 Convertible

Identification Data

AUSTIN HEALEY 3000   **Mechanical Service Parts List AKD 3523**

Model	Car No. Prefix	Commencing		Finishing	
		Car No.	Engine No.	Car No.	Engine No.
Austin-Healey 3000 (Mark II)	BJ7	17551	29F/101 29FF/101	25314	29F/6188 29FF/164
Austin-Healey 3000 (Mark III)	BJ8	25315	29K/101 29KF/101 29KFA/224	43026	29K/17636 29KF/223 29KFA/399

Identification Data

AUSTIN HEALEY 3000   **Body Service Parts List AKD 3524**

MODEL		COMMENCING	FINISHING
Mark II (Series BJ7)	ENGINE No.	29F-101 29FF-101	29F-6188 29FF-164
	CAR No.	H-BJ7-17551	H-BJ7-25314
	BODY No.	17424	70760
Mark III (Series BJ8)	ENGINE No.	29K-101 29KF-101 29KFA-224	29K-17636 29KF-223 29KFA-399
	CAR No.	H-BJ8-25315	H-BJ8-43026
	BODY No.	70761	87903

CONTENTS

●EXPLANATORY

● The range of parts in this List covers all serviceable components on model/models to the standard specification. Where the part is confined to one specification this is clearly defined in the Description or Remarks column, and where the part listed is not serviced, this is indicated by the letters NSP in the Part No. column.

● This List is provided with a Group Index on the title-page, and also more detailed indexes at the beginning of each separate Section. Additionally, a Part Number Index is provided in the preface pages.

● The Part Number Index will be issued twice yearly.

● Items comprising an assembly (or sub-assembly) are inset for easy reference. This principle is followed in all Parts Lists, typical examples being given below.

Examples :

| Crankshaft | AMK 2254 |
| Plug | AMK 97 |

Panel assembly—rear lower	CZA 418
Angle—attachment—rear bumper	CZA 147
Bracket—rear bumper support	CZA 164

● The word 'Quantity' as shown in the heading of all text pages is intended to convey that all figures appearing in that column are quantities used on a particular application and not quantities used per vehicle.

● The assemblies and components in the plate illustrations are identified by numbers which correspond with the illustration references appearing on the facing text page in the column immediately following the Part Number. Note the use of squares, rectangles, and circles on the Illustration Plates. The square/rectangle indicates an assembly which comprises all component parts shown enclosed. The components can, in turn, be supplied separately providing Illustration Numbers are shown against them. A circle embracing certain components is used to give a magnified view of the items which are too small to show up in detail if illustrated on the same scale as the other parts on the plate.

● It is essential first to identify the part against the illustration in the appropriate Section of the List, and then make use of the illustration reference number to locate the correct Part Number and official description on the adjacent page, taking into account Engine, Car, and Commission Numbers, etc.

● ABBREVIATIONS: Standard abbreviations are employed. The complete range of abbreviations covering all lists is given below.

A	Ambulance	I.P.T.O.	Independent Power Take-off	(RA)	Rear axle number
A/R	As required	J	Convertible	RH	Right-hand
(B)	Body number	K	Truck	RHD	Right-hand drive
(BP)	Belt pulley number	KPH	Kilometres per hour	RHT	Right-hand thread
B.R.S.	British Road Services	L	Hire Car	(RP)	Rear pulley number
C	Chassis number	LC	Low compression	S	4-door Saloon
(C)	Car number	LH	Left-hand	(S)	Super de-luxe
(CB)	Cab number	LHD	Left-hand drive	ST	Soft Top
(CN)	Commission number	LHT	Left-hand thread	STD	Standard
CP	Chrome-plated	LWB	Long wheelbase	SWB	Short wheelbase
D	Coupé	M	Limousine	2S	2-door Saloon
(D)	De-luxe	MB	Minibus/Omnicoach	T	4-seater Tourer
DC	Double-coil	MPH	Miles per hour	T.I.B.	Technical Information
D/E	Double-ended	N	2-seater Tourer		Bulletin
dia	Diameter	No.	Number	U	Pick-up
E	G.P.O. Engineering	NSP	Non-serviceable part	UK	Gt. Britain and Northern
(E)	Engine number	OD	Outside diameter		Ireland
EXP	Export	(OD)	Overdrive number	U/S	Undersize
(FA)	Front axle number	O/S	Oversize	V	Van
G	G.P.O. Postal	P	Hard Top	W	Dual-purpose (wood
(G)	Gearbox number	pr	Pair		framing)
GP	General Purpose Carrier	psi	Pounds/square inch	WB	Wheelbase
H	Hearse	PSV	Public Service Vehicle	Ws	Dual-purpose (all-metal)
HC	High compression	P.T.O.	Power Take-off	W.S.E.	When stock exhausted
(HU)	Hydraulic unit number	Q	Chassis and Cab	X	Taxi
ID	Inside diameter	R	Chassis and Scuttle		

●EXPLANATORY—*continued*

● Amendments to this List will be effected by means of revised pages. Should it be necessary to add an additional page or pages to interrupt the existing sequence of page numbers, the added pages will be numbered as in the following examples, which illustrate what would happen if it became necessary (A) to extend the information on a text page beyond the limits of that page or (B) to add an illustration page between existing illustration pages. Use of the decimal notation avoids the necessity of re-numbering and reprinting all pages in any section after the newly introduced page.

Example (A)

Existing text pages	...	...	...	... BA 5, BA 6, BA 7, etc.
Added text pages	...	...	...	... BA 5·1, BA 5·2, BA 5·3
Page sequence will then read		...	...	... BA 5, BA 5·1, BA 5·2, BA 5·3, BA 6, etc.

Example (B)

Existing plates ...	...	...	...	... A 5, A 6, A 7, etc.
Added plates ...	...	...	...	... A 5·1, A 5·2, A 5·3
Plate sequence will then read		...	...	... A 5, A 5·1, A 5·2, A 5·3, A 6, etc.

● Each circulation of revised pages will be issued under a cover page. This cover page will always appear as the first page and will, in addition to indicating the circulation number, show all part numbers with their page reference that are new and additional to this list.

● Where information on a page has been revised this is shown by the inclusion of a dagger †, indicating what has been revised at that time.

● As revised pages are issued a complete index showing all the pages/plates, with their latest issue, now comprising this Service Parts List will be added to the list and reprinted with each circulation of revised pages.

● **Claims under Warranty**

Claims for the replacement of material or parts under Warranty must always be submitted to the supplying Distributor or Dealer, or when this is not possible to the nearest Distributor or Dealer, informing them of the vendor's name and address.

Power Unit Identification
Serial Number Prefix Code

The engine number prefix comprises a series of letters and numbers, presenting in code the cubic capacity and make, the ancillaries fitted, and the type of compression.

1st PREFIX GROUP—Cubic capacity, make, and type

1st Prefix number: 29—2900 cc
1st Prefix letter: F—Variation of engine type
2nd Prefix letter: F—Variation for France
3rd Prefix letter: A—Variation for France (2900 cc)

2nd PREFIX GROUP—Gearbox and ancillaries

R—Overdrive (Laycock)
U—Centre gear change gearbox

3rd GROUP—Compression and serial number

H—High compression and serial number of unit

CODE EXAMPLE

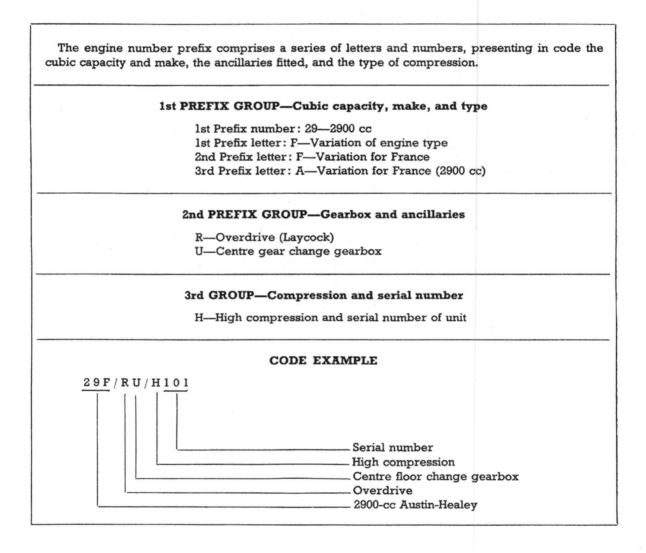

29F/RU/H101

— Serial number
— High compression
— Centre floor change gearbox
— Overdrive
— 2900-cc Austin-Healey

Always quote these prefixes with Engine Serial Numbers

Vehicle Identification
Serial Number Prefix Letter Code

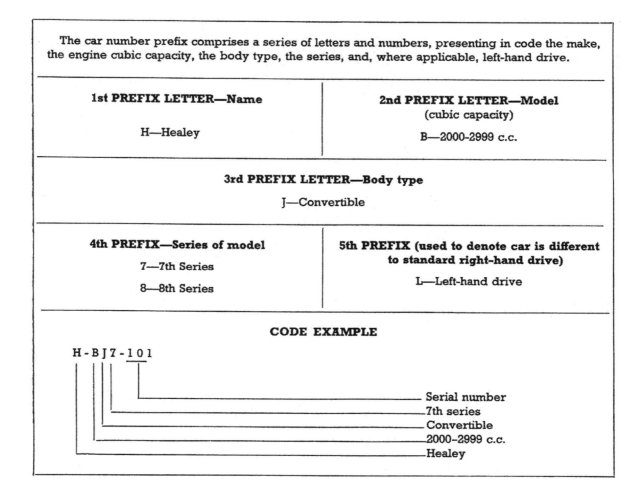

The car number prefix comprises a series of letters and numbers, presenting in code the make, the engine cubic capacity, the body type, the series, and, where applicable, left-hand drive.

1st PREFIX LETTER—Name	2nd PREFIX LETTER—Model (cubic capacity)
H—Healey	B—2000-2999 c.c.

3rd PREFIX LETTER—Body type

J—Convertible

4th PREFIX—Series of model	5th PREFIX (used to denote car is different to standard right-hand drive)
7—7th Series	L—Left-hand drive
8—8th Series	

CODE EXAMPLE

H - B J 7 - 1 0 1

—————— Serial number
—————— 7th series
—————— Convertible
—————— 2000-2999 c.c.
—————— Healey

Always quote these prefixes with Car Number

Location of Unit Numbers

The **Car Number** (A) and the **Body Number** (B) are stamped on plates secured to the right-hand side of the dash panel

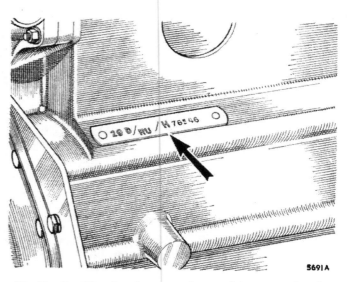

The **Engine Number** is stamped on a plate secured to the front left-hand side of the cylinder block

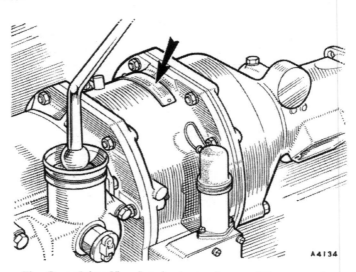

The **Overdrive Number** is stamped on a plate secured to the top of the unit

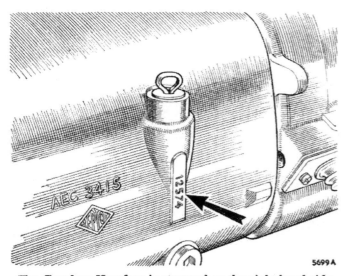

The **Gearbox Number** is stamped on the right-hand side of the gearbox casing

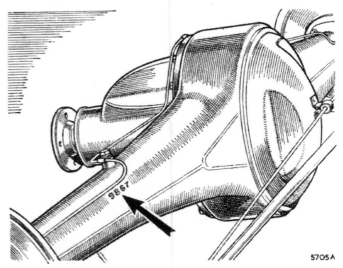

The **Rear Axle Number** is stamped on the rear left-hand side of the axle

AUSTIN-HEALEY

MK. 2 and MK. 3
SERIES BJ7 and BJ8
MECHANICAL
SERVICE PARTS LIST
AKD 3523

CONTENTS

Identification Data

AUSTIN HEALEY 3000

Mechanical Service Parts List AKD 3523

Model	Car No. Prefix	Commencing		Finishing	
		Car No.	Engine No.	Car No.	Engine No.
Austin-Healey 3000 (Mark II)	BJ7	17551	29F/101 29FF/101	25314	29F/6188 29FF/164
Austin-Healey 3000 (Mark III)	BJ8	25315	29K/101 29KF/101 29KFA/224	43026	29K/17636 29KF/223 29KFA/399

Part Number Index

The following is a complete index of parts in this List, giving the page reference of each part number

Part Number	Page	Part Number	Page	Part Number	Page	Part Number	Page	Part Number	Page
1A 1829	MA 20	ACB 9274	MK 5	AEC 162	MA 7	AEC 682	MA 12	AEC 1332	MA 14
1A 1880	MN 3	ACB 9407	MA 16	AEC 183	MA 6	AEC 685	MA 12	AEC 1337 03	MA 2
1A 2104	MA 15	ACB 9425	MJ 2·1	AEC 191	MA 5	AEC 686	MA 12	AEC 1337 06	MA 2
1A 3073	MA 12	ACB 9427	MJ 2·1	AEC 202	MA 6·1	AEC 687	MA 12	AEC 1337 13	MA 2
1A 3073	MF 1·1	ACB 9428	MJ 2·1	AEC 202	MA 14	AEC 689	MA 6·1	AEC 1337 16	MA 2
1A 3073	MF 7			AEC 203	MA 9	AEC 698	MA 9	AEC 1337 23	MA 2
1A 4744	MK 1·1	ACC 5062	MA 21	AEC 205	MA 9	AEC 698	MA 14	AEC 1337 26	MA 2
1A 4744	MK 6	ACC 5137	MA 14	AEC 205	MA 14	AEC 699	MA 9	AEC 1337 33	MA 2
1A 4745	MK 1·1	ACC 5137	MA 17	AEC 216	MA 11	AEC 699	MA 14	AEC 1337 36	MA 2
1A 4745	MK 6	ACC 5137	MA 18	AEC 216	MA 14	AEC 701	MA 12	AEC 1337 43	MA 2
1A 4746	MK 1·1			AEC 223	MA 9	AEC 702	MD 3	AEC 1337 46	MA 2
1A 4746	MK 6	ACG 5002	MH 5	AEC 224	MA 9	AEC 703	MD 3	AEC 1341	MA 9
1A 4751	MK 1·1			AEC 238	MA 12	AEC 724	MA 7	AEC 1353	MA 1·1
1A 4751	MK 6	ACH 5854	MD 1·1	AEC 242	MA 12	AEC 731	MA 14	AEC 1377	MA 15
1A 4752	MK 1·1	ACH 8979	MO 1·1	AEC 243	MA 12	AEC 731	MA 15	AEC 1378	MA 15
1A 4752	MK 6	ACH 9041	MB 2	AEC 244	MA 12	AEC 736	MA 7	AEC 1489	MA 1·1
1A 4753	MK 1·1	ACH 9042	MA 21	AEC 245	MA 7	AEC 744	MA 4	AEC 1490	MA 1·1
1A 4753	MK 6			AEC 0245 10	MA 7	AEC 745	MA 4	AEC 2008	MA 7
1A 4754	MK 1·1	ADA 2657	MN 12	AEC 247	MA 5	AEC 746	MA 4	AEC 2018	MA 11
1A 4754	MK 6			AEC 264	MA 6	AEC 747	MA 4	AEC 2020	MA 11
1A 4756	MK 1·1	ADB 826	MN 10	AEC 0264 10	MA 6	AEC 748	MA 4	AEC 2021	MA 11
1A 4760	MK 1·1			AEC 0264 20	MA 6	AEC 749	MA 4	AEC 2026	MA 4
1A 4785	MK 5	ADC 560	MN 10	AEC 265	MA 6	AEC 787	MA 6·1	AEC 2029	MA 5
1A 4788	MK 1·1			AEC 266	MA 8	AEC 796	MA 12	AEC 2030	MA 5
1A 9209	MA 16	ADP 210	MA 8	AEC 278	MA 4	AEC 810	MA 5	AEC 2032	MA 5
1A 9211	MA 16	ADP 210	MA 15	AEC 279	MA 4	AEC 829	MA 5	AEC 2033	MA 5
1A 9222	MH 4			AEC 283	MA 9	AEC 853	MA 1·1	AEC 2033	MA 14
1A 9223	MH 4	AEA 420	MA 6	AEC 284	MA 9	AEC 865	MA 5	AEC 2037	MA 6
				AEC 290	MA 6	AEC 871	MA 15	AEC 2040	MA 4
2A 263	MA 12	AEB 3105	MF 2	AEC 293	MA 12	AEC 872	MA 1·1	AEC 2041	MA 8
2A 504	MD 1·1	AEB 3105	MF 5	AEC 313	MA 6	AEC 875	MA 7	AEC 2044	MA 7
2A 700	MA 10	AEB 3111	MF 2	AEC 313	MA 14	AEC 875	MA 14	AEC 2075	MA 21
2A 770	MA 6·1	AEB 3111	MF 5	AEC 315	MA 9	AEC 876	MA 1·1	AEC 2078	MA 12
2A 778	MA 11	AEB 3111	MF 8	AEC 315	MA 14	AEC 876	MA 7	AEC 2079	MA 12
2A 2088	MD 1·1	AEB 3111	MF 11	AEC 328	MA 4	AEC 879	MA 3·1	AEC 2091	MA 21
2A 3254	MF 3	AEB 3112	MF 2	AEC 332	MA 4	AEC 882	MA 4	AEC 2097	MA 4
2A 3254	MF 9	AEB 3112	MF 5	AEC 333	MA 4	AEC 885	MA 6	AEC 2127	MA 21
2A 3602	MF 7	AEB 3115	MF 2	AEC 339	MA 5	AEC 888	MA 9	AEC 2133	MD 1·1
2A 3602	MF 10	AEB 3115	MF 5	AEC 339	MA 14	AEC 888	MA 14	AEC 2163	MA 6·1
2A 4144	MK 2	AEB 3115	MF 8	AEC 340	MA 5	AEC 889	MA 16	AEC 2178	MA 8
2A 5006	MH 4	AEB 3115	MF 11	AEC 341	MA 1·1	AEC 890	MA 16	AEC 2179	MA 8
2A 5176	MH 5	AEB 3124	MF 2	AEC 343	MA 1·1	AEC 903	MA 3	AEC 2181	MA 8
2A 5304	MM 4	AEB 3124	MF 5	AEC 346	MA 7	AEC 0903 10	MA 3	AEC 2184	MA 12
2A 5346	MM 2·1	AEB 3124	MF 8	AEC 348	MA 6	AEC 0903 20	MA 3	AEC 2193 03	MA 2
2A 5393	MH 4	AEB 3124	MF 11	AEC 349	MA 6	AEC 0903 30	MA 3	AEC 2193 06	MA 2
2A 7142	MH 1·1	AEB 3130	MF 3	AEC 350	MA 15	AEC 0903 40	MA 3	AEC 2193 13	MA 2
2A 7142	MH 1·1	AEB 3130	MF 6	AEC 375	MD 3	AEC 905	MA 3·1	AEC 2193 16	MA 2
2A 7227	MM 2·1	AEB 3130	MF 9	AEC 385	MF 1·1	AEC 906	MA 3	AEC 2193 23	MA 2
2A 9013	MN 8·1	AEB 3130	MF 12	AEC 385	MF 7	AEC 0906 10	MA 3	AEC 2193 26	MA 2
2A 9013	MN 8·4	AEB 3162	MF 2	AEC 398	MA 1·1	AEC 0906 20	MA 3	AEC 2193 33	MA 2
		AEB 3162	MF 8	AEC 435	MA 6·1	AEC 0906 30	MA 3	AEC 2193 36	MA 2
12A 24	MA 6·1	AEB 3163	MF 2	AEC 440	MD 3	AEC 0906 40	MA 3	AEC 2193 43	MA 2
12A 1139	MA 6·1	AEB 3163	MF 8	AEC 441	MD 3	AEC 907	MA 3	AEC 2193 46	MA 2
12A 1139	MA 14	AEB 3202	MF 3	AEC 448	MA 6	AEC 0907 10	MA 3	AEC 2195	MA 3
12A 1170	MA 6·1	AEB 3202	MF 9	AEC 449	MA 15	AEC 0907 20	MA 3	AEC 2195 10	MA 3
12A 1175	MA 6·1	AEB 3203	MF 2	AEC 450	MA 15	AEC 0907 30	MA 3	AEC 2195 20	MA 3
12A 1176	MA 6·1	AEB 3203	MF 5	AEC 461	MA 6	AEC 0907 40	MA 3	AEC 2195 30	MA 3
12A 1177	MA 6·1	AEB 3204	MF 2	AEC 463	MA 7	AEC 908	MA 3	AEC 2195 40	MA 3
12A 1205	MA 12	AEB 3204	MF 5	AEC 474	MA 6·1	AEC 0908 10	MA 3	AEC 2196	MA 3
		AEB 3212	MF 2	AEC 478	MA 6·1	AEC 0908 20	MA 3	AEC 2196 10	MA 3
22A 75	MF 3	AEB 3212	MF 5	AEC 479	MA 15	AEC 0908 30	MA 3	AEC 2196 20	MA 3
22A 75	MF 6			AEC 479	MF 1·1	AEC 0908 40	MA 3	AEC 2196 30	MA 3
22A 75	MF 9	AEC 27	MA 7	AEC 479	MF 4	AEC 910	MA 12	AEC 2196 40	MA 3
22A 75	MF 12	AEC 28	MA 4	AEC 479	MF 7	AEC 915	MA 7	AEC 2197	MA 3
22A 136	MA 12	AEC 47	MA 4	AEC 479	MF 10	AEC 928	MA 9	AEC 2197 10	MA 3
		AEC 76	MA 13	AEC 482	MA 5	AEC 929	MA 9	AEC 2197 20	MA 3
AAA 1891	MN 13	AEC 87	MA 7	AEC 491	MA 7	AEC 930	MA 9	AEC 2197 30	MA 3
AAA 4258	MR 2	AEC 108	MA 9	AEC 496	MB 2	AEC 932	MA 13	AEC 2197 40	MA 3
AAA 5981	MB 3	AEC 108	MA 14	AEC 604	MA 1·1	AEC 950	MA 14	AEC 3072	MF 2
		AEC 110	MA 1·1	AEC 616	MA 7	AEC 950	MA 15	AEC 3072	MF 5
ACA 5000	MH 5	AEC 128	MA 6·1	AEC 621	MA 6	AEC 962	MA 7	AEC 3088	MF 1·1
ACA 5216	MR 2	AEC 128	MA 14	AEC 667	MA 9	AEC 981	MD 1·1	AEC 3088	MF 4
ACA 5297	MJ 1·1	AEC 135	MA 7	AEC 671	MA 9	AEC 982	MD 1·1	AEC 3088	MF 7
ACA 5297	MJ 2	AEC 0135 10	MA 7	AEC 672	MA 1·1	AEC 996	MA 7	AEC 3088	MF 10
ACA 5453	MA 21	AEC 139	MA 1·1	AEC 675	MA 10	AEC 1011	MA 6	AEC 3102	MF 1·1
		AEC 143	MA 7	AEC 678	MA 12	AEC 1024	MA 13	AEC 3102	MF 4
ACB 5311	MA 20	AEC 144	MA 7	AEC 679	MA 12	AEC 1025	MA 13	AEC 3102	MF 7
ACB 5311	MA 21	AEC 158	MA 8	AEC 680	MA 12	AEC 1097	MA 7	AEC 3102	MF 10
ACB 5856	MM 2	AEC 160	MA 7	AEC 681	MA 12	AEC 1332	MA 8	AEC 3105	MF 1·1

Part Number	Page	Part Number	Page	Part Number	Page	Part Number	Page	Part Number	Page	Part Number	Page
AEC 3105	MF 4	AEC 3340	MF 5	AEC 3626	MF 3	AHA 5217	MR 2	AHB 8708	MN 12
AEC 3105	MF 7	AEC 3340	MF 8	AEC 3626	MF 6	AHA 5450	MA 19	AHB 8939	ME 3
AEC 3105	MF 10	AEC 3340	MF 11	AEC 3626	MF 6	AHA 5689	MA 17	AHB 8944	MA 21
AEC 3106	MF 1·1	AEC 3342	MF 3	AEC 3626	MF 9	AHA 5689	MA 19	AHB 8946	MC 2
AEC 3106	MF 4	AEC 3342	MF 6	AEC 3626	MF 12	AHA 5690	MA 17	AHB 8949	MA 20
AEC 3106	MF 7	AEC 3342	MF 9	AEC 3636	MF 3	AHA 5690	MA 19	AHB 8950	MA 20
AEC 3106	MF 10	AEC 3342	MF 12	AEC 3636	MF 6	AHA 6173	MA 18	AHB 8970	MC 2
AEC 3112	MF 1·1	AEC 3343	MF 3	AEC 3636	MF 9	AHA 6367	MA 21	AHB 8971	MC 2
AEC 3112	MF 4	AEC 3343	MF 6	AEC 3636	MF 12	AHA 7373	MP 1·1	AHB 8975	MA 17
AEC 3112	MF 7	AEC 3343	MF 9	AEC 3649	MF 2	AHA 7374	MP 1·1	AHB 8976	MA 17
AEC 3112	MF 10	AEC 3343	MF 12	AEC 3649	MF 5	AHA 7375	MP 1·1	AHB 8983	MR 2
AEC 3115	MF 2	AEC 3393	MF 2	AEC 3654	MF 3	AHA 7376	MP 1·1	AHB 8984	MN 8·3
AEC 3115	MF 5	AEC 3393	MF 5	AEC 3654	MF 6			AHB 8985	MN 8·3
AEC 3116	MF 2	AEC 3417	MF 2	AEC 3656	MF 3	AHB 5397	MA 15	AHB 8993	MA 17
AEC 3116	MF 5	AEC 3418	MF 2	AEC 3656	MF 6	AHB 5401	MC 2	AHB 8993	MA 18
AEC 3119	MF 2	AEC 3418	MF 8	AEC 3656	MF 9	AHB 5402	MC 2	AHB 8996	MA 17
AEC 3119	MF 5	AEC 3419	MF 3	AEC 3656	MF 12	AHB 6000	MJ 2·1	AHB 9021	MA 20
AEC 3119	MF 8	AEC 3419	MF 9	AEC 3657	MF 1·1	AHB 6002	MD 3	AHB 9022	MA 20
AEC 3119	MF 11	AEC 3461	MF 1·1	AEC 3657	MF 4	AHB 6003	MD 3	AHB 9053	MN 4
AEC 3121	MF 2	AEC 3461	MF 4	AEC 3658	MF 3	AHB 6006	MA 18	AHB 9067	MM 2
AEC 3121	MF 5	AEC 3461	MF 7	AEC 3658	MF 6	AHB 6009	MA 18	AHB 9109	MM 3
AEC 3121	MF 8	AEC 3461	MF 10	AEC 3659	MF 3	AHB 6013	MA 21	AHB 9110	MM 4
AEC 3121	MF 11	AEC 3468	MF 2	AEC 3659	MF 6	AHB 6014	MA 21	AHB 9111	MM 4
AEC 3168	MF 1·1	AEC 3469	MF 2	AEC 3659	MF 9	AHB 6018	MA 21	AHB 9112	MM 4
AEC 3168	MF 4	AEC 3469	MF 5	AEC 3659	MF 12	AHB 6019	MD 3	AHB 9113	MM 4
AEC 3168	MF 7	AEC 3472	MF 2	AEC 3661	MF 13	AHB 6021	MA 21	AHB 9117	MM 3·1
AEC 3168	MF 10	AEC 3472	MF 5	AEC 3671	MF 3	AHB 6022	MA 19	AHB 9118	MM 3·1
AEC 3178	MF 2	AEC 3481	MF 2	AEC 3671	MF 6	AHB 6022	MD 10	AHB 9119	MM 3
AEC 3178	MF 5	AEC 3481	MF 5	AEC 3671	MF 9	AHB 6023	MA 19	AHB 9120	MM 4
AEC 3180	MF 2	AEC 3482	MF 2	AEC 3671	MF 12	AHB 6026	MJ 2	AHB 9126	MM 4
AEC 3180	MF 5	AEC 3482	MF 5	AEC 3679	MF 2	AHB 6027	MJ 2	AHB 9127	MM 4
AEC 3180	MF 8	AEC 3484	MF 5	AEC 3679	MF 5	AHB 6105	MA 18	AHB 9142	MN 11
AEC 3180	MF 11	AEC 3484	MF 11	AEC 3679	MF 8	AHB 6106	MA 18	AHB 9145	MN 12
AEC 3181	MF 2	AEC 3484 03	MF 5	AEC 3679	MF 11	AHB 6114	MA 21	AHB 9162	MJ 1·1
AEC 3181	MF 5	AEC 3484 03	MF 11	AEC 3681	MF 2	AHB 6126	MA 19	AHB 9163	MJ 2
AEC 3181	MF 8	AEC 3484 06	MF 5	AEC 3681	MF 5	AHB 6127	MA 19	AHB 9164	MJ 2
AEC 3181	MF 8	AEC 3484 06	MF 11	AEC 3681	MF 8	AHB 6220	MA 18	AHB 9182	MM 1·1
AEC 3181	MF 11	AEC 3485	MF 5	AEC 3681	MF 11	AHB 6223	MA 18	AHB 9183	ME 2
AEC 3182	MF 2	AEC 3485	MF 11	AEC 3693	MF 1·1	AHB 6224	MA 18	AHB 9185	MM 1·1
AEC 3182	MF 5	AEC 3486	MF 5	AEC 3683	MF 4	AHB 6225	MA 18	AHB 9188	MA 20
AEC 3183	MF 2	AEC 3487	MF 3	AEC 3683	MF 7	AHB 6226	MA 18	AHB 9190	MA 20
AEC 3183	MF 5	AEC 3487	MF 6	AEC 3683	MF 10	AHB 6228	MA 20	AHB 9204	MA 20
AEC 3184	MF 2	AEC 3487	MF 9	AEC 3689	MF 3	AHB 6413	MN 11	AHB 9378	MD 2
AEC 3184	MF 5	AEC 3487	MF 12	AEC 3689	MF 6	AHB 6414	MN 11	AHB 9383	MD 1·1
AEC 3185	MF 2	AEC 3492	MF 1·1	AEC 3689	MF 9	AHB 6415	MN 12	AHB 9386	MD 1·1
AEC 3185	MF 5	AEC 3492	MF 4	AEC 3689	MF 12	AHB 6504	MN 3	AHB 9389	MA 17
AEC 3185	MF 8	AEC 3492	MF 7			AHB 6660	MH 5	AHB 9549	MN 11
AEC 3185	MF 11	AEC 3492	MF 10	AED 159	MA 7	AHB 6696	MH 5	AHB 9551	MN 11
AEC 3186	MF 2	AEC 3520	MF 3			AHB 6698	MH 5	AHB 9609	MJ 3
AEC 3186	MF 5	AEC 3520	MF 6	AEG 3113	MF 3	AHB 6703	MH 5	AHB 9766	MD 3
AEC 3187	MF 3	AEC 3533	MF 1·1	AEG 3113	MF 6	AHB 6704	MH 5	AHB 9769	MA 20
AEC 3187	MF 6	AEC 3533	MF 4	AEG 3113	MF 9	AHB 6705	MH 5	AHB 9771	MA 21
AEC 3187	MF 9	AEC 3533	MF 7	AEG 3113	MF 12	AHB 6706	MH 5	AHB 9795	MA 20
AEC 3187	MF 12	AEC 3533	MF 10	AEG 3122	MF 3	AHB 6707	MH 5	AHB 9798	MA 21
AEC 3188	MF 3	AEC 3547	MF 1·1	AEG 3122	MF 6	AHB 6711	MA 18	AHB 9800	MA 21
AEC 3188	MF 6	AEC 3547	MF 4	AEG 3122	MF 9	AHB 6712	MM 4	AHB 9801	MA 21
AEC 3188	MF 9	AEC 3554	MF 4	AEG 3122	MF 12	AHB 6713	MM 4	AHB 9802	MA 21
AEC 3188	MF 12	AEC 3555	MF 1·1	AEG 3123	MF 3	AHB 6715	MD 1·1	AHB 9839	MA 21
AEC 3189	MF 3	AEC 3557	MF 3	AEG 3123	MF 6	AHB 6853	MA 20	AHB 9840	MA 21
AEC 3189	MF 6	AEC 3557	MF 6	AEG 3123	MF 9	AHB 6895	MO 1·1	AHB 9848	MA 21
AEC 3189	MF 9	AEC 3557	MF 9	AEG 3123	MF 12	AHB 6918	MN 11	AHB 9866	MA 20
AEC 3189	MM 12	AEC 3557	MF 12	AEG 3124	MF 3	AHB 6926	MM 2	AHB 9887	MM 4
AEC 3193	MF 2	AEC 3559	MF 1·1	AEG 3124	MF 6	AHB 7033	MN 12	AHB 9898	MA 21
AEC 3193	MF 5	AEC 3559	MF 4	AEG 3124	MF 9	AHB 7098	MA 13	AHB 9905	MA 21
AEC 3198	MF 3	AEC 3565	MF 2	AEG 3124	MF 12	AHB 7109	MA 13	AHB 9909	MD 3
AEC 3198	MF 9	AEC 3565	MF 5			AHB 7117	MN 12	AHB 9957	MA 20
AEC 3207	MF 1·1	AEC 3601	MF 1·1	AEH 592	MA 1·1	AHB 7118	MN 11	AHB 9958	MA 20
AEC 3207	MF 4	AEC 3601	MF 4			AHB 7119	MN 12	AHB 9961	MA 20
AEC 3207	MF 7	AEC 3601	MF 7	AEJ 17	ME 1·1	AHB 7120	MN 11	AHB 9963	MA 20
AEC 3207	MF 10	AEC 3601	MF 10	AEJ 20	MF 4	AHB 7120	MN 11	AHB 9965	MA 20
AEC 3208	MF 2	AEC 3605	MF 1·1	AEJ 20	MF 10	AHB 7128	MM 2	AHB 9969	MA 20
AEC 3208	MF 5	AEC 3605	MF 6	AEJ 22	MN 1·1	AHB 7129	MM 2	AHB 9974	ML 2
AEC 3208	MF 8	AEC 3605	MF 7	AEJ 25	MB 1·1	AHB 7130	MK 5	AHB 9975	ML 2
AEC 3208	MF 11	AEC 3605	MF 12	AEJ 30	ME 1·1	AHB 7136	MN 8·4	AHB 9977	MH 5
AEC 3221	MF 1·1	AEC 3620	MF 1·1	AEJ 42	MF 13	AHB 7137	MD 1·1	AHB 9978	MH 5
AEC 3221	MF 4	AEC 3623	MF 13	AEJ 51	MF 1·1	AHB 7193	MM 2	AHB 9980	MH 5
AEC 3221	MF 7	AEC 3624	MF 3	AEJ 51	MF 4	AHB 8312	MJ 2	AHB 9981	MH 5
AEC 3221	MF 10	AEC 3624	MF 6	AEJ 51	MF 7	AHB 8314	MJ 2	AHB 9982	MH 5
AEC 3298	MF 1·1	AEC 3625	MF 3	AEJ 51	MF 10	AHB 8315	MD 1·1	AHB 9983	MH 5
AEC 3298	MF 4	AEC 3625	MF 6	AEJ 52	MA 7	AHB 8385	MN 1·1	AHB 9984	MH 5
AEC 3298	MF 7	AEC 3625	MF 9			AHB 8388	MJ 1·1	AHB 9985	MH 5
AEC 3298	MF 10	AEC 3625	MF 12	AEK 113	MA 7	AHB 8389	MJ 1·1	AHB 9996	ML 2
AEC 3340	MF 2			AEK 113	MA 14	AHB 8707	MN 11		

Part Number	Page	Part Number	Page	Part Number	Page	Part Number	Page	Part Number	Page
AHH 5297	MD 1·1	ATB 7265	MK 2	AUA 575	MD 2·1	AUB 6022	MD 2·1	1B 4501	MK 5
AHH 5414	MN 10	ATB 7285	MH 2	AUA 585	MD 2	AUB 6025	MD 2	1B 4513	MK 5
AHH 5839	MR 2	ATB 7285	MK 2	AUA 585	MD 2·1	AUB 6034	MD 2	1B 4517	MK 1·1
AHH 5986	MR 2	ATB 7289	MM 4	AUA 692	MB 1·1	AUB 6034	MD 2·1	1B 4525	MK 5
AHH 5987	MR 2			AUA 692	MD 2·1	AUB 6061	MD 2·1	1B 4526	MK 5
AHH 6503	MA 20	ATC 4257	MK 2	AUA 699	MD 2	AUB 6062	MD 2·1	1B 4527	MK 2
AHH 6866	MM 4	ATC 7060	MH 2	AUA 699	MD 2·1	AUB 6071	MD 2	1B 4528	MK 2
AHH 7078	MH 5	ATC 7061	MH 1·1	AUA 869	MD 2	AUB 6080	MD 2·1	1B 4529	MK 2
AHH 7315	MP 1·1	ATC 7062	MH 1·1	AUA 869	MD 2·1	AUB 6080	MD 2·1	1B 5329	MM 5
AHH 7316	MP 1·1	ATC 7071	MG 1	AUA 878	MD 2	AUB 6097	MD 2	1B 6127	MJ 3
AHH 7317	MP 1·1	ATC 7071	MH 3	AUA 878	MD 2·1	AUB 6097	MD 2·1	1B 6137	MJ 3
AHH 7318	MP 1·1	ATC 7083	MH 1·1	AUA 1433	MD 2			1B 6138	MJ 3
AHH 8001	MP 1·1	ATC 7084	MH 1·1	AUA 1433	MD 2·1	AUC 1833	MD 1·1	1B 6195	MJ 3
		ATC 7085	MH 2	AUA 1435	MD 2	AUC 1833	MD 2	1B 6199	MJ 3
AJA 11	MB 3	ATC 7089	MH 2	AUA 1435	MD 2·1	AUC 2141	MD 1·1	1B 6214	MJ 2·1
AJA 5081	MN 5	ATC 7091	MH 2	AUA 1453	MD 2	AUC 2141	MD 2	1B 6226	MN 9
AJA 5081	MN 6	ATC 7092	MH 1·1	AUA 1455	MD 2	AUC 2588	MD 2·1	1B 6256	MJ 3
AJA 5081	MN 7	ATC 7093	MH 1·1	AUA 1455	MD 2·1	AUC 2698	MD 1·1	1B 6257	MJ 1·1
AJA 5081	MN 7·1	ATC 7094	MH 1·1	AUA 1456	MD 2	AUC 2698	MD 2	1B 6257	MJ 2
AJA 5081	MN 7·2	ATC 7095	MH 1·1	AUA 1456	MD 2·1	AUC 4454	MA 21	1B 6257	MJ 3
AJA 5081	MN 7·3	ATC 7096	MH 1·1	AUA 1459	MD 2			1B 6258	MJ 3
		ATC 7097	MH 1·1	AUA 1459	MD 2·1	AUE 38	MD 2	1B 6277	MJ 1·1
AJC 5011	MA 10	ATC 7098	MH 1·1	AUA 1466	MD 2			1B 6277	MJ 3
AJC 5033	MA 5	ATC 7099	MH 1·1	AUA 1468	MD 2	AUF 301	MD 2·1	1B 6278	MJ 1·1
AJC 5095	MB 1·1	ATC 7700	MF 1·1	AUA 1468	MD 2·1			1B 6278	MJ 3
AJC 5116	MN 8·3	ATC 7100	MF 7	AUA 1500	MD 2	AWZ 109	MA 20	1B 6281	MJ 3
AJC 5159	MA 4	ATC 7100	MH 2	AUA 1661	MD 2			1B 6282	MJ 3
AJC 5159 10	MA 4	ATC 7101	MH 2	AUA 1661	MD 2·1	AYH 4040	MK 2	1B 6286	MJ 3
AJC 5159 20	MA 4	ATC 7104	MH 1·1	AUA 1662	MD 2			1B 6287	MJ 3
AJC 5159 30	MA 4	ATC 7106	MH 1·1	AUA 1662	MD 2·1	1B 1033	MA 4	1B 6299	MJ 3
AJC 5159 40	MA 4	ATC 7107	MH 1·1	AUA 1863	MD 2	1B 1219	MA 5	1B 6300	MJ 2·1
AJC 6042	MA 1·1	ATC 7108	MH 1·1	AUA 1863	MD 2·1	1B 1233	MA 10	1B 6301	MJ 2·1
		ATC 7109	MH 1·1	AUA 4083	MD 2	1B 1233	MA 14	1B 6303	MN 9
AJD 1042	MD 2·1	ATC 7111	MH 1·1	AUA 4611	MD 2	1B 1314	MA 16	1B 6340	MJ 3
AJD 1252 Z	MN 2	ATC 7112	MH 1·1	AUA 4645	MD 2	1B 1315	MA 16	1B 7354	MK 5
AJD 1703 N	MN 3	ATC 7113	MH 1·1	AUA 4646	MD 2	1B 1714	MA 6	1B 7355	MK 5
AJD 3202 Z	MN 10	ATC 7114	MH 1·1	AUA 4647	MD 2	1B 2178	MA 12	1B 7356	MK 5
AJD 6257 Z	MN 9	ATC 7115	MH 1·1	AUA 5059	MD 2·1	1B 2261	MD 3	1B 7362	MM 5
AJD 8012 Z	MN 8·2	ATC 7116	MH 1·1	AUA 5060	MD 2·1	1B 2721	MN 4	1B 7366	MH 4
AJD 8012 Z	MN 8·3	ATC 7124	MH 1·1	AUA 6021	MD 2	1B 2736	MD 1·1	1B 7386	MG 2
AJD 8019 Z	MN 3	ATC 7125	MH 1·1	AUA 6021	MD 2	1B 2796	MN 12	1B 7424	MM 5
AJD 8052 C	MN 8·3	ATC 7152	MH 2	AUA 6021	MD 2·1	1B 2801	MN 12	1B 7437	MH 3
AJD 8612	MN 2	ATC 7153	MH 2	AUA 6036	MD 2	1B 2804	MN 3	1B 7438	MH 3
		ATC 7154	MH 2	AUA 6036	MD 2·1	1B 2805	MN 7·3	1B 7463	ML 2
AJG 5047	MN 9	ATC 7155	MH 2	AUA 6058	MD 2	1B 2836	MN 4	1B 7464	ML 2
		ATC 7156	MH 2			1B 2837	MN 4	1B 7470	ML 2
AJH 5079	MN 10	ATC 7157	MH 2	AUB 521	MD 2	1B 2847	MN 11	1B 7472	ML 2
AJH 5176	MO 2	ATC 7158	MH 2	AUB 521	MD 2·1	1B 3346	MF 1·1	1B 7473	ML 2
AJH 5178	MO 2	ATC 7158	MH 2	AUB 579	MD 2	1B 3346	MF 4	1B 7474	MG 2
AJH 5184	MO 1·1	ATC 7172	MH 2	AUB 581	MD 2	1B 3346	MF 7	1B 7480	MH 4
		ATC 7189	MH 1·1	AUB 582	MD 2	1B 3346	MF 10	1B 7489	MG 2
AJR 211	MB 2	ATC 7236	MH 2	AUB 593	MD 2	1B 3346	MF 14	1B 7490	MH 3
		ATC 7237	MH 2	AUB 597	MD 2·1	1B 3650	MF 5	1B 7526	MH 3
AKF 1439	MD 1·1	ATC 7251	MM 5	AUB 609	MD 2·1	1B 3655	MA 15	1B 8036	MP 1·1
AKF 1446	MP 1·1	ATC 7257	MH 2	AUB 611	MD 2·1	1B 3664	MF 8	1B 8037	MP 1·1
AKF 1447	MP 1·1	ATC 7262	MH 1·1	AUB 617	MD 2·1	1B 3668	MF 11	1B 8038	MP 1·1
AKF 1448	MP 1·1	ATC 7263	MH 1·1	AUB 618	MD 2·1	1B 3668	MF 8	1B 8039	MP 1·1
AKF 1449	MP 1·1	ATC 7266	MH 1·1	AUB 624	MD 2	1B 3669	MF 11	1B 8040	MP 1·1
AKF 1450	MP 1·1	ATC 7267	MH 1·1	AUB 625	MD 2	1B 3710	MF 3	1B 8041	MP 1·1
AKF 1451	MP 1·1	ATC 7268	MH 1·1	AUB 652	MD 2·1	1B 3710	MF 6	1B 8048	MP 1·1
		ATC 7288	MH 1·1	AUB 653	MD 2·1	1B 3710	MF 9	1B 8057	MP 1·1
ANK 3458	MN 10	ATC 7290	MH 1·1	AUB 660	MD 2·1	1B 3710	MF 12	1B 8347	MA 16
ANK 3459	MN 10	ATC 7309	MH 1·1	AUB 662	MD 2·1	1B 3736	MF 3	1B 8751	ME 2
ANK 4646	MN 3	ATC 7310	MH 1·1	AUB 675	MD 2·1	1B 3736	MF 6	1B 8751	MM 1·1
		ATC 7315	MH 1·1	AUB 676	MD 2·1	1B 3736	MF 9	1B 8817	ME 2
ARB 97	MA 18	ATC 7344	MH 2	AUB 693	MD 2·1	1B 3736	MF 12	1B 8832	MA 16
ARB 98	MA 18	ATC 7394	MH 2	AUB 694	MD 2·1	1B 3766	MF 2	1B 8896	MM 5
ARB 99	MA 19	ATC 7564	MH 1·1	AUB 695	MD 2·1	1B 3766	MF 8	1B 8926	MM 2·1
ARB 100	MA 19	ATC 7568	MH 1·1	AUB 696	MD 2·1	1B 3836	MF 3	1B 8930	MH 4
		ATC 7569	MH 2	AUB 697	MD 2·1	1B 3836	MF 6	1B 8995	MR 2
ARH 1542	MC 2	ATC 7588	MH 2	AUB 698	MD 2·1	1B 3836	MF 9	1B 8997	MR 2
ARH 1662	MC 2	ATC 7589	MH 2	AUB 702	MD 2·1	1B 3836	MF 12	1B 9030	MN 3
		ATC 7593	MH 2	AUB 703	MD 2·1	1B 4316	MK 2	1B 9031	MN 3
ATA 7043	MH 1·1	ATC 7595	MH 2	AUB 704	MD 2·1	1B 4365	MK 1·1	1B 9061	MO 1·1
ATA 7232	MH 1·1			AUB 706	MD 2	1B 4366	MK 1·1	1B 9074	MM 5
		AUA 73	MD 2	AUB 706	MD 2·1	1B 4392	MK 2	1B 9078	MN 12
ATB 4098	MK 2	AUA 504	MD 2	AUB 707	MD 2·1	1B 4400	MK 2	1B 9080	MN 12
ATB 4238	MK 2	AUA 565	MD 2	AUB 711	MD 2·1	1B 4422	MA 16	1B 9100	MN 8
ATB 4239	MK 2	AUA 565	MD 2·1	AUB 716	MD 2·1	1B 4428	MA 16	1B 9101	MN 8·2
ATB 4240	MK 2	AUA 566	MD 2	AUB 759	MD 2·1	1B 4457	MK 1·1	1B 9140	MO 2
ATB 4241	MK 2	AUA 566	MD 2·1	AUB 6003	MD 2	1B 4475	MK 1·1	1B 9141	MO 2
ATB 4242	MK 2	AUA 573	MD 2·1	AUB 6915	MD 2	1B 4476	MK 1·1		
ATB 7258	MK 1·1	AUA 574	MD 2·1	AUB 6022	MD 2	1B 4486	MK 5		

Part Number	Page	Part Number	Page	Part Number	Page	Part Number	Page	Part Number	Page	Part Number	Page
DMK 5418	MA 17	FNZ 105	MM 5	1G 9384	MA 16	8G 4194	MK 1·1	68G 277	MA 1·1	2H 10	MC 2
		FNZ 106	MA 10	1G 9516	ME 3	8G 4217	MK 1·1	68G 278	MA 1·1	2H 35	MB 3
1F 657	MA 20	FNZ 106	MA 15	1G 9529	ME 3	8G 4219	MK 1·1	68G 309	MA 1·1	2H 35	MN 13
1F 1293	MA 20	FNZ 106	MA 16	1G 9622	ME 3	8G 7070	MH 3	68G 310	MA 1·1	2H 174	MM 2·1
1F 6153	MJ 2·1	FNZ 106	MA 17	1G 9622	MM 2·1	8G 7131	MH 1·1			2H 400	MM 2·1
		FNZ 106	MF 3			8G 8249	ME 3	88G 235	MD 2	2H 731	MA 6
3F 90	MN 13	FNZ 106	MF 6	8G 507	MA 1·1	8G 8279	MK 3	88G 257	MD 1·1	2H 1082	MD 1·1
		FNZ 106	MF 9	8G 548	MN 3	8G 8280	MH 3	88G 264	MA 6	2H 2065	MN 11
FHS 0510	MF 13	FNZ 106	MF 12	8G 554	MK 2	8G 8281	MH 3	88G 275	MH 2	2H 2617	MN 11
FHS 0511	MF 13	FNZ 106	MG 2	8G 576	MB 2·1	8G 8282	MH 3	88G 275	MK 2	2H 2617	MN 12
FHS 0513	MF 15	FNZ 106	MH 1·1	8G 612	MA 8	8G 8354	ME 1·1	88G 278	MH 4	2H 2635	MN 9
FHS 2511	MD 3	FNZ 106	MH 3	8G 616	MB 3	8G 8355	ME 1·1	88G 278	MK 5	2H 2704	MN 11
FHS 2512	MD 3	FNZ 106	MH 4	8G 624	MJ 2·1	8G 8476	MK 3	88G 293	MM 5	2H 2704	MN 12
FHS 2516	MD 3	FNZ 106	MH 5	8G 637	MO 1·1	8G 8648	MM 4	88G 298	MA 21	2H 3271	MB 2
		FNZ 106	MJ 3	8G 654	MD 1·1	8G 8649	MH 3	88G 320	MF 1·1	2H 3406	MN 11
FNN 104	MA 9	FNZ 106	MK 2	8G 728	MB 3	8G 8650	MH 3	88G 320	MF 1·1	2H 3406	MN 12
FNN 104	MF 15	FNZ 106	MK 4	8G 2287	MA 4	8G 8660	MK 3	88G 329	MR 2	2H 4185	MN 3
FNN 105	MA 1·1	FNZ 106	ML 2	8G 2287 10	MA 4	8G 8703	MM 3	88G 333	MD 3	2H 4243	MB 3
FNN 105	MA 8	FNZ 106	MN 2	8G 2287 20	MA 4	8G 8807	ME 2	88G 423	MA 8	2H 4244	MB 3
FNN 105	MA 9	FNZ 107	MA 16	8G 2287 30	MA 4	8G 8807	MM 1·1	88G 423	MA 12	2H 4245	MB 3
FNN 105	MA 12	FNZ 107	MH 4	8G 2287 40	MA 4	8G 8811	ME 1·1	88G 424	MA 11	2H 4246	MB 3
FNN 107	MA 12	FNZ 107	MH 5	8G 2291	MA 14	8G 8911	MM 3	88G 440	MN 3	2H 4685	MA 9
FNN 107	MH 1·1	FNZ 107	ML 2	8G 2327	MA 14	8G 8943	MK 4	88G 446	MA 11	2H 4933	MA 12
FNN 204	MF 13	FNZ 204	MM 5	8G 2339	MA 4	8G 8981	MG 2	88G 484	MK 2	2H 4935	MA 15
FNN 206	MA 7	FNZ 205	MD 1·1	8G 2360	MA 4					2H 4978	MN 11
FNN 207	MN 1·1	FNZ 205	MF 13	8G 2360 10	MA 4	11G 176	MA 8	1H 55	MA 20	2H 4992	MN 11
FNN 505	MF 6	FNZ 205	MH 3	8G 2360 20	MA 4	11G 221	MB 2	1H 723	MA 7		
FNN 505	MF 12	FNZ 205	MH 5	8G 2360 30	MA 4	11G 2007	MN 3	1H 726	MA 7	3H 660	MJ 1·1
FNN 506	MA 7	FNZ 205	MM 4	8G 2360 40	MA 4	11G 2100	MD 1·1	1H 1111	MA 7	3H 914	MN 11
FNN 612	MH 2	FNZ 206	MA 16	8G 2407	MA 14	11G 9093	MN 9	1H 1153	MA 11	3H 964	MA 12
		FNZ 206	ME 3	8G 2522	MA 3·1			1H 2112	MM 2	3H 1454	MN 9
FNZ 103	MA 20	FNZ 206	MH 4	8G 2522 10	MA 3·1	12G 350	MB 3	1H 3087	MF 3	3H 1589	MH 2
FNZ 103	MA 21	FNZ 206	MM 2	8G 2522 20	MA 3·1			1H 3087	MF 6	3H 1655	MB 3
FNZ 103	MD 1·1	FNZ 206	MM 2·1	8G 2522 30	MA 3·1	14G 1702	MN 1·1	1H 3087	MF 9	3H 1656	MB 3
FNZ 103	ME 2	FNZ 210	MJ 3	8G 2522 40	MA 3·1	14G 3722	MN 10	1H 3087	MF 12	3H 1657	MB 3
FNZ 103	MM 2	FNZ 307	MJ 3	8G 2562 03	MA 2	14G 5509	MN 1·1	1H 3131	MF 3	3H 1658	MB 3
FNZ 103	MM 4	FNZ 407	MJ 3	8G 2562 13	MA 2			1H 3131	MF 6	3H 1659	MB 3
FNZ 103	MN 4	FNZ 407	MK 2	8G 2562 23	MA 2	18G 8011	MM 4	1H 3131	MF 9	3H 1660	MB 3
FNZ 103	MN 8	FNZ 408	MK 5	8G 2562 33	MA 2	18G 8126	MM 3	1H 3131	MF 12	3H 1836	MN 4
FNZ 103	MN 8·1	FNZ 506	ML 2	8G 2562 43	MA 2	18G 8163	MK 3	1H 3364	MF 1·1		
FNZ 103	MN 8·2	FNZ 507	MK 1·1	8G 2562 06	MA 2	18G 8178	MK 3	1H 3364	MF 7		
FNZ 103	MN 8·4	FNZ 507	ML 2	8G 2562 16	MA 2	18G 8341	MM 3	1H 3364	MH 1·1		
FNZ 103	MN 12	FNZ 508	ML 2	8G 2562 26	MA 2	18G 8400	MK 4	1H 4092	MK 5		
FNZ 104	MA 20	FNZ 612	MF 2	8G 2562 36	MA 2	18G 8401	MH 3	1H 5719	MM 4		
FNZ 104	MA 21	FNZ 612	MF 8	8G 2562 46	MA 2	18G 8402	MH 3				
FNZ 104	MB 2	FNZ 2210	MJ 3	8G 2563 03	MA 2	18G 8430	MM 2·1				
FNZ 104	MD 1·1			8G 2563 06	MA 2	18G 8441	MM 2·1				
FNZ 104	ME 2	1G 838	MA 6	8G 2563 13	MA 2						
FNZ 104	MF 13	1G 1814	MA 6·1	8G 2563 16	MA 2	21G 9057	MN 5				
FNZ 104	MH 4	1G 2268	MD 3	8G 2563 23	MA 2	21G 9057	MN 6				
FNZ 104	MH 5	1G 2342	MA 8	8G 2563 26	MA 2	21G 9057	MN 7				
FNZ 104	MJ 3	1G 2342	MA 12	8G 2563 33	MA 2	21G 9057	MN 7·1				
FNZ 104	MK 1·1	1G 2697	MA 20	8G 2563 36	MA 2	21G 9057	MN 7·2				
FNZ 104	MK 6	1G 3410	MA 12	8G 2563 43	MA 2	21G 9057	MN 8				
FNZ 104	MM 1·1	1G 3709	MF 3	8G 2563 46	MA 2	21G 9057	MN 8·1				
FNZ 104	MM 2	1G 3709	MF 6	8G 2564	MA 3·1	21G 9057	MN 8·2				
FNZ 104	MM 4	1G 4271	MK 1·1	8G 2564 10	MA 3·1	21G 9057	MN 8·4				
FNZ 104	MM 5	1G 4276	MK 5	8G 2564 20	MA 3·1	21G 9090	MN 11				
FNZ 104	MN 9	1G 4279	MK 5	8G 2564 30	MA 3·1						
FNZ 105	MA 15	1G 4346	MK 1·1	8G 2564 40	MA 3·1	24G 1345	MN 3				
FNZ 105	MA 16	1G 4348	MK 1·1	8G 2565	MB 3	24G 1482	MA 21				
FNZ 105	MA 17	1G 4349	MK 2	8G 3001	MG 2						
FNZ 105	MA 18	1G 4350	MK 1·1	8G 3013	MF 2	48G 171	MA 10				
FNZ 105	MA 19	1G 4505	MK 1·1	8G 3013	MF 5						
FNZ 105	MA 20	1G 4505	MK 6	8G 3014	MF 8	68G 200	MA 15				
FNZ 105	MB 2	1G 5753	MH 4	8G 3014	MF 11	68G 204	MA 1·1				
FNZ 105	MC 2	1G 6236	MJ 1·1	8G 3015	MF 8	68G 207	MA 1·1				
FNZ 105	MD 2	1G 6236	MJ 3	8G 3015	MF 11	68G 212	MA 1·1				
FNZ 105	MD 3	1G 6236	MM 5	8G 3016	MF 7	68G 217	MA 1·1				
FNZ 105	MF 13	1G 6353	MJ 3	8G 3016	MF 10	68G 220	MA 1·1				
FNZ 105	MF 15	1G 6354	MJ 3	8G 3023	MF 8	68G 223	MA 1·1				
FNZ 105	MH 5	1G 7484	MM 5	8G 3023	MF 11	68G 230	MA 1·1				
FNZ 105	MJ 3	1G 7485	MM 5	8G 3024	MF 8	68G 249	MA 1·1				
FNZ 105	MK 3	1G 7549	MM 5	8G 3024	MF 11	68G 252	MA 1·1				
FNZ 105	MK 4	1G 7574	MM 5	8G 3025	MF 8	68G 259	MA 1·1				
FNZ 105	MK 5	1G 8084	MP 1·1	8G 3025	MF 11	68G 262	MA 1·1				
FNZ 105	MM 2·1	1G 9310	ME 2	8G 3026	MF 8	68G 265	MA 1·1				
FNZ 105	MM 3·1	1G 9310	MM 1·1	8G 3026	MF 11	68G 267	MA 1·1				
		1G 9314	MM 1·1	8G 3027	MF 2	68G 270	MA 15				
		1G 9320	MH 4	8G 3027	MF 5	68G 271	MA 1·1				
		1G 9321	MH 4	8G 3028	MF 2	68G 273	MA 1·1				
		1G 9321	MH 5	8G 3028	MF 5	68G 274	MA 1·1				
		1G 9382	MA 16	8G 4191	MK 1·1	68G 275	MA 1·1				
						68G 276	MA 1·1				

Part Number	Page	Part Number	Page	Part Number	Page	Part Number	Page	Part Number	Page	Part Number	Page
3H 1894	MM 2·1	7H 4989	MH 3	7H 5879	MF 15	13H 297	MM 2	17H 2805	MJ 2·1		
3H 1910	MN 4	7H 4990	MH 3	7H 5881	MF 15	13H 337	MN 3	17H 2807	MJ 2·1		
3H 2138	MB 1·1	7H 4997	MH 3	7H 5883	MF 15	13H 349	MN 6	17H 2873	MA 10		
3H 2144	MN 13	7H 4998	MH 3	7H 884	MF 15	13H 469	MN 10	17H 2877	MA 10		
3H 2287	ME 3	7H 5000	MN 2	7H 5885 E	MF 15	13H 496	MN 5	17H 3529	MA 10		
3H 2287	MM 2·1	7H 5001	MN 2	7H 5885 F	MF 15	13H 709	MJ 2·1	17H 3530	MA 10		
3H 2429	MM 4	7H 5002	MN 2	7H 5885 G	MF 15	13H 760	MA 13	17H 3693	MA 10		
3H 2502	MA 1·1	7H 5004	MN 2	7H 5885 H	MF 15	13H 772	MA 11	17H 3745	MO 2		
3H 2615	MO 1·1	7H 5005	MN 2	7H 5885 J	MF 15	13H 818	ME 1·1	17H 4010	ME 2		
3H 2695	MB 2	7H 5006	MN 2	7H 5889	MF 15	13H 837	MN 2	17H 4011	ME 3		
3H 2696	MB 2	7H 5007	MN 2	7H 5894	MF 15	13H 848	MA 13	17H 4132	ME 3		
3H 2825	MN 3	7H 5008	MN 2	7H 5897	MF 13	13H 957	MA 8	17H 4132	MM 1·1		
3H 3028	MK 1·1	7H 5009	MN 2	7H 5898	MF 14	13H 998	MA 10	17H 4132	MM 4		
3H 3058	MN 3	7H 5010	MN 2	7H 6079	MJ 1·1	13H 1564	MF 8	17H 4141	MM 4		
3H 3079	MH 4	7H 5011	MN 2	7H 6079	MJ 2	13H 1564	MF 11	17H 4238	MM 2		
3H 3079	MK 5	7H 5012	MN 2	7H 6116	MJ 1·1	13H 1565	MF 8	17H 4507	MH 3		
3H 3096	MN 3	7H 5013	MN 2	7H 6116	MJ 2	13H 1565	MF 11	17H 4508	MM 2		
3H 3098	MN 3	7H 5021	MN 1·1	7H 6118	MJ 1·1	13H 1573	MM 3	17H 4509	MM 3		
3H 3099	MN 3	7H 5025	MN 1·1	7H 6118	MJ 2	13H 1581	ME 1·1	17H 4513	ME 2		
3H 3100	MN 3	7H 5066	MN 4	7H 6128	MJ 1·1	13H 1583	ME 1·1	17H 4513	MM 1·1		
		7H 5067	MN 4	7H 6128	MJ 2	13H 1596	MM 4	17H 4514	MM 2		
7H 25	MA 10	7H 5111	MN 8	7H 6129	MJ 1·1	13H 1739	ME 1·1	17H 4515	MM 2		
7H 28	MA 10	7H 5111	MN 8	7H 6129	MJ 2	13H 1950	MB 3	17H 4516	ME 3		
7H 147	MA 10	7H 5121	MN 8·3	7H 6130	MJ 2	13H 1953	MB 3	17H 4517	ME 3		
7H 1709	MP 1·1	7H 5123	MN 8·3	7H 6155	MJ 1·1	13H 2109	MN 9	17H 4518	MM 2		
7H 1756	MA 10	7H 5128	MN 4	7H 6155	MJ 2	13H 2110	MN 9	17H 4519	MM 2		
7H 1758	MA 10	7H 5130	MN 10	7H 6167	MJ 1·1	13H 2127	ME 1·1	17H 4528	MM 2		
7H 1759	MA 10	7H 5140	MN 9	7H 6167	MJ 2	13H 2154	MF 4	17H 4546	MH 3		
7H 1761	MA 10	7H 5142	MN 9	7H 6267	MJ 1·1	13H 2303	MM 2·1	17H 4554	ME 3		
7H 1762	MA 10	7H 5143	MN 9	7H 6267	MJ 2	13H 2317	MA 8	17H 4556	MM 2		
7H 1764	MA 10	7H 5156	MN 2	7H 6391	MJ 1·1	13H 2567	MF 3	17H 4557	MM 2		
7H 1765	MA 10	7H 5182	MN 8	7H 6391	MJ 2	13H 2567	MF 6	17H 4559	MM 2		
7H 1804	MP 1·1	7H 5182	MN 8·1	7H 6392	MJ 1·1	13H 2567	MF 9	17H 4561	ME 2		
7H 1805	MP 1·1	7H 5182	MN 8·2	7H 6392	MJ 2	13H 2567	MF 12	17H 4561	MM 1·1		
7H 1806	MP 1·1	7H 5182	MN 8·4	7H 6436	MJ 1·1	13H 2639	MN 9	17H 4561	MM 4		
7H 3001	ME 1·1	7H 5185	MN 8·3	7H 6436	MJ 2	13H 2972	MJ 2·1	17H 4596	MM 4		
7H 3042	ME 1·1	7H 5202	MN 8	7H 6460	MJ 2	13H 3860	MM 3	17H 4597	MM 4		
7H 3048	ME 1·1	7H 5202	MN 8·1	7H 6507	MJ 1·1	13H 3585	MA 8	17H 4601	MM 4		
7H 3067	ME 1·1	7H 5202	MN 8·4	7H 6507	MJ 2	13H 3747	ME 1·1	17H 4602	MM 4		
7H 3069	ME 1·1	7H 5339	MN 2	7H 6515	MJ 2	13H 3910	ME 1·1	17H 4603	MM 4		
7H 3078	ME 1·1	7H 5468	MN 9	7H 6589	MJ 1·1	13H 4070	MA 8	17H 4635	ME 2		
7H 3082	ME 1·1	7H 5469	MN 9	7H 6589	MJ 2	13H 4180	MJ 2·1	17H 4637	MK 3		
7H 3092	ME 1·1	7H 5471	MN 9	7H 6598	MJ 1·1	13H 4485	MN 3	17H 4639	MK 3		
7H 3120	ME 1·1	7H 5474	MN 9	7H 6598	MJ 2	13H 4486	MN 3	17H 4639	MK 4		
7H 3195	ME 1·1	7H 5483	MN 5	7H 6599	MJ 1·1	13H 4757	ME 1·1	17H 4640	MK 3		
7H 3239	ME 1·1	7H 5498	MN 2	7H 6599	MJ 2			17H 4640	MK 4		
7H 3777	MJ 3	7H 5512	MN 9	7H 6620	MJ 1·1	17H 3	MA 10	17H 4641	MH 3		
7H 3835	MG 2	7H 5522	MN 4	7H 6620	MJ 2	17H 4	MA 10	17H 4642	MK 3		
7H 3836	MG 2	7H 5525	MN 1·1	7H 6838	MN 5	17H 31	MA 5	17H 4665	MM 2		
7H 3858	MG 2	7H 5528	MN 1·1	7H 6892	MJ 3	17H 341	MA 5	17H 4666	MM 2		
7H 3902	MG 2	7H 5540	MN 4	7H 6893	MJ 3	17H 342	MA 5	17H 4679	MK 3		
7H 3905	MG 2	7H 5822	MF 13	7H 6894	MB 3	17H 630	MO 2	17H 4690	MH 3		
7H 3912	MG 2	7H 5825	MF 13	7H 6946	MB 1·1	17H 775	MA 10	17H 4694	MH 3		
7H 3913	MG 2	7H 5827	MF 13	7H 6958	MM 3	17H 786	MM 5	17H 4712	ME 3		
7H 3956	MG 2	7H 5829	MF 13	7H 6959	MM 3	17H 787	MM 5	17H 4743	ME 2		
7H 3962	MG 2	7H 5831	MF 13	7H 6960	MM 3	17H 788	MM 5	17H 4752	ME 2		
7H 4419	ME 3	7H 5833	MF 13	7H 6961	MM 3	17H 789	MM 5	17H 4814	MK 3		
7H 4419	MH 3	7H 5836	MF 14	7H 6962	MM 3	17H 790	MM 5	17H 4815	MK 3		
7H 4419	MK 3	7H 5837	MF 14	7H 6963	MM 3	17H 932	MO 1·1	17H 4827	ME 2		
7H 4419	MK 4	7H 5839	MF 14	7H 6964	MM 3	17H 940	MA 10	17H 4827	MM 1·1		
7H 4429	MH 3	7H 5840	MF 14	7H 6965	MM 3	17H 942	MA 10	17H 4827	MM 4		
7H 4451	ME 2	7H 5841	MF 14	7H 6966	MM 3	17H 1061	MO 2	17H 4831	ME 2		
7H 4451	MM 1·1	7H 5845	MF 14	7H 6967	MM 3	17H 1148	MA 10	17H 4831	MM 1·1		
7H 4461	MH 3	7H 5846	MF 14	7H 8196	MF 13	17H 1150	MA 10	17H 4896	MM 4		
7H 4596	MH 3	7H 5849	MF 14	7H 8273	MF 15	17H 1152	MA 10	17H 4897	MM 4		
7H 4726	MM 2	7H 5851	MF 13			17H 1167	MA 10	17H 4898	MM 4		
7H 4751	ME 2	7H 5852	MF 13	11H 921	MK 1·1	17H 1173	MA 10	17H 4899	MM 4		
7H 4751	MM 1·1	7H 5857	MF 14	11H 924	MK 1·1	17H 1272	MA 10	17H 4900	MM 4		
7H 4751	MM 4	7H 5861	MF 15	11H 924	MK 6	17H 1304	MO 2	17H 4908	MM 3		
7H 4752	ME 2	7H 5862	MF 15	11H 1051	MR 2	17H 1343	MO 2	17H 4910	MM 3		
7H 4752	MM 1·1	7H 5863	MF 15	11H 1686	MR 2	17H 1476	MA 10	17H 4913	MM 3		
7H 4752	MM 4	7H 5866	MF 15			17H 1642	MO 1·1	17H 4914	MM 3		
7H 4756	ME 2	7H 5867	MF 15	12H 51	MB 2	17H 1658	MO 2	17H 4915	MM 3·1		
7H 4867	ME 2	7H 5868	MF 15	12H 650	MA 7	17H 1662	MO 2	17H 4917	MM 3		
7H 4867	MM 2	7H 5870	MF 15	12H 736	MA 15	17H 1761	MA 10	17H 4929	MM 3		
7H 4904	MH 3	7H 5872 A	MF 14	12H 941	MA 6·1	17H 1822	MO 1·1	17H 4930	MM 3		
7H 4906	MH 3	7H 5872 B	MF 14	12H 1001	MD 1·1	17H 2142	MJ 3	17H 4931	MM 3·1		
7H 4907	MH 3	7H 5872 C	MF 14	12H 2097	MA 11	17H 2143	MJ 3	17H 4937	MM 3		
7H 4944	ME 2	7H 5872 D	MF 14	12H 2269	MA 11	17H 2144	MJ 3	17H 4946	ME 2		
7H 4944	MM 1·1	7H 5872 E	MF 14			17H 2392	MB 1·1	17H 4950	MM 3·1		
7H 4970	ME 3	7H 5872 F	MF 14	13H 110	MN 9	17H 2472	MN 1·1	17H 4951	MM 3		
7H 4973	ME 3	7H 5872 G	MF 14	13H 252	MN 4	17H 2660	MJ 1·1	17H 4952	MM 3		
7H 4973	MH 3	7H 5873	MF 14	13H 297	ME 2	17H 2724	ME 1·1	17H 4958	MK 3		

Part Number	Page	Part Number	Page	Part Number	Page	Part Number	Page	Part Number	Page
17H 4959	MK 3	17H 5878	MF 14	27H 2945	MK 4	27H 6713	MN 7·3	37H 5530	MN 7·2
17H 4960	MK 3	17H 5879	MF 14	27H 2946	MK 4	27H 6713	MN 8	37H 5531	MN 8·2
17H 5043	MN 1·1	17H 5977	MF 14	27H 2947	MK 4	27H 6713	MN 8·1		
17H 5065	MB 1·1	17H 6103	MJ 1·1	27H 2948	MK 4	27H 6713	MN 8·4	47H 5010	MN 9
17H 5069	MB 1·1	17H 6103	MJ 2	27H 2949	MK 4	27H 6873	MM 3	47H 5011	MN 9
17H 5095	MB 1·1	17H 6106	MJ 1·1	27H 2950	MK 4	27H 6874	MM 3	47H 5033	MN 8
17H 5110	MB 1·1	17H 6106	MJ 2	27H 2951	MK 4	27H 6960	MM 3·1	47H 5124	MN 6
17H 5113	MB 1·1	17H 6107	MJ 1·1	27H 2953	MK 4	27H 6967	MN 5	47H 5124	MN 7
17H 5117	MB 1·1	17H 6108	MJ 1·1	27H 2988	MK 4	27H 6967	MN 7·1	47H 5125	MN 6
17H 5158	MB 1·1	17H 6109	MJ 1·1	27H 2989	MK 4	27H 6967	MN 7·2	47H 5125	MN 7
17H 5166	MB 1·1	17H 6110	MJ 1·1	27H 3234	ME 1·1	27H 6995	MJ 3	47H 5125	MN 7·1
17H 5205	MN 5	17H 6161	MJ 2	27H 3338	MN 5	27H 6995	MM 5	47H 5126	MN 5
17H 5205	MN 6	17H 6162	MJ 2	27H 3338	MN 6	27H 7562	MM 3	47H 5126	MN 6
17H 5205	MN 7	17H 6163	MJ 2	27H 3338	MN 7	27H 7816	MN 2	47H 5126	MN 7
17H 5205	MN 7·1	17H 6164	MJ 2	27H 3338	MN 7·1	27H 7824	MN 7·1	47H 5126	MN 7·1
17H 5205	MN 7·2	17H 6536	MJ 2	27H 3338	MN 7·2	27H 7993	MK 3	47H 5126	MN 7·2
17H 5230	MN 7·3	17H 6542	MJ 1·1	27H 3338	MN 7·3	27H 7994	MK 3	47H 5126	MN 7·3
17H 5231	MN 5	17H 6543	MJ 1·1	27H 3573	MD 1·1	27H 8056	MM 3	47H 5160	MN 3
17H 5231	MN 6	17H 6544	MJ 2	27H 3588	MN 13	27H 8067	MJ 2	47H 5204	MN 3
17H 5231	MN 7	17H 6545	MJ 2	27H 3800	MN 8·1	27H 8068	MJ 2	47H 5166	MN 11
17H 5231	MN 7·1	17H 6679	MA 5	27H 3800	MN 8·4	27H 8136	MN 1·1	47H 5212	MN 4
17H 5231	MN 7·2	17H 6681	MA 5	27H 3817	MN 1·1	27H 8198	MM 3	47H 5240	MN 9
17H 5231	MN 7·3	17H 6763	MN 8	27H 4146	MN 6	27H 8199	MM 3	47H 5241	MN 9
17H 5243	MB 1·1	17H 6763	MN 8·1	27H 4146	MN 7	27H 8203	MN 5	47H 5242	MN 9
17H 5255	MN 10	17H 6764	MN 8	27H 4678	MN 8	27H 8204	MN 6	47H 5243	MN 9
17H 5259	MN 9	17H 6764	MN 8·1	27H 4678	MN 8·1	27H 8205	MN 7	47H 5244	MN 9
17H 5273	MN 7·3	17H 6765	MN 8	27H 4678	MN 8·2	27H 8206	MN 7·2	47H 5245	MN 9
17H 5277	MN 7·3	17H 6765	MN 8·1	27H 4678	MN 8·4	27H 8207	MN 7·3	47H 5247	MN 9
17H 5306	MN 5	17H 6765	MN 8·2	27H 4717	MM 4	27H 8209	MN 5	47H 5249	MB 1·1
17H 5306	MN 7·2	17H 6765	MN 8·4	27H 4754	MM 4	27H 8284	MN 7·1	47H 5250	MB 1·1
17H 5375	MN 7·2	17H 6766	MN 8·2	27H 4829	MN 1·1	27H 8287	MN 7·1	47H 5316	MN 10
17H 5394	MN 5	17H 6865	MB 1·1	27H 4886	MN 8	27H 8495	MN 5	47H 5389	MN 1·1
17H 5394	MN 6	17H 6965	MB 1·1	27H 4886	MN 8·1	27H 9196	MM 2	47H 5392	MN 1·1
17H 5394	MN 7·1	17H 8041	MB 1·1	27H 4886	MN 8·4	27H 9197	MM 2	47H 5394	MN 1·1
17H 5394	MN 7·2	17H 8112	ME 2	27H 4927	MN 8·2	27H 9198	MM 2	47H 5413	MN 1·1
17H 5394	MN 7·3	17H 8112	MM 1·1	27H 4929	MN 8·1	27H 9199	MM 2	47H 5414	MN 1·1
17H 5396	MN 10	17H 8113	ME 2	27H 4929	MN 8·4	27H 9391	MJ 2·1	47H 5415	MN 1·1
17H 5423	MB 1·1	17H 8113	MM 1·1	27H 4930	MN 8·1	27H 9394	MJ 2·1	47H 5416	MN 1·1
17H 5431	MN 10	17H 8153	MJ 1·1	27H 5253	MN 5			47H 5419	MN 11
17H 5434	MN 1·1	17H 8153	MJ 2	27H 5253	MN 6	37H 140	MA 10	47H 5481	MN 3
17H 5437	MB 1·1	17H 8157	MF 14	27H 5253	MN 7	37H 614	MO 2	47H 5496	MN 11
17H 5441	MN 10	17H 8619	MP 1·1	27H 5253	MN 7·1	37H 1173	MA 10	47H 5499	MN 11
17H 5442	MN 10	17H 8620	MP 1·1	27H 5253	MN 7·2	37H 1204	MO 2	47H 5524	MM 5
17H 5469	MB 1·1	17H 8659	MJ 2·1	27H 5278	MN 3	37H 1206	MO 2	47H 5528	MN 7·1
17H 5475	MN 10	17H 8799	ME 1·1	27H 5309	MN 10	37H 1207	MO 2	47H 5589	MN 4
17H 5527	MB 1·1	17H 8844	MB 1·1	27H 5316	MB 1·1	37H 1342	MB 3		
17H 5531	MB 1·1	17H 9170	MJ 3	27H 5354	MN 5	37H 1366	MN 3	57H 5018	MN 7·3
17H 5546	MN 7·2	17H 9276	ML 2	27H 5354	MN 6	37H 1368	MN 7	57H 5050	MB 1·1
17H 5594	MN 9	17H 9391	MN 10	27H 5354	MN 7	37H 2099	MN 3	57H 5085	MN 1·1
17H 5804	MF 15			27H 5354	MN 7·1	37H 2151	ME 1·1	57H 5128	MN 8·3
17H 5808	MF 13	27H 984	MO 2	27H 5354	MN 7·2	37H 3054	ML 2	57H 5138	MN 9
17H 5809	MF 13	27H 985	MO 2	27H 5354	MN 7·3	37H 3055	ML 2	57H 5241	MB 1·1
17H 5811	MF 13	27H 992	MO 1·1	27H 5374	MN 10	37H 5169	MN 10	57H 5292	MN 7·3
17H 5815	MF 13	27H 1142	MA 10	27H 5584	MN 1·1	37H 5181	MN 11	57H 5294	MN 10
17H 5818	MF 15	27H 1143	MA 10	27H 5545	MN 8	37H 5190	MN 5	57H 5309	MN 9
17H 5819	MF 15	27H 1144	MA 10	27H 5545	MN 8·2	37H 5190	MN 6	57H 5310	MN 9
17H 5821	MF 15	27H 1473	MN 9	27H 5556	MN 9	37H 5190	MN 7	57H 5368	MN 8·3
17H 5822	MF 15	27H 1983	MA 10	27H 5557	MN 9	37H 5190	MN 7·1	57H 5369	MN 2
17H 5823	MF 15	27H 2122	MB 1·1	27H 5576	MN 3	37H 5190	MN 7·2	57H 5396	MN 4
17H 5824	MF 15	27H 2291	MN 2	27H 5578	MN 12	37H 5190	MN 7·3	57H 5397	MN 4
17H 5825	MF 13	27H 2315	MF 13	27H 5873	MN 4	37H 5288	MN 1	57H 5398	MN 4
17H 5827	MF 14	27H 2318	ME 1·1	27H 5903	MN 13	37H 5308	MN 1	57H 5420	MB 1·1
17H 5833	MF 15	27H 2333	MN 5	27H 5941	MM 3·1	37H 5437	MN 1	57H 5427	MN 1·1
17H 5844	MF 15	27H 2347	MJ 2	27H 5979	MN 5	37H 5445	MB 1·1	57H 5428	MN 1·1
17H 5846	MF 15	27H 2348	MJ 2	27H 6202	MN 8	37H 5452	MN 8	57H 5429	MN 1·1
17H 5847	MF 14	27H 2349	MJ 2	27H 6202	MN 8·1	37H 5452	MN 8·1	57H 5431	MN 1·1
17H 5848	MF 14	27H 2350	MJ 2	27H 6202	MN 8·4	37H 5452	MN 8·4	57H 5432	MN 1·1
17H 5854	MF 15	27H 2412	MF 13	27H 6236	MJ 2·1	37H 5459	MN 8	57H 5433	MN 1·1
17H 5855	MF 15	27H 2413	MF 13	27H 6237	MJ 2·1	37H 5459	MN 8·2	57H 5445	MN 11
17H 5856	MF 13	27H 2414	MF 13	27H 6238	MJ 2·1	37H 5487	MN 1·1	57H 5456	MN 5
17H 5857	MF 13	27H 2418	MM 3	27H 6241	MN 8	37H 5519	MN 8	57H 5456	MN 6
17H 5858	MF 13	27H 2419	MM 3·1	27H 6242	MN 8	37H 5520	MN 8·1	57H 5456	MN 7
17H 5859	MF 15	27H 2420	MM 3·1	27H 6245	MJ 2·1	37H 5520	MN 8·4	57H 5456	MN 7·3
17H 5862	MF 13	27H 2568	MN 10	27H 6482	MN 5	37H 5527	MN 5	57H 5457	MN 5
17H 5863	MF 15	27H 2573	MA 10	27H 6482	MN 6	37H 5527	MN 6	57H 5457	MN 6
17H 5864	MF 15	27H 2576	MH 3	27H 6482	MN 7	37H 5527	MN 7	57H 5457	MN 7
17H 5965	MF 15	27H 2724	MN 8	27H 6482	MN 7·2	37H 5527	MN 7·1	57H 5457	MN 7·1
17H 5867	MF 15	27H 2724	MN 8·2	27H 6482	MN 7·3	37H 5528	MN 8	57H 5457	MN 7·2
17H 5869	MF 15	27H 2725	MN 8	27H 6713	MN 5	37H 5528	MN 8·1	57H 5478	MB 1·1
17H 5873	MF 14	27H 2725	MN 8·2	27H 6713	MN 6	37H 5530	MN 5	57H 5485	MN 1·1
17H 5874	MF 14	27H 2817	MN 6	27H 6713	MN 7	37H 5530	MN 6	57H 5488	MB 1·1
17H 5975	MF 13	27H 2817	MN 7	27H 6713	MN 7·1	37H 5530	MN 7	57H 5489	MB 1·1
17H 5876	MF 14	27H 2821	MN 9	27H 6713	MN 7·2	37H 5530	MN 7·1		

Part Number Index—continued

Part Number	Page	Part Number	Page	Part Number	Page	Part Number	Page	Part Number	Page	Part Number	Page
57H 5490	MB 1·1	HBZ 0638	MJ 3	HZS 0606	MA 16	2K 2561	MA 7	2K 8929	MJ 2·1	53K 1477	MA 15
57H 5496	MN 8	HBZ 0722	MH 5	HZS 0606	MM 3	2K 4936	MO 1·1	2K 8951	MK 1·1	53K 1551	MJ 3
57H 5496	MN 8·2	HBZ 0728	MK 1·1	HZS 0607	MA 16	2K 4954	MA 1·1	2K 9579	MP 1·1	53K 1662	MK 1·1
57H 5554	MN 10	HBZ 0730	MK 1·1	HZS 0607	MA 17	2K 4954	MA 14			53K 1764	MK 1·1
57H 5559	MN 10			HZS 0607	MH 4	2K 4954	MC 2	6K 35	ME 3	53K 1770	MK 1·1
57H 5586	MN 10	HCN 0631	MA 10	HZS 0608	ME 3	2K 4970	MA 12	6K 35	MM 2·1	53K 1770	MK 6
				HZS 0608	MK 5	2K 4974	MA 11	6K 35	MO 1·1	53K 3061	MD 1·1
67H 5024	MN 6	HCS 126	MC 2			2K 4874	MK 1·1	6K 56	MA 12	53K 3503	MA 21
67H 5024	MN 7	HCS 0709	MD 3	1K 21	MA 12	2K 4975	MC 2	6K 431	MA 9		
67H 5024	MN 7·3	HCS 1217	MC 2	1K 51	MA 1·1	2K 5057	MJ 2·1	6K 433	MA 8	54K 1723	MF 3
67H 5025	MN 5	HCS 2228	MD 1·1	1K 105	MA 9	2K 5090	MA 21	6K 467	MA 20	54K 1723	MF 6
67H 5025	MN 6			1K 106	MA 9	2K 5197	MA 6·1	6K 499	MF 1·1	54K 1723	MF 9
67H 5025	MN 7	HNS 0403	MA 6·1	1K 141	MA 9	2K 5197	MA 9	6K 499	MF 4	54K 1723	MF 12
67H 5025	MN 7·1	HNS 0404	MA 8	1K 204	MB 2	2K 5213	MM 5	6K 499	MF 7		
67H 5025	MN 7·2	HNS 0404	MA 9	1K 369	MA 4	2K 5215	MO 1·1	6K 499	MF 10	5L 286	MN 11
67H 5025	MN 7·3	HNS 0405	MA 12	1K 372	MA 7	2K 5217	MM 2·1	6K 499	MH 1·1	5L 287	MN 11
67H 5026	MN 5	HNS 0406	MA 9	1K 618	MA 17	2K 5218	MM 2·1	6K 638	MD 1·1	5L 289	MN 11
67H 5026	MN 6	HNS 0407	MA 12	1K 618	MA 18	2K 5221	MM 5	6K 638	MD 1·1		
67H 5026	MN 7	HNS 0503	MA 1·1	1K 624	MA 5	2K 5243	MM 5	6K 649	MB 2	LNN 208	MA 1·1
67H 5026	MN 7·1	HNS 0506	MA 5	1K 800	MA 7	2K 5291	MM 5	6K 650	MB 2		
67H 5026	MN 7·2	HNS 0506	MA 6·1	1K 1056	MA 8	2K 5505	MF 2	6K 681	MF 2	LNZ 105	MK 5
67H 5026	MN 7·3	HNS 0506	ME 1·1	1K 1056	MA 14	2K 5505	MF 8	6K 681	MF 5	LNZ 205	MA 17
67H 5028	MN 6	HNS 0506	MJ 1·1	1K 2524	MA 12	2K 5507	MF 15	6K 681	MF 8	LNZ 205	MA 18
67H 5028	MN 7	HNS 0506	MJ 2	1K 3055	MF 2	2K 5616	MM 5	6K 681	MF 11	LNZ 205	MA 19
67H 5028	MN 7·1	HNS 0506	MJ 2	1K 3055	MF 11	2K 5622	ME 3	6K 777	MF 2	LNZ 205	MM 1·1
67H 5028	MN 7·2	HNS 0507	MA 5	1K 4055	MF 5	2K 5914	MG 2	6K 777	MF 5	LNZ 206	MA 12
67H 5029	MN 3	HNS 0507	MA 6·1	1K 4055	MF 8	2K 5923	MA 7	6K 777	MF 8	LNZ 206	MG 2
		HNS 0507	MA 13			2K 5976	MA 21	6K 777	MF 11	LNZ 206	MH 3
97H 626	MN 1·1	HNS 0509	MA 12	2K 1345	MF 1·1	2K 6012	MA 1·1	6K 780	MF 2	LNZ 206	MH 4
97H 2797	MJ 2·1	HNS 0509	MF 1·1	2K 1345	MF 7	2K 6057	MJ 2	6K 780	MF 5	LNZ 206	MH 5
		HNS 0509	MF 4	2K 1351	MF 7	2K 6167	MN 12	6K 780	MF 8	LNZ 206	MK 5
HBN 0412	MA 5	HNS 0509	MF 10	2K 1351	MF 10	2K 6192	MA 15	6K 780	MF 11	LNZ 206	MN 1·1
HBN 0509	MF 7	HNS 0514	MF 13	2K 1358	MA 1·1	2K 6193	MA 15	6K 873	MA 7		
HBN 0510	MA 6·1	HNS 0607	ME 1·1	2K 1369	MO 2	2K 6534	MA 7	6K 9582	MK 5	LWN 204	MA 8
HBN 0510	MA 12	HNS 0608	MA 5	2K 1381	MN 4	2K 6541	MH 1·1	6K 9777	MN 8·3	LWN 204	MA 9
HBN 0510	MF 1·1			2K 2163	MA 12	2K 6650	MA 1·1			LWN 204	MA 12
HBN 0510	MF 7	HZS 0403	ME 2			2K 6930	MM 5	10K 5451	MM 2·1	LWN 204	MB 2
HBN 0512	MF 1·1	HZS 0403	MK 4			2K 7440	MF 3	10K 7089	MF 1·1	LWN 204	MF 1·1
HBN 0512	MF 4	HZS 0403	MM 2			2K 7500	MF 9	10K 7089	MF 4	LWN 204	MF 4
HBN 0512	MF 7	HZS 0403	MM 5			2K 7500	MA 6	10K 7089	MF 7	LWN 204	MF 7
HBN 0512	MF 10	HZS 0404	MA 9			2K 7552	MF 4	10K 7089	MF 10	LWN 204	MF 10
HBN 0515	MF 1·1	HZS 0404	MD 2			2K 7914	MF 10			LWN 205	MA 1·1
HBN 0515	MF 4	HZS 0404	ME 2			2K 8209	MJ 3	11K 8309	MM 3·1	LWN 205	MA 5
HBN 0515	MF 7	HZS 0404	MH 4			2K 8377	MA 9	11K 9095	MN 12	LWN 205	MA 8
HBN 0515	MG 2	HZS 0404	MH 5			2K 8645	MN 1·1	11K 9181	MN 12	LWN 205	MA 9
HBN 0518	MF 1·1	HZS 0404	MM 2			2K 8725	MA 4			LWN 205	MA 12
HBN 0518	MF 4	HZS 0404	MN 3					21K 8341	MM 4	LWN 205	MA 13
HBN 0518	MF 7	HZS 0405	MA 12					21K 8342	MM 4	LWN 205	ME 1·1
HBN 0518	MF 10	HZS 0405	MA 16					21K 9068	MN 3	LWN 205	MF 1·1
HBZ 0409	MM 1·1	HZS 0405	MD 1·1							LWN 205	MF 4
HBZ 0410	MM 2·1	HZS 0405	MH 4					41K 5011	MM 2	LWN 205	MF 6
HBZ 0410	MM 4	HZS 0405	MH 5							LWN 205	MF 7
HBZ 0411	ME 2	HZS 0405	MK 5					51K 370	MJ 3	LWN 205	MF 9
HBZ 0418	MJ 3	HZS 0406	MF 12					51K 490	MA 8	LWN 205	MF 10
HBZ 0422	MP 1·1	HZS 0406	MM 2·1					51K 505	MF 6	LWN 205	MF 12
HBZ 0511	MA 18	HZS 0408	MB 2					51K 505	MF 12	LWN 206	MA 5
HBZ 0512	MJ 1·1	HZS 0409	MA 20					51K 562	MA 15	LWN 206	MA 7
HBZ 0512	MJ 2	HZS 0415	MM 2					51K 590	MA 7	LWN 206	ME 1·1
HBZ 0513	MA 19	HZS 0420	MB 2					51K 591	MA 7	LWN 207	MA 12
HBZ 0516	MA 19	HZS 0504	MK 4							LWN 305	MA 12
HBZ 0516	MC 2	HZS 0505	MA 16					53K 320	MJ 3	LWN 305	MF 2
HBZ 0518	MA 18	HZS 0505	MC 2					53K 124	MF 13	LWN 305	MF 5
HBZ 0524	MJ 3	HZS 0505	MM 1·1					53K 126	MF 13	LWN 305	MF 8
HBZ 0526	MA 15	HZS 0506	MA 16					53K 128	MA 21	LWN 305	MF 11
HBZ 0611	MF 3	HZS 0506	MA 17					53K 129	MN 4	LWN 307	MH 1·1
HBZ 0611	MF 6	HZS 0506	MA 18					53K 165	MD 1·1	LWN 403	MD 2
HBZ 0611	MF 9	HZS 0506	MA 21					53K 329	MK 1·1	LWN 403	MD 2·1
HBZ 0611	MF 12	HZS 0506	MJ 3					53K 329	MK 6	LWN 404	MA 12
HBZ 0612	MF 3	HZS 0506	MK 5					53K 330	MK 2	LWN 406	MA 6·1
HBZ 0612	MF 6	HZS 0506	MM 2·1					53K 365	MJ 3	LWN 406	MA 16
HBZ 0612	MF 9	HZS 0506	MM 3·1					53K 485	MA 1·1	LWN 406	ME 3
HBZ 0612	MF 12	HZS 0506	MM 5					53K 507	MA 15	LWN 406	MM 2·1
HBZ 0615	MN 2	HZS 0507	MA 17					53K 563	MA 15	LWN 406	MN 9
HBZ 0616	MK 2	HZS 0508	MA 18					53K 564	MA 15		
HBZ 0618	MK 5	HZS 0508	MA 20					53K 1016	MA 21	LWZ 203	MA 20
HBZ 0620	MK 2	HZS 0508	MA 21					53K 1048	MG 2	LWZ 203	MA 21
HBZ 0620	MK 5	HZS 0508	ME 2					53K 1048	ML 2	LWZ 203	MD 1·1
HBZ 0620	MN 2	HZS 0508	MM 1·1					53K 1433	MA 11	LWZ 203	ME 3
HBZ 0624	MJ 3	HZS 0509	MA 6·1					53K 1435	MF 1·1	LWZ 203	MF 13
HBZ 0626	MJ 3	HZS 0509	MA 18					53K 1435	MF 4	LWZ 203	MF 14
HBZ 0632	MA 10	HZS 0509	MA 20					53K 1435	MF 7	LWZ 203	MM 2
HBZ 0636	MA 10	HZS 0604	MN 12					53K 1435	MF 10	LWZ 203	MM 4
								53K 1473	MA 15		

Part Number	Page	Part Number	Page	Part Number	Page	Part Number	Page
LWZ 203	MM 5	LWZ 304	MH 4	PMZ 0307	MB 2	PWZ 107	ML 2
LWZ 203	MN 3	LWZ 304	MH 5	PMZ 0307	MM 2·1	PWZ 108	ME 2
LWZ 203	MN 4	LWZ 304	MJ 3	PMZ 0307	MN 4	PWZ 204	MB 2
LWZ 203	MN 7·3	LWZ 304	MK 5	PMZ 0307	MO 1·1	PWZ 204	MH 4
LWZ 203	MN 8·3	LWZ 304	MM 1·1	PMZ 0308	MA 7	PWZ 204	MH 5
LWZ 203	MN 9	LWZ 304	MM 2·1	PMZ 0308	MD 1·1	PWZ 204	MM 5
LWZ 203	MN 12	LWZ 304	MM 4	PMZ 0308	MF 13	PWZ 205	MA 17
LWZ 204	MA 20	LWZ 305	MA 5	PMZ 0308	MF 14	PWZ 205	MA 19
LWZ 204	MD 1·1	LWZ 305	MA 18	PMZ 0308	MN 3	PWZ 205	MB 2
LWZ 204	MD 2	LWZ 305	MB 2	PMZ 0308	MN 4	PWZ 205	MC 2
LWZ 204	ME 2	LWZ 305	MD 2	PMZ 0308	MN 9	PWZ 205	MM 1·1
LWZ 204	MF 13	LWZ 305	MJ 3	PMZ 0308	MN 12	PWZ 205	MM 3·1
LWZ 204	MH 4	LWZ 305	MK 3	PMZ 0310	MD 1·1	PWZ 206	MA 16
LWZ 204	MH 5	LWZ 305	MK 4	PMZ 0310	ME 2	PWZ 206	MH 4
LWZ 204	MK 1·1	LWZ 305	MM 5	PMZ 0314	MN 4	PWZ 207	MH 4
LWZ 204	MK 4	LWZ 306	MA 17	PMZ 0314	MM 2	PWZ 207	MK 5
LWZ 204	MK 6	LWZ 306	ME 3	PMZ 0314	MM 4	PWZ 305	MA 18
LWZ 204	MM 2	LWZ 306	MG 2	PMZ 0316	MJ 2		
LWZ 204	MM 5	LWZ 306	MH 1·1	PMZ 0318	MN 4	RFN 106	MN 13
LWZ 204	MN 3	LWZ 306	MH 4	PMZ 0320	MN 4	RFN 303	MN 13
LWZ 204	MN 9	LWZ 306	MJ 3	PMZ 0408	MN 9	RFN 403	MO 1·1
LWZ 204	MP 1·1	LWZ 306	MK 2	PMZ 0410	MA 20	RFN 405	MN 13
LWZ 205	MA 15	LWZ 306	MK 5	PMZ 0410	MN 3	RFN 405	MO 2
LWZ 205	MA 16	LWZ 306	ML 2	PMZ 0412	MA 20		
LWZ 205	MA 17	LWZ 307	ML 2	PMZ 0412	MH 4	RMP 0310	MP 1·1
LWZ 205	MA 18	LWZ 308	ML 2	PMZ 0412	MH 5		
LWZ 205	MA 20	LWZ 403	MJ 2	PMZ 0510	MA 17	RMZ 0310	MN 7·3
LWZ 205	MA 21	LWZ 403	MN 8				
LWZ 205	MC 1	LWZ 403	MN 8·1	PTZ 803	MN 13	RPS 1210	MF 3
LWZ 205	MD 1·1	LWZ 403	MN 8·4	PTZ 1003	MD 1·1	RPS 1210	MF 6
LWZ 205	MD 3	LWZ 403	MN 8·2	PTZ 1004	MM 2·1	RPS 1210	MF 9
LWZ 205	ME 2	LWZ 404	MA 9	PTZ 1004	MM 4	RPS 1210	MF 12
LWZ 205	MF 13	LWZ 506	MK 3	PTZ 1004	MN 12	RPS 1222	MH 1·1
LWZ 205	MF 15	LWZ 507	MK 3				
LWZ 205	MJ 1·1	LWZ 507	MK 4	PWN 104	MA 9	TPS 0405	MF 13
LWZ 205	MJ 2			PWN 105	MA 9	TPS 0610	MF 1·1
LWZ 205	MK 4	NCS 0408	MA 9	PWN 106	MA 5	TPS 0610	MF 4
LWZ 205	MK 5	NCS 0507	MA 12	PWN 106	MA 7	TPS 0610	MF 7
LWZ 205	MM 1·1	NCS 0606	MA 6	PWN 106	MA 10	TPS 0610	MF 10
LWZ 205	MM 2·1			PWN 106	MA 12		
LWZ 205	MM 3·1	NZS 103	MM 5	PWN 107	MA 1·1	TRS 1519	MK 1·1
LWZ 205	MN 3			PWN 112	MF 15	TRS 1519	MK 6
LWZ 206	MA 6	PCR 0307	ME 3	PWN 112	MJ 1·1		
LWZ 206	MA 10	PCR 0307	MM 4	PWN 112	MJ 3	UHN 305	MM 5
LWZ 206	MA 15	PCR 0307	MO 1·1	PWN 112	MJ 2	UHN 400	MG 2
LWZ 206	MA 16	PCR 0311	MN 12	PWN 204	MB 2	UHN 400	MJ 3
LWZ 206	MF 3	PCR 0407	MN 12			UHN 490	MK 1·1
LWZ 206	MF 6	PCR 0505	MA 21	PWZ 102	MN 4	UHN 490	MM 5
LWZ 206	MF 9	PCR 0507	MD 1·1	PWZ 102	MN 8		
LWZ 206	MF 12	PCR 0507	MN 12	PWZ 102	MN 8·1	WKN 305	MF 2
LWZ 206	MH 3	PCR 0507	MN 12	PWZ 102	MN 8·2	WKN 305	MF 8
LWZ 206	MH 4	PCR 0509	MN 12	PWZ 102	MN 8·4	WKN 404	MF 3
LWZ 206	MH 5	PCR 0607	MM 4	PWZ 103	MN 3	WKN 404	MF 6
LWZ 206	MK 1·1	PCR 0607	MN 12	PWZ 103	MN 4	WKN 404	MF 9
LWZ 206	MK 4	PCR 0609	MM 5	PWZ 103	MN 8·3	WKN 404	MF 12
LWZ 206	MM 3·1	PCR 0707	MN 12	PWZ 103	MN 9	WKN 405	MA 9
LWZ 206	MN 2	PCR 0709	MN 12	PWZ 103	MN 12	WKN 405	MN 1·1
LWZ 206	MN 12	PCR 1007	MD 1·1	PWZ 104	MA 21	WKN 606	MA 5
LWZ 207	MA 16			PWZ 104	MB 1·1	WKN 608	MA 4
LWZ 207	MH 4	PJZ 602	MN 5	PWZ 104	MD 1·1	WKN 608	MA 6
LWZ 207	MH 5	PJZ 602	MN 6	PWZ 104	MD 2		
LWZ 207	MK 1·1	PJZ 602	MN 7	PWZ 104	MH 4	WNZ 103	MB 2
LWZ 207	MK 3	PJZ 602	MN 7·1	PWZ 104	MH 5	WNZ 104	MN 1·1
LWZ 207	ML 2	PJZ 602	MN 7·2	PWZ 104	MM 5		
LWZ 212	MF 2	PJZ 602	MN 7·3	PWZ 104	MN 3	ZCS 0505	MA 1·1
LWZ 212	MF 8			PWZ 104	MN 9		
LWZ 212	MH 2	PMP 0218	MN 8	PWZ 104	MP 1·1	ZPS 0306	MD 1·1
LWZ 302	MN 3	PMP 0218	MN 8·1	PWZ 105	MA 15		
LWZ 302	MN 8	PMP 0218	MN 8·2	PWZ 105	MA 16		
LWZ 302	MN 8·1	PMP 0218	MN 8·4	PWZ 105	MA 18		
LWZ 302	MN 8·2			PWZ 105	MA 20		
LWZ 302	MN 8·4	PMZ 0207	MN 3	PWZ 105	MA 21		
LWZ 302	MO 1·1	PMZ 0207	MN 8	PWZ 105	MC 2		
LWZ 303	MA 20	PMZ 0207	MN 8·1	PWZ 105	MD 3		
LWZ 303	MA 21	PMZ 0207	MN 8·2	PWZ 105	ME 3		
LWZ 303	MD 2·1	PMZ 0207	MN 8·4	PWZ 105	MF 13		
LWZ 304	MA 16	PMZ 0305	MB 2	PWZ 105	MM 5		
LWZ 304	MA 20	PMZ 0305	MD 1·1	PWZ 106	MA 15		
LWZ 304	MB 2	PMZ 0306	MA 21	PWZ 106	MA 20		
LWZ 304	ME 2	PMZ 0306	ME 3	PWZ 106	MK 3		
LWZ 304	MF 7	PMZ 0306	MM 5	PWZ 106	MK 5		
LWZ 304	MF 10	PMZ 0306	MN 8	PWZ 106	ML 2		
		PMZ 0307	MA 21	PWZ 107	MH 4		

ENGINE

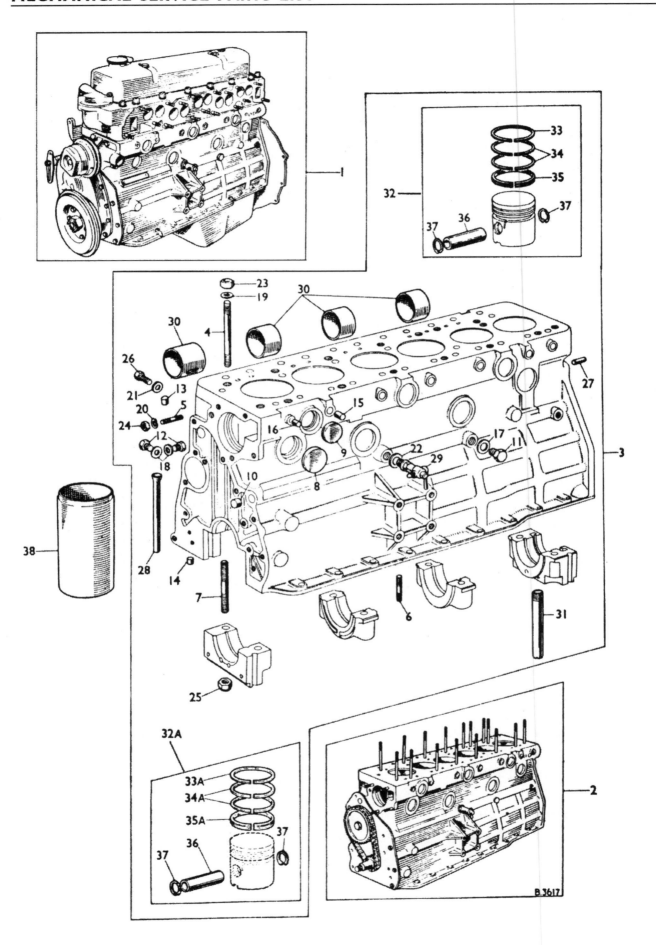

B.3617

	DESCRIPTION	Part No.	Illus. No.	Quantity	Change Point	REMARKS
	ENGINE					
	ENGINE UNIT					
	Engine unit—stripped					
	2912-cc	AEC 1489	1	1	(E) 29F/H101 to 4878	
		68G 217	1	1	(E) 29F/H4879 to 6188	W.S.E. use 68G 259
		68G 259	1	1	(E) 29F/H6189 on	
		68G 267	1	1	(E) 29K/H101 to 278	W.S.E. use 68G 277
		68G 277	1	1	(E) 29K/H279 to 10271 (E) 29KFA/H224 to 326	
		68G 309	1	1	(E) 29K/H10272 on (E) 29KFA/H327 on	
	2860-cc **France**	68G 212	1	1	(E) 29FF/H101 to 149	
		68G 220	1	1	(E) 29FF/H150 to 164	W.S.E. use 68G 262
		68G 262	1	1	(E) 29FF/H165 on	
		†68G 278	1	1	(E) 29KF/H101 to 223	W.S.E. use 68G 310
		68G 310	1	1	(E) 29KF/H224 on	
	Engine unit—half					
	2912-cc	AEC 1490	2	1	⎫ (E) 29F/H101 to 6188	W.S.E. use 68G 230
		68G 230	2	1	⎭	
		†68G 265	2	1	(E) 29K/H101 to 278	W.S.E. use 68G 275 together with 1 off oil level indicator 12B 771
		68G 275	2	1	(E) 29K/H279 on (E) 29KFA/H224 on	
	2860-cc **France**	68G 207	2	1	⎫ (E) 29FF/H101 to 164	W.S.E. use 68G 252 together with oil level indicator 12B 771
		68G 252	2	1	⎭	
		68G 276	2	1	(E) 29KF/H101 on	
	Block assembly—cylinder					
	2912-cc	†AEC 1353	3	1	(E) 29F/H101 to 278	W.S.E. use 68G 223 together with 1 off oil level indicator 12B 771
		†68G 223	3	1		
		†68G 271	3	1	(E) 29K/H101 to 278	W.S.E. use 68G 273 together with 1 off oil level indicator 12B 771
		68G 273	3	1	(E) 29K/H279 on (E) 29KFA/H224 on	
	2860-cc **France**	68G 204	3	1	⎫ (E) 29FF/H101 to 164	W.S.E. use 68G 249 together with oil level indicator 12B 771
		68G 249	3	1	⎭	
		68G 274	3	1	(E) 29KF/H101 on	
	Stud					
	Cylinder head	AEC 604	4	16		
	Water pump	53K 485	5	4		
	Oil pump	AEC 341	6	3		W.S.E. use CHS 0510
	Oil pump	CHS 0510	6	3		
	Main bearing cap	AEC 872	7	8		
	Plug					
	Core—large	AEH 592	8	5		
	Core—small	AEC 876	9	4		
	Oil gallery	8G 507	10	2		
	Oil filter feed hole	AEC 110	11	1		
	Oil pump feed hole	HNS 0503	12	2		
	Oil pump boss	2K 6012	13	1		
	Tensioner feed hole	2K 6650	14	1		
	Water gallery—large	2K 1358	15	5		
	Water gallery—small	2K 6650	16	2		
	Washer					
	Plug—oil filter feed hole	AEC 343	17	1		
	Plug—oil pump feed hole	AEC 398	18	2		
	Stud—cylinder head (steel)	PWN 107	19	16		
	Spring—stud—water pump	LWN 205	20	4		
	Screw—blanking (copper)	AEC 398	21	4		
	Tap—water drain	2K 4954	22	1		
	Nut					
	Stud—cylinder head	AEC 139	23	16		
	Stud—water pump	FNN 105	24	4		
	Stud—main bearing cap	LNN 208	25	8		
	Screw—blanking—fuel pump flange	ZCS 0505	26	2		
	Dowel—rear plate to block	1K 51	27	2		
	Tube—oil level indicator	AEC 672	28	1		
	Tap—water drain	3H 2502	29	1		
	Liner—camshaft	AJC 6042	30	1 set		
	Cap—main bearing					
	Front	NSP		1		
	No. 2	NSP		1		
	No. 3	NSP		1		
	Rear	NSP		1		
	Tube—drain	AEC 853	31	1		

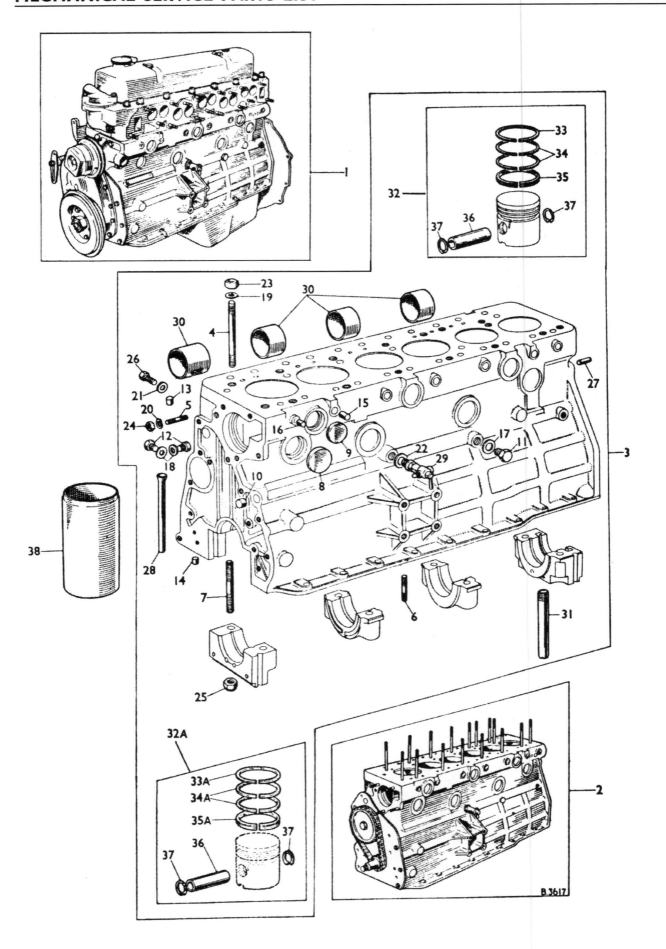

B.3617

DESCRIPTION		Part No.	Illus. No.	Quantity	Change Point	REMARKS

Engine Unit—*continued*

DESCRIPTION		Part No.	Illus. No.	Quantity	Change Point	REMARKS
Piston assembly—Grade 3						
Standard		AEC 1337 03	32	6		
·010″ (·254 mm) O/S		AEC 1337 13	32	6		
·020″ (·508 mm) O/S		AEC 1337 23	32	6		
·030″ (·762 mm) O/S		AEC 1337 33	32	6		
·040″ (1·016 mm) O/S		AEC 1337 43	32	6	(E) 29F/H101 to H6188	
Piston assembly—Grade 6						
Standard		†AEC 1337 06	32	6		
·010″ (·254 mm) O/S		†AEC 1337 16	32	6		W.S.E. use 8G 2562 and
·020″ (·508 mm) O/S		†AEC 1337 26	32	6		oversizes
·030″ (·762 mm) O/S		†AEC 1337 36	32	6		
·040″ (1·016 mm) O/S		†AEC 1337 46	32	6		
Piston assembly—Grade 3						
Standard		†12B 1159 03	32	6		
·010″ (·254 mm) O/S		†12B 1159 13	32	6		
·020″ (·508 mm) O/S		†12B 1159 23	32	6		
·030″ (·762 mm) O/S		†12B 1159 33	32	6		
·040″ (1·016 mm) O/S		†12B 1159 43	32	6	(E) 29K/H101 on	W.S.E. use 8G 2562 in
Piston assembly—Grade 6	2912-cc †				(E) 29KFA/H224 on	grades 3 or 6 and oversizes
Standard		†12B 1159 06	32	6		
·010″ (·254 mm) O/S		†12B 1159 16	32	6		
·020″ (·508 mm) O/S		†12B 1159 26	32	6		
·030″ (·762 mm) O/S		†12B 1159 36	32	6		
·040″ (1·016 mm) O/S		†12B 1159 46	32	6		
Piston assembly—engine set—Grade 3						
Standard		8G 2562 03	32	1		
·010″ (·254 mm) O/S		8G 2562 13	32	1		
·020″ (·508 mm) O/S		8G 2562 23	32	1		
·030″ (·762 mm) O/S		8G 2562 33	32	1		
·040″ (1·016 mm) O/S		8G 2562 43	32	1		
Piston assembly—engine set—Grade 6						
Standard		8G 2562 06	32	1		
·010″ (·254 mm) O/S		8G 2562 16	32	1		
·020″ (·508 mm) O/S		8G 2562 26	32	1		
·030″ (·762 mm) O/S		8G 2662 36	32	1		
·040″ (1·016 mm) O/S		8G 2562 46	32	1		
Piston assembly—Grade 3						
Standard		†AEC 2193 03	32A	6		
·010″ (·254 mm) O/S		†AEC 2193 13	32A	6		
·020″ (·508 mm) O/S		†AEC 2193 23	32A	6		
·030″ (·762 mm) O/S		†AEC 2193 33	32A	6		
·040″ (1·016 mm) O/S		†AEC 2193 43	32A	6	(E) 29FF/H101 to H164	W.S.E. use 12B 1187 in
Piston assembly—Grade 6						grades 3 or 6 and oversizes
Standard		†AEC 2193 06	32A	6		
·010″ (·254 mm) O/S		†AEC 2193 16	32A	6		
·020″ (·508 mm) O/S		†AEC 2193 26	32A	6		
·030″ (·762 mm) O/S		†AEC 2193 36	32A	6		
·040″ (1·016 mm) O/S		†AEC 2193 46	32A	6		
Piston assembly—Grade 3						
Standard		†12B 1187 03	32A	6		
·010″ (·254 mm) O/S		12B 1187 13	32A	6		
·020″ (·508 mm) O/S		†12B 1187 23	32A	6		
·030″ (·762 mm) O/S		†12B 1187 33	32A	6		
·040″ (1·016 mm) O/S		†12B 1187 43	32A	6	(E) 29KF/H101 on	W.S.E. use 8G 2563 in
Piston assembly—Grade 6	2860-cc France					grades 3 or 6 and oversizes
Standard		†12B 1187 06	32A	6		
·010″ (·254 mm) O/S		†12B 1187 16	32A	6		
·020″ (·508 mm) O/S		†12B 1187 26	32A	6		
·030″ (·762 mm) O/S		†12B 1187 36	32A	6		
·040″ (1·016 mm) O/S		†12B 1187 46	32A	6		
Piston assembly—engine set—Grade 3						
Standard		8G 2563 03	32A	1		
·010″ (·254 mm) O/S		8G 2563 13	32A	1		
·020″ (·508 mm) O/S		8G 2563 23	32A	1		
·030″ (·762 mm) O/S		8G 2563 33	32A	1		
·040″ (1·016 mm) O/S		8G 2563 43	32A	1		
Piston assembly—engine set—Grade 6						
Standard		8G 2563 06	32A	1		
·010″ (·254 mm) O/S		8G 2563 16	32A	1		
·020″ (·508 mm) O/S		8G 2563 26	32A	1		
·030″ (·762 mm) O/S		8G 2563 36	32A	1		
·040″ (1·016 mm) O/S		8G 2563 46	32A	1		

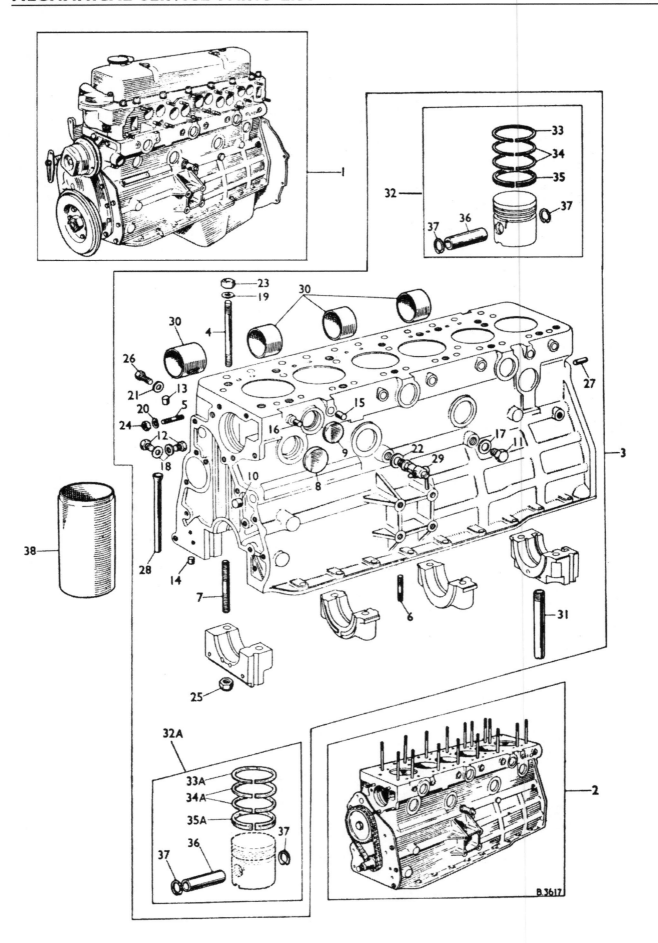

B.3617

DESCRIPTION	Part No.	Illus. No.	Quantity	Change Point	REMARKS

Engine Unit—*continued*

Ring—compression—top

DESCRIPTION	Part No.	Illus. No.	Quantity	Change Point	REMARKS
Standard	†AEC 906	33	6		
·010″ (·254 mm) O/S	†AEC 0906 10	33	6		
·020″ (·508 mm) O/S	†AEC 0906 20	33	6	(E) 29F/H101 to H6188	
·030″ (·762 mm) O/S	†AEC 0906 30	33	6		
·040″ (1·016 mm) O/S **2912-cc**	†AEC 0906 40	33	6		W.S.E. use ring—piston—engine set 8G 2522 and oversizes
Standard	†12B 1165	33	6		
·010″ (·254 mm) O/S	†12B 1165 10	33	6	(E) 29K/H101 on	
·020″ (·508 mm) O/S	†12B 1165 20	33	6	(E) 29KFA/H224 on	
·030″ (·762 mm) O/S	†12B 1165 30	33	6		
·040″ (1·016 mm) O/S	†12B 1165 40	33	6		
Standard	†AEC 2195	33A	6		
·010″ (·254 mm) O/S	†AEC 2195 10	33A	6		
·020″ (·508 mm) O/S	†AEC 2195 20	33A	6	(E) 29FF/H101 to H164	
·030″ (·762 mm) O/S	†AEC 2195 30	33A	6		
·040″ (1·016 mm) O/S **2860-cc**	†AEC 2195 40	33A	6		W.S.E. use ring—piston—engine set 8G 2564 and oversizes
Standard **France**	†12B 1188	33A	6		
·010″ (·254 mm) O/S	†12B 1188 10	33A	6		
·020″ (·508 mm) O/S	†12B 1188 20	33A	6	(E) 29KF/H101 on	
·030″ (·762 mm) O/S	†12B 1188 30	33A	6		
·040″ (1·016 mm) O/S	†12B 1188 40	33A	6		

Ring—compression—taper

DESCRIPTION	Part No.	Illus. No.	Quantity	Change Point	REMARKS
Standard	†AEC 907	34	12		
·010″ (·254 mm) O/S	†AEC 0907 10	34	12		
·020″ (·508 mm) O/S	†AEC 0907 20	34	12	(E) 29F/H101 to H6188	
·030″ (·762 mm) O/S	†AEC 0907 30	34	12		
·040″ (1·016 mm) O/S **2912-cc**	†AEC 0907 40	34	12		W.S.E. use ring—piston—engine set 8G 2522 and oversizes
Standard	†AEC 903	34	12		
·010″ (·254 mm) O/S	†AEC 0903 10	34	12		
·020″ (·508 mm) O/S	†AEC 0903 20	34	12	(E) 29K/H101 on	
·030″ (·762 mm) O/S	†AEC 0903 30	34	12	(E) 29KFA/H224 on	
·040″ (1·016 mm) O/S	†AEC 0903 40	34	12		
Standard	†AEC 2196	34A	12		
·010″ (·254 mm) O/S	†AEC 2196 10	34A	12		
·020″ (·508 mm) O/S	†AEC 2196 20	34A	12	(E) 29FF/H101 to H164	
·030″ (·762 mm) O/S	†AEC 2196 30	34A	12		
·040″ (1·016 mm) O/S **2860-cc**	†AEC 2196 40	34A	12		W.S.E. use ring—piston—engine set 8G 2564 and oversizes
Standard **France**	†12B 1189	34A	12		
·010″ (·254 mm) O/S	†12B 1189 10	34A	12		
·020″ (·508 mm) O/S	†12B 1189 20	34A	12	(E) 29KF/H101 on	
·030″ (·762 mm) O/S	†12B 1189 30	34A	12		
·040″ (1·016 mm) O/S	†12B 1189 40	34A	12		

Ring—scraper

DESCRIPTION	Part No.	Illus. No.	Quantity	Change Point	REMARKS
Standard	†AEC 908	35	6		
·010″ (·254 mm) O/S	†AEC 0908 10	35	6		
·020″ (·508 mm) O/S	†AEC 0908 20	35	6	(E) 29F/H101 to H6188	
·030″ (·762 mm) O/S	†AEC 0908 30	35	6		
·040″ (1·016 mm) O/S **2912-cc**	†AEC 0908 40	35	6		W.S.E. use ring—piston—engine set 8G 2522 and oversizes
Standard	†12B 1160	35	6		
·010″ (·254 mm) O/S	†12B 1160 10	35	6	(E) 29K/H101 on	
·020″ (·508 mm) O/S	†12B 1160 20	35	6	(E) 29KFA/H224 on	
·030″ (·762 mm) O/S	†12B 1160 30	35	6		
·040″ (1·016 mm) O/S	†12B 1160 40	35	6		
Standard	†AEC 2197	35A	6		
·010″ (·254 mm) O/S	†AEC 2197 10	35A	6		
·020″ (·508 mm) O/S	†AEC 2197 20	35A	6	(E) 29FF/H101 to H164	
·030″ (·762 mm) O/S	†AEC 2197 30	35A	6		
·040″ (1·016 mm) O/S **2860-cc**	†AEC 2197 40	35A	6		W.S.E. use ring—piston—engine set 8G 2564 and oversizes
Standard **France**	†12B 1190	35A	6		
·010″ (·254 mm) O/S	†12B 1190 10	35A	6		
·020″ (·508 mm) O/S	†12B 1190 20	35A	6	(E) 29KF/H101 on	
·030″ (·762 mm) O/S	†12B 1190 30	35A	6		
·040″ (1·016 mm) O/S	†12B 1190 40	35A	6		

Ring—piston—engine set—2912-cc

DESCRIPTION	Part No.	Illus. No.	Quantity	Change Point	REMARKS
Standard	8G 2522		1		
·010″ (·254 mm) O/S	8G 2522 10		1		
·020″ (·508 mm) O/S	8G 2522 20		1		
·030″ (·762 mm) O/S	8G 2522 30		1		
·040″ (1·016 mm) O/S	8G 2522 40		1		

Ring—piston—engine set—2860-cc

DESCRIPTION	Part No.	Illus. No.	Quantity	Change Point	REMARKS
Standard	8G 2564		1		
·010″ (·254 mm) O/S	8G 2564 10		1		
·020″ (·508 mm) O/S	8G 2564 20		1		
·030″ (·762 mm) O/S	8G 2564 30		1		
·040″ (1·016 mm) O/S	8G 2564 40		1		
Pin—gudgeon	AEC 905	36	6		
Circlip	CCN 214	37	12		
Liner—cylinder block **2912-cc**	†AEC 879	38	6		For service purposes only

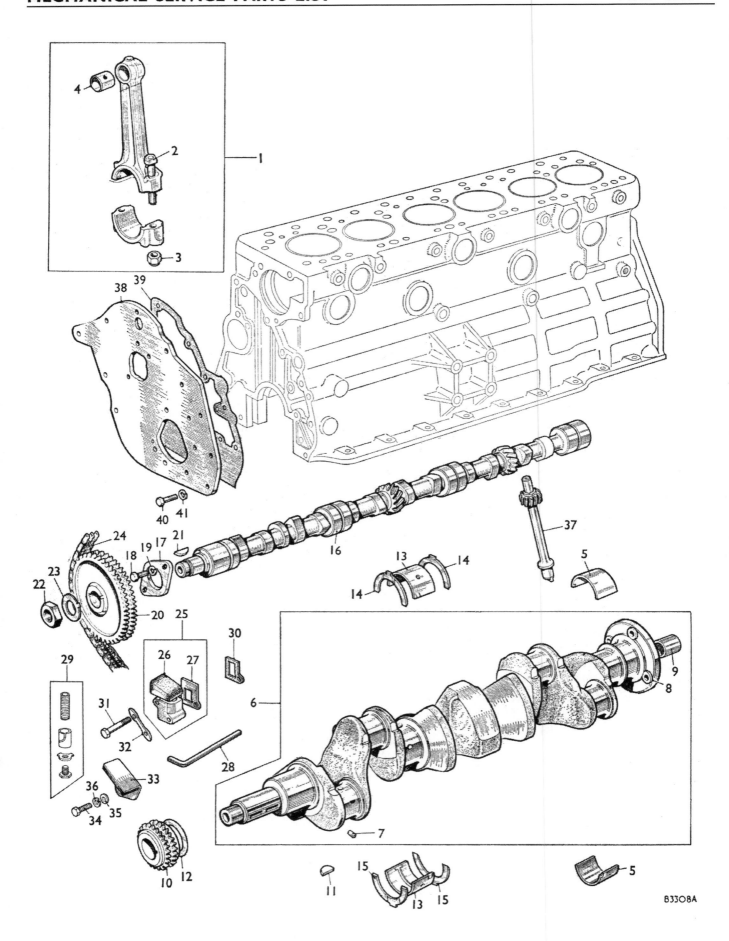

B3308A

	DESCRIPTION	Part No.	Illus. No.	Quantity	Change Point	REMARKS

† **Engine Unit**—*continued*

CONNECTING RODS—BEARINGS

DESCRIPTION	Part No.	Illus. No.	Quantity	Change Point	REMARKS
Connecting rod and cap	8G 2339	1	1 set		
Bolt—cap	AEC 2097	2	12		
Nut—bolt	AEC 328	3	12		
Bush—small end	AEC 882	4	6		
Bearing—connecting rod					
Standard	AJC 5159	5	1 set		
·010″ (·254 mm) U/S	AJC 515910	5	1 set		
·020″ (·508 mm) U/S	AJC 515920	5	1 set		
·030″ (·762 mm) U/S	AJC 515930	5	1 set		
·040″ (1·016 mm) U/S	AJC 515940	5	1 set		

CRANKSHAFT—BEARINGS—GEARS

DESCRIPTION	Part No.	Illus. No.	Quantity	Change Point	REMARKS
Crankshaft	AEC 28	6	1		
Restrictor	1B 1033	7	6		
Nut—flywheel bolt	AEC 2040	8	4		
Bush—drive gear	1K 369	9	1		
Gear—crankshaft	AEC 2026	10	1		
Key—gear	WKN 608	11	1		
Washer—packing	2K 8725	12	A/R		
Bearing—main					
Standard	8G 2287	13	1 set		W.S.E.; use 8G 2360 and oversizes
·010″ (·254 mm) U/S	8G 228710	13	1 set	(E) 29F/H101 to H2011	
·020″ (·508 mm) U/S	8G 228720	13	1 set		
·030″ (·762 mm) U/S	8G 228730	13	1 set		
·040″ (1·016 mm) U/S	8G 228740	13	1 set		
Standard	†8G 2360	13	1 set		
·010″ (·254 mm) U/S	†8G 236010	13	1 set		
·020″ (·508 mm) U/S	8G 236020	13	1 set	(E) 29/H2012 on	
·030″ (·762 mm) U/S	8G 236030	13	1 set		
·040″ (1·016 mm) U/S	8G 236040	13	1 set		
Washer—thrust—upper					
Standard	†AEC 278	14	2		Two used of selected size
·0025″ (·0635 mm) O/S	†AEC 332	14	2		
·005″ (·127 mm) O/S	†AEC 744	14	2		
·0075″ (·190 mm) O/S	†AEC 746	14	2		
·010″ (·254 mm) O/S	†AEC 748	14	2		
Washer—thrust—lower					
Standard	†AEC 279	15	2		Two used of selected size
·0025″ (·0635 mm) O/S	†AEC 333	15	2		
·005″ (·127 mm) O/S	†AEC 745	15	2		
·0075″ (·190 mm) O/S	†AEC 747	15	2		
·010″ (·254 mm) O/S	†AEC 749	15	2		
Crankshaft (with bearings)	†AEC 47		1		U.K. market; Exchange Unit Scheme only

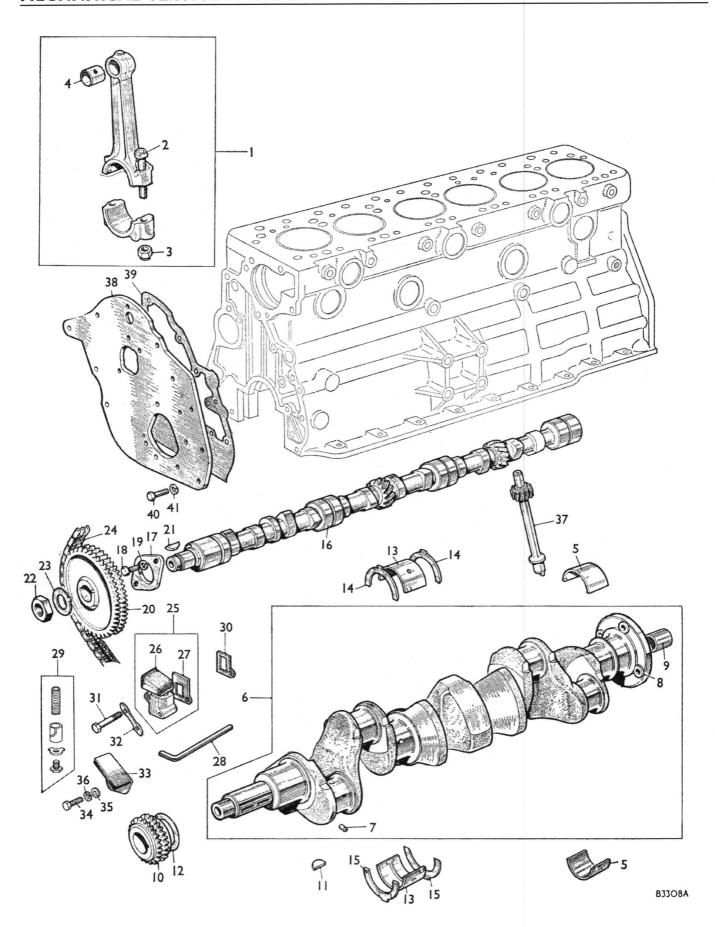

B3308A

		DESCRIPTION	Part No.	Illus. No.	Quantity	Stock recoms. DIST. Exp.	UK	D	Change Point	REMARKS

† **Engine Unit**—*continued*

CAMSHAFT—GEAR

DESCRIPTION	Part No.	Illus. No.	Quantity	Exp.	UK	D	Change Point	REMARKS
Camshaft	AEC 2029	16	1				(E) 29F/H101 to H2285	
	12B 594	16	1	★	★		(E) 29F/H2286 to H6188 29FF/H101 to H164	
	AEC 865	16	1	★	★		(E) 29K/H101 on (E) 29KF/H101 on (E) 29KFA/H224 on	
Plate—locating	†AEC 810	17	1					W.S.E.; use 1K 624
Plate—locating	†1K 624	17	1					
Screw	HNS 0507	18	2					
Washer—spring	LWN 205	19	2					
Gear—camshaft	AEC 482	20	1	★	★			
Key	WKN 606	21	1					
Nut—gear	AEC 247	22	1					
Washer—lock	1B 1219	23	1					
Chain—camshaft drive	AEC 191	24	1	★	★	★		
Tensioner assembly—chain (with Allen key)	NSP		1					Was 17H 342; use 17H 6681 together with Allen key 17H 6679
Tensioner assembly—chain	17H 6681	25	1					
Head—slipper	17H 31	26	1					
Back plate	AJC 5033	27	1					
Key—Allen	17H 6679	28	1					
Kit—chain tensioner servicing	17H 341	29	1					For service purposes only
Spring	NSP		1					
Plug—bottom	NSP		1					
Washer—tab	NSP		1					
Cylinder	NSP		1					
Joint—tensioner	AEC 339	30	1	★	★	★		
Bolt	HBN 0412	31	2					
Washer—lock—bolt	AEC 340	32	1					
Damper—chain	AEC 2030	33	1	★	★			
Screw	HNS 0608	34	1					
Washer	PWN 106	35	1					
Washer	LWN 206	36	1					

OIL PUMP SPINDLE

DESCRIPTION	Part No.	Illus. No.	Quantity	Exp.	UK	D	Change Point	REMARKS
Spindle—driving—oil pump	AEC 829	37	1					

FRONT MOUNTING PLATE

DESCRIPTION	Part No.	Illus. No.	Quantity	Exp.	UK	D	Change Point	REMARKS
Plate—engine mounting—front	AEC 2032	38	1	★	★			
Joint—mounting plate to crankcase	AEC 2033	39	1	★	★			
Screw	HNS 0506	40	6					
Washer—spring	LWZ 305	41	6					

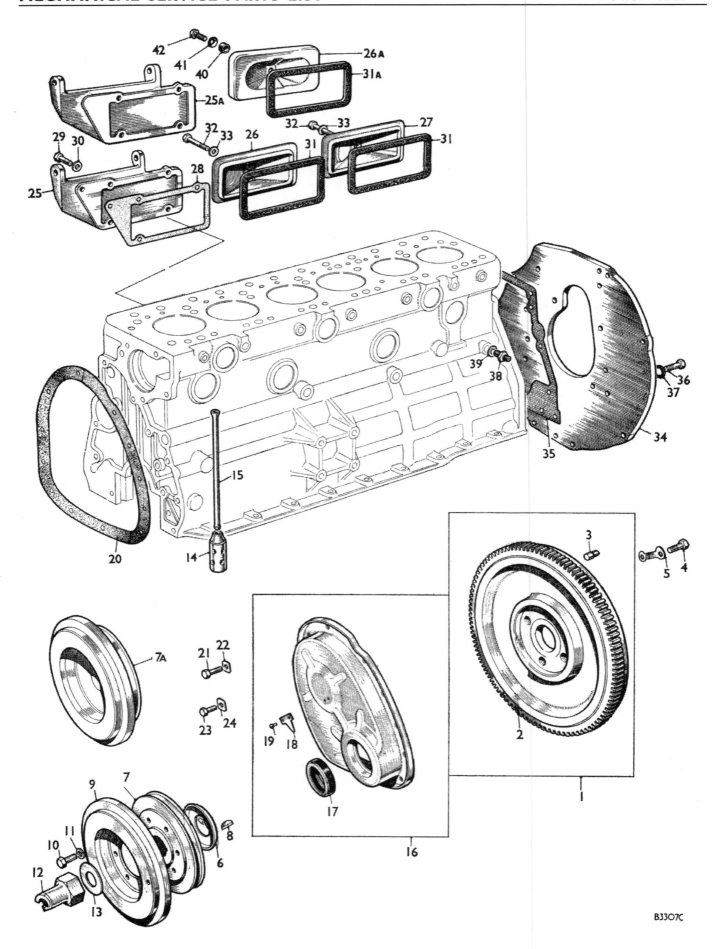

B3307C

	DESCRIPTION	Part No.	Illus. No.	Quantity	Change Point	REMARKS
	Engine Unit—*continued*					
	FLYWHEEL					
	Flywheel	AEC 885	1	1	(E) 29F/H101 to H4878	
					(E) 29FF/H101 to H149	
	Flywheel	22B 136	1	1 ★ ★	(E) 29F/H4879 on	
					(E) 29FF/H150 on	
	Ring—starter	1B 1714	2	1 ★		
	Dowel—clutch to flywheel	AEC 2037	3	2	(E) 29F/H101 to H4878	
					(E) 29FF/H101 to H149	
	Dowel—clutch to flywheel	AEA 420	3	3	(E) 29F/H4979 on	
					(E) 29FF/H160 on	
	Bolt—flywheel to crankshaft	AEC 265	4	4		
	Washer lock bolt	2K 7552	5	2		
	CRANKSHAFT OIL THROWER—					
	PULLEY—DAMPER—STARTING NUT					
	Thrower—oil	1G 838	6	1		
	Pulley—crankshaft	†AEC 290	7	1	⎤ (E) 29F/H101 to 6188	
	Damper—crankshaft	†AEC 183	9	1	⎦ (E) 29FF/H101 to 164	
					(E) 29K/H101 to 10271	
					(E) 29KF/H101 to 223	
					(E) 29KFA/H224 to 326	
	*Pulley—crankshaft (with Damper)					
	½″ (12·7 mm) Grove	†12B 1274	7A	1	(E) 29K/H10272 on	
					(E) 29KF/H 224 on	
					(E) 29KFA/H 327 on	
	Key	WKN 608	8	1		
	Screw	NCS 0606	10	6		
	Washer—spring	LWZ 206	11	6		
	Nut—starting	AEC 448	12	1		
	Washer—nut	2H 731	13	1	(E) 29F/H101 to H3385	W.S.E.; use 12B 681
	Washer—nut	12B 681	13	1	(E) 29F/H3386 on	
	TAPPETS AND PUSH RODS					
	Tappets					
	Standard	AEC 264	14	12 ★ ★		
	·010″ (·254 mm) O/S	AEC 026410	14	A/R		
	·020″ (·508 mm) O/S	AEC 026420	14	A/R		
	Push rod	88G 264	15	12		Part No. change; Part No. change; was AEC 150 and AEC 2015

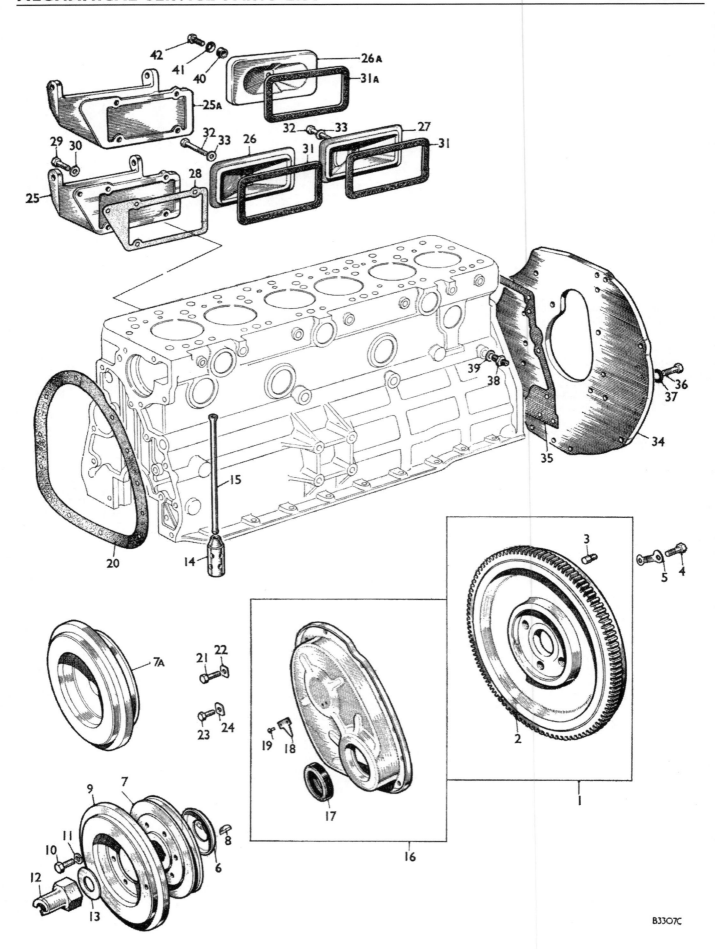

B3307C

	DESCRIPTION	Part No.	Illus. No.	Quantity	Change Point	REMARKS
	Engine Unit—*continued*					
	CYLINDER FRONT AND SIDE COVERS					
	Cover—front	AEC 1011	16	1		
	Seal	AEC 621	17	1		
	Pointer-timing	AEC 348	18	1		
	Rivet—pointer	AEC 349	19	2		
	Joint—front cover	AEC 202	20	1		
	Screw	HNS 0507	21	7		Correction; was HNS 0570
	Washer	2K 7440	22	7		
	Screw	HNS 0403	23	5		
	Washer	2K 5197	24	5		
	Cover—cylinder side					
	Front	AEC 689	25	1	(E) 29F/H101 to H6188 (E) 29FF/H101 to H164	
	Front	AEC 2163	25A	1	(E) 29K/H101 on †(E) 29KFA/H224 on (E) 29KF/H101 on	
	Centre	2A 770	26	1	(E) 29F/101 to 3593	
		12H 941	26	1	(E) 29F/3954 on	W.S.E.; use 12A 1170 together with 1 off washer 12A 1175, 1 off bush 12A 1176, 1 off cup washer, 12A 1177 and 1 off screw HZS 0509
		12A 1170	26A	1		
	Rear	12B 682	27	1		
	Joint—front side cover	AEC 313	28	1		
	Screw	HNS 0506	29	5		
	Washer	AEC 435	30	5		
	Joint—centre and rear side covers	12A 24	31	2		W.S.E.; use 12A 1139
	Joint—centre and rear side covers	12A 1139	31	2		For use with 12B 682 and 12A 941
	Bolt	HBN 0510	32	2		
	Washer	AEC 461	33	2		
	Joint—centre side cover	12A 1175	31A	1		
	Bush	12A 1176	40	1		Required when cover 12A 1170 is fitted
	Washer—cup	12A 1177	41	1		
	Screw	HZS 0509	42	1		
	REAR MOUNTING PLATE					
	Plate—engine mounting—rear	AEC 474	34	1		
	Joint—plate to crankcase	AEC 128	35	1		
	Bolt	AEC 478	36	11		
	Washer—shakeproof	LWN 406	47	11		
	OIL PIPE UNION					
	Union oil gauge pipe	1G 1814	38	1		
	Washer—union	AEC 787	39	1		

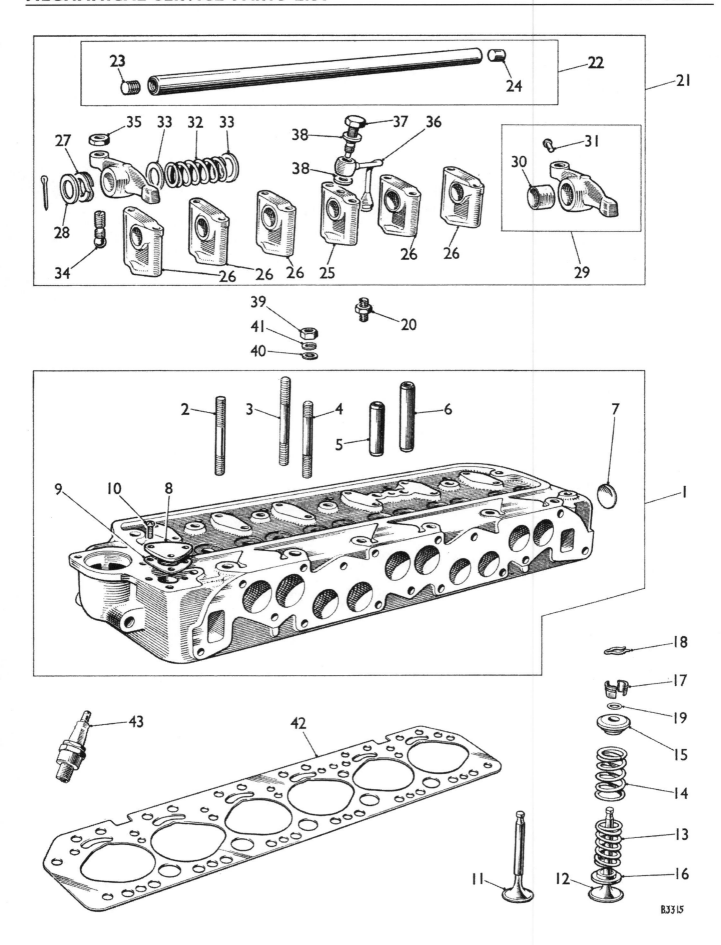

B3315

	DESCRIPTION	Part No.	Illus. No.	Quantity	Stock recoms. DIST. Exp.	UK	D	Change Point	REMARKS

Engine Unit—*continued*

CYLINDER HEAD—VALVES—GUIDES—SPRINGS—ROCKERS

DESCRIPTION	Part No.	Illus. No.	Quantity	Exp.	UK	D	Change Point	REMARKS
Head—cylinder	AEC 2008	1	1	★	★			
Stud								
Rocker bracket and cover	AEC 491	2	2					
Rocker bracket—long	51K 591	3	6					
Rocker bracket—short	51K 590	4	4					
Guide—valve								
Inlet—standard	AEC 135	5	6	★	★			
Inlet ·010" (·254 mm) O/S, O/D	AEC 013520	5	6					
Exhaust—standard	AEC 245	6	6	★	★			
Exhaust ·010" (·254 mm) O/S,O/D	AEC 024510	6	6					
Plug—core hole	AEC 876	7	1					
Plate—blanking—thermal switch hole	AEC 996	8	1					
Washer—joint—plate	AEC 962	9	1					
Screw	PMZ 0308	10	3					
Valve—inlet	AEC 724	11	6	★	★	★		
Valve—exhaust	AEC 915	12	6	★	★	★		
Springs—valve								
Inner	1H 723	13	12	★	★	★		
Outer	12H 650	14	12	★	★	★	(E) 29F/H101 to H2285	
Outer	6K 873	14	12	★	★	★	(E) 29F/H2286 to H6188	
							(E) 29FF/H101 to H164	
Outer	1H 1111	14	12	★	★	★	(E) 29K/H101 on	
							(E) 29KFA/H224 on	
							(E) 29KF/H101 on	
Cap—spring	AEC 736	15	12	★	★			
Collar—spring	1H 726	16	12	★	★			
Retainer—spring	1K 800	17	12prs.	★	★			
Circlip—retainer	1K 372	18	12	★	★			
Grommet—valve stem	AEK 113	19	12	★	★			
Union—rocker oil feed pipe	AEC 463	20	1					
Shaft assembly—valve rocker	†AEC 1097	21	1					]W.S.E.; use component parts
Shaft—rocker	AEC 27	22	1					
Plug—screwed	2K 6534	23	1					
Plug—plain	ID 1977	24	1					
Bracket—rocker shaft—tapped	AEC 616	25	1					
Bracket—rocker shaft—plain	11B 121	26	5					
Washer—spring—rocker shaft	2K 2561	27	2					
Washer—plain—rocker shaft	AEC 144	28	2					
Rocker assembly	†AED 159	29	12	★	★			Correction; was AEC 159
Bush	11B 511	30	12	★	★			
Rivet	5C 2436	31	12					
Spring—rocker spacing	2K 5923	32	5					
Washer—rocker spacing	AEC 143	33	12					
Screw—rocker adjusting	AEC 2044	34	12					
Nut—locking—screw	FNN 206	35	12					
Pipe—rocker oil feed	AEC 160	36	1					
Bolt—pipe to rocker bracket	AEC 162	37	1					
Washer—bolt	AEC 346	38	2					
Nut—rocker bracket stud	FNN 506	39	12					
Washer—plain—nut	PWN 106	40	12					
Washer—spring—nut	LWN 206	41	12					
Washer—joint—cylinder head	AEC 875	42	1					
Plug—sparking	AEJ 52	43	6	★	★	★		

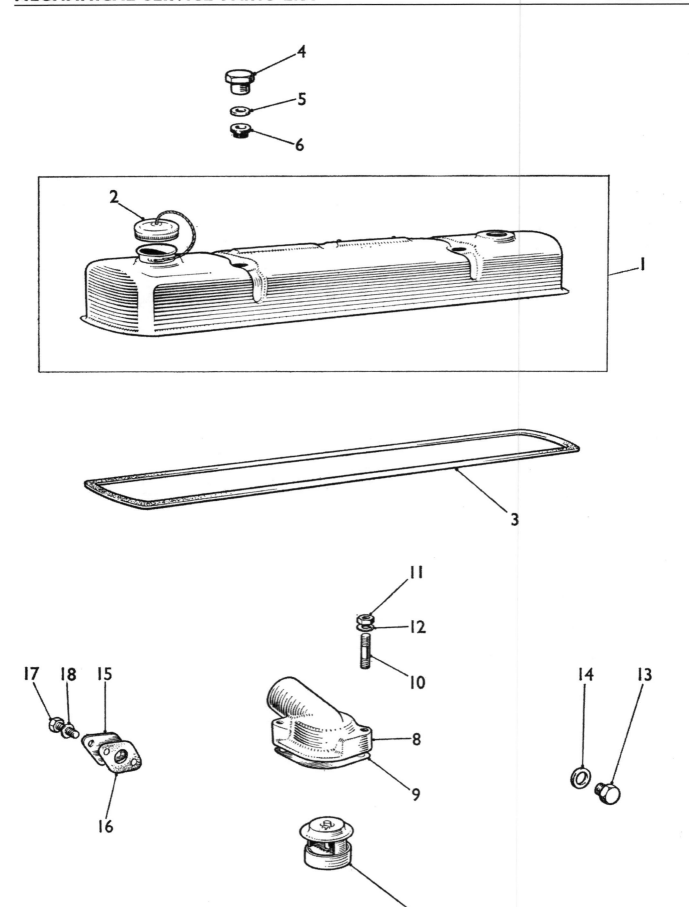

B3314

DESCRIPTION	Part No.	Illus. No.	Quantity	Change Point	REMARKS
Engine Unit—*continued*					
VALVE ROCKER COVER AND OIL FILLER					
Cover—valve rocker	AEC 2041	1	1		W.S.E. use 12B 1384
Cover—valve rocker	12B 1384	1	1		
Cap—oil filler	8G 612	2	1		
Gasket—cover to head	AEC 1332	3	1		
Nut—rocker cover	AEC 2181	4	2		
Washer—nut	AEC 2179	5	2		
Bush (rubber)	AEC 2178	6	2		
Thermostat	13H 957	7	1		
	13H 2317	7	1		W.S.E. use 13H 4070
	13H 3585	7	1		
	13H 4070	7	1		
Elbow—water outlet	AEC 158	8	1		
Gasket—elbow	1K 1056	9	1		
Stud—elbow to cylinder head	51K 490	10	2		
Nut—stud	FNN 105	11	2		
Washer—spring—stud	LWN 205	12	2		
Plug—thermal indicator boss	ADP 210	13	1		
Washer—plug	6K 433	14	1		
Plate—heater outlet blanking	AEC 266	15	1		
Gasket—blanking plate	†1G 2342	16	2		W.S.E. use 88G 423
Gasket—blanking plate	†88G 423	16	2		
Screw—blanking plate	HNS 0404	17	2		
Washer—spring	LWN 204	18	2		
Sleeve—thermostat blanking	11G 176		1		For use in extremely hot climates in lieu of thermostat, optional extra

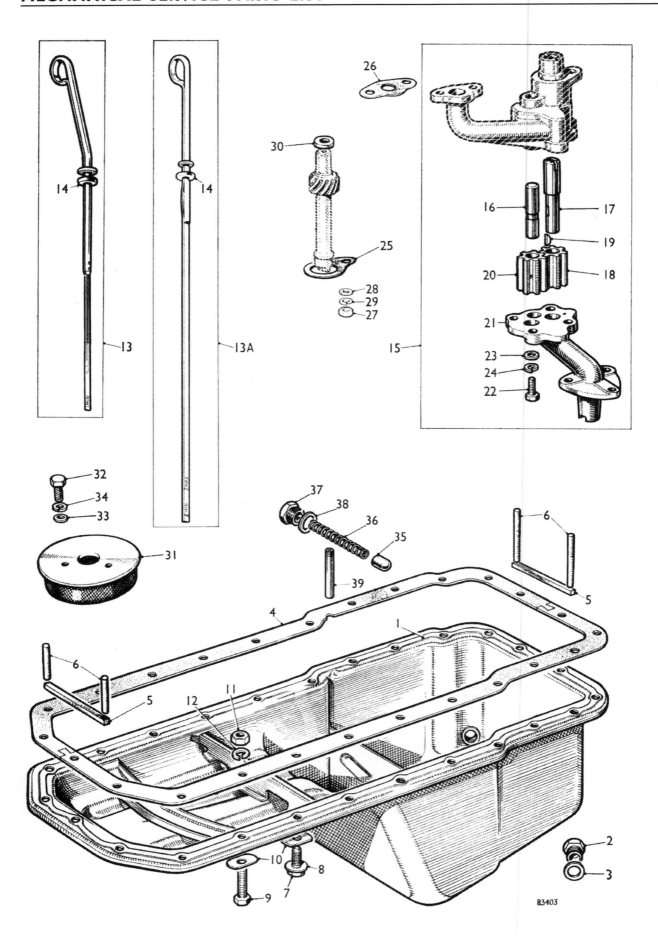

B.3403

DESCRIPTION	Part No.	Illus. No.	Quantity	Exp.	UK	D	Change Point	REMARKS
Engine Unit—*continued*								
SUMP—OIL LEVEL INDICATOR								
Sump—oil	AEC 203	1	1	★	★			
Plug—drain	2H 4685	2	1					
Washer—plug (copper)	AEC 699	3	1					
Joint—sump to crankcase	AEC 205	4	1	★	★	★		
Seal—front and rear main bearing cap	AEC 108	5	2	★	★	★		
Plug—front and rear main bearing cap	AEC 888	6	4	★	★			
Bolt	HZS 0404	7	23					
Washer—spring	LWZ 404	8	23					
Bolt	HNS 0408	9	2					
Washer	2K 5197	10	25					
Nut	FNN 104	11	2					
Washer—spring	LWN 204	12	2					
Indicator—oil level	AEC 667	13	1				(E) 29F/H101 to 29K/H278 / (E) 29FF/H101 to H164	
Indicator—oil level	12B 771	13A	1				(E) 29K/H279 on / †(E) 29KFA/H224 on / (E) 29KF/H101 on	
Washer—indicator (rubber)	AEC 671	14	1					
OIL PUMP—PIPE—OIL RELEASE VALVE								
Pump assembly—oil	AEC 1341	15	1	★	★			
Body	N.S.P.		1					
Shaft—driven	AEC 928	16	1					
Shaft—driving	AEC 929	17	1					
Gear—driving	1K 105	18	1					
Key	WKN 405	19	1					
Gear—driven	1K 106	20	1					
Cover—body	AEC 930	21	1					
Screw	NCS 0408	22	4					
Washer—plain	PWN 104	23	4					
Washer—spring	LWN 204	24	4					
Joint—pump body to block	AEC 698	25	1	★	★			
Joint—flange to block	AEC 315	26	1	★	★			
Nut	FNN 105	27	3					
Washer								
Plain	PWN 105	28	3					
Spring	LWN 205	29	3					
Thrust—driving spindle	AEC 223	30	1					
Strainer—oil	AEC 224	31	1					
Bolt	HNS 0406	32	3					
Washer—plain	PWN 104	33	3					
Washer—spring	LWN 204	34	3					
Valve—oil release	AEC 283	35	1	★	★			
Spring—valve	AEC 284	36	1	★	★			
Plug—valve	2K 8377	37	1					
Washer—plug (copper)	6K 431	38	1					
Pipe—valve drain	1K 141	39	1					

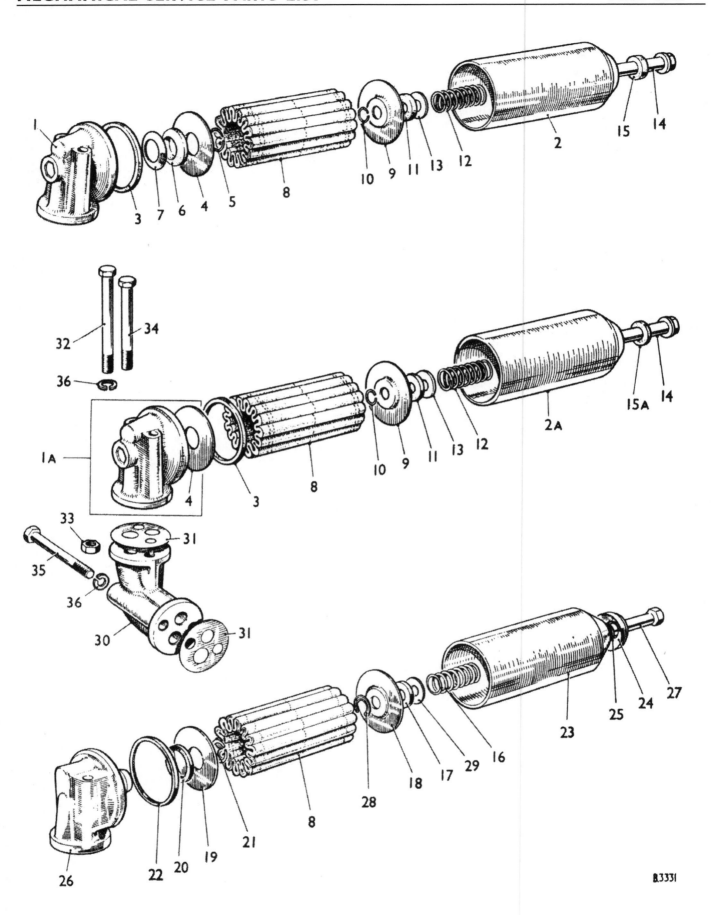

83331

	DESCRIPTION	Part No.	Illus. No.	Quantity	Change Point	REMARKS

Engine Unit—*continued*

    OIL FILTER (EXTERNAL)

DESCRIPTION	Part No.	Illus. No.	Quantity	Change Point	REMARKS
Filter—oil (Tecalemit)	NSP		1		Alternative to Purolator
Head (for use with BSF thread centre bolt)	AJC 5011	1	1		
Head (for use with UNF thread centre bolt)	17H 940	1	1		
Sump	17H 3	2	1		
Seal—sump to head	13H 998	3	1		Part No. change; was 17H 4
Plate—element clamp	7H 147	4	1		
Circlip—plate to head	2A 700	5	1		
Washer (felt)	7H 1756	6	1	(E) 29F/H101 to H2268	
Washer (dished)	7H 1761	7	1		
Element	48G 171	8	1		
Plate—pressure	17H 942	9	1		
Circlip—plate to centre bolt	17H 2877	10	1		
Washers (felt)	7H 1758	11	1		
Spring—pressure plate	7H 1764	12	1		
Washer—spring	7H 1765	13	1		
Bolt—centre (BSF thread)	7H 1762	14	1		
Bolt—centre (UNF thread)	†17H 775	14	1		W.S.E. use 17H 1272
Bolt—centre (UNF thread)	†17H 1272	14	1		
Seal—bolt to sump	7H 1759	15	1		
Filter—oil (Tecalemit)	NSP		1		Alternative to Purolator
Head assembly	17H 2873	1A	1		
Plate—element clamp	7H 147	4	1		
Sump	17H 3529	2A	1		
Seal—sump to head	13H 998	3	1		Part No. change; was 17H 4
Element	48G 171	8	1	(E) 29F/H2269 on	
Plate—pressure	17H 942	9	1		
Circlip—plate to centre bolt	17H 2877	10	1		
Washer (felt)	7H 1758	11	1		
Spring—pressure plate	7H 1764	12	1		
Washer	7H 1765	13	1		
Bolt—centre	17H 3530	14	1		
Seal—bolt to sump	37H 1173	15A	1		
Filter—oil (Purolator)	NSP		1		Alternative to Tecalemit
Element	48G 171	8	1		
Spring	7H 25	16	1		
Seal	7H 28	17	1		
Plate—pressure	17H 1148	18	1		
Plate—clamping	17H 1150	19	1		
Gasket	17H 1152	20	1		
Ring—snap	17H 1167	21	1		
Seal	27H 1983	22	1		
Sump	27H 1144	23	1		W.S.E. use 37H 140
Sump	37H 140	23	1		
Collar	27H 1143	24	1		
Seal—'O' section	17H 1173	25	1		
Head	17H 3693	26	1		
Bolt—centre	27H 1142	27	1		
Circlip	†17H 1476	28	1		W.S.E. use 27H 2573
Circlip	†27H 2573	28	1		
Washer	PWN 106	29	1		
Plate—adaptor	AEC 675	30	1		
Gasket—plate to crankcase	1B 1233	31	1		
Gasket—filter to plate	1B 1233	31	1		
Bolt—filter to plate	HBZ 0636	32	1		
Nut—bolt	FNZ 106	33	1		
Screw—filter to plate	HCN 0631	34	1		
Bolt—plate to crankcase	HBZ 0632	35	2		
Washer—spring—bolt	LWZ 206	36	4		

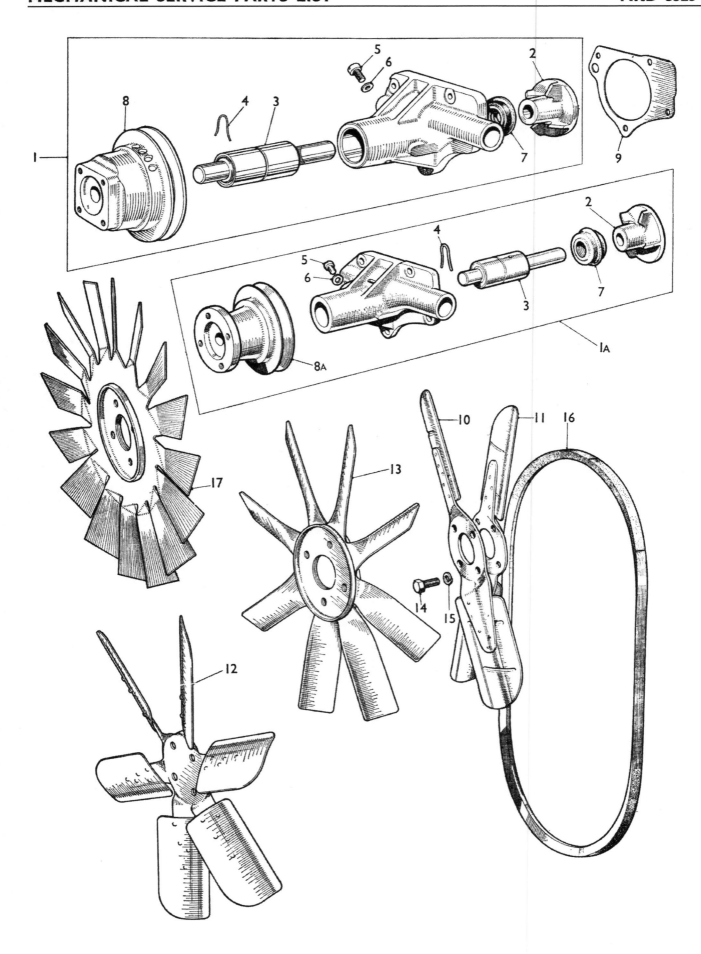

	DESCRIPTION	Part No.	Illus. No.	Quantity	Change Point	REMARKS
	Engine Unit—*continued*					
	WATER PUMP					
	Pump assembly—water	AEC 2018	1	1	⎤	
	Body	NSP		1		
	Vane	AEC 2020	2	1	(E) 29F/H101 to 6188	
	Bearing and spindle assembly	1H 1153	3	1	(E) 29FF/H101 to 164	
	Wire—bearing locating	2A 778	4	1	(E) 29K/H101 to 10271	
	Screw—lubricating point	53K 1433	5	1	(E) 29KF/H101 to 223	
	Washer (fibre)	2K 4974	6	1	(E) 29KFA/H224 to 826	
	Seal	88G 446	7	1		Was 13H 772
	Pulley	AEC 2021	8	1	⎦	
	Pump assembly—water	12B 706	1A	1		W.S.E. use 12B 2056
	Pump assembly—water	12B 2056	1A	1		
	Body	NSP		1	⎤	
	Vane	AEC 2020	2	1		
	Bearing and spindle	1H 1153	3	1		For use with 12B 705
		†12H 2097	3	1		For use with 12B 2056; W.S.E. use 12H 2269
		†12H 2269	3	1	(E) 29K/H10272 on	
	Wire—bearing locating	2A 778	4	1	(E) 29KF/H224 on	
	Screw—lubricating point	53K 1433	5	1	(E) 29KFA/H327 on	
	Washer (fibre)	2K 4974	6	1		
	Seal	88G 446	7	1		
	Pulley—'V' type	12B 700	8A	1		
	Gasket—pump to crankcase	†88G 424	9	1	⎦	Was AEC 216

† Revised Information.   43   Issue 5   **MA 11**

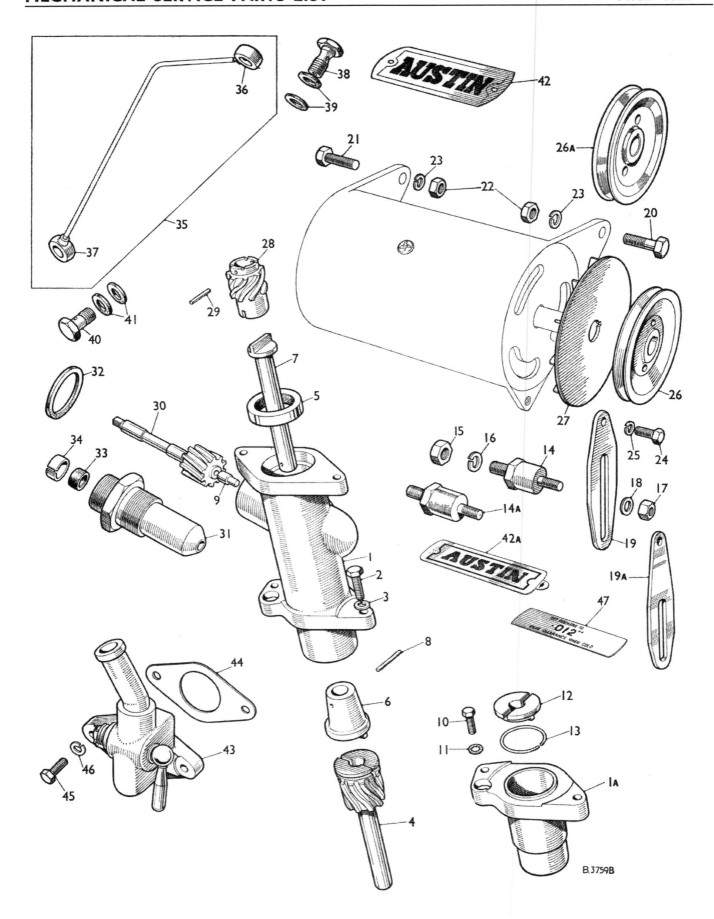

B.3759B

	DESCRIPTION	Part No.	Illus. No.	Quantity	Change Point	REMARKS

Engine Unit—*continued*

DISTRIBUTOR AND DYNAMO MOUNTING

DESCRIPTION	Part No.	Illus. No.	Qty	Change Point	REMARKS
Housing—distributor and tachometer	AEC 685	1	1		
Screw	HNS 0407	2	3		
Washer—spring	LWN 204	3	3		
Gear—distributor driving	AEC 242	4	1		
Seal—oil—distributor	AEC 681	5	1		
Dog—driving	AEC 678	6	1	See (1) foot of page	
Extension—driving spindle	AEC 686	7	1		
Peg—spindle	2K 2163	8	1		
Button—tachometer pinion thrust	1A 3073	9	1		
Housing—distributor	1K 2524	1A	1		
Screw	HNS 0405	10	1		
Washer—shakeproof	LWN 404	11	1	See (2) foot of page	
Gear—distributor driving	AEC 242	4	1		
Coupling—distributor to gear	AEC 243	12	1		
Circlip—coupling	AEC 244	13	1		
Pillar—dynamo adjusting link	AEC 293	14	1	See (1) foot of page	
Pillar—dynamo adjusting link	AEC 2079	14A	1	See (2) foot of page	
Nut	FNN 107	15	1		
Washer—spring	LWN 207	16	1		
Nut	LNZ 206	17	1		
Washer—plain	PWN 106	18	1		

DYNAMO LINK, FAN, PULLEY AND TACHOMETER DRIVE

DESCRIPTION	Part No.	Illus. No.	Qty	Change Point	REMARKS
Link—dynamo adjusting	AEC 238	19	1	See (3) foot of page	
Link—dynamo adjusting	AEC 2184	19A	1	See (5) foot of page	
Bolt	HBN 0510	20	1		
Screw	HNS 0509	21	1		
Nut	FNN 105	22	2		
Washer—spring	LWN 205	23	2		
Screw	NCS 0507	24	1		
Washer—spring	LWN 805	25	1		
Pulley—dynamo	AEC 910	26	1	See (1) foot of page	
	AEC 2078	26	1	See (4) foot of page	
	12B 701	26A	1	See (5) foot of page	
Fan—dynamo	1B 2178	27	1	See (1) foot of page	
Fan—dynamo	17D 11	27	1	See (2) foot of page	
Gear—tachometer driving	AEC 679	28	1		
Peg—gear	2K 2163	29	1		
Pinion—tachometer	AEC 680	30	1		
Bush—pinion	AEC 701	31	1		
Gasket—bush to housing	2K 4970	32	1		
Seal—oil—pinion	3H 964	33	1		
Ring—oil seal—retaining	1G 3410	34	1		
Pipe—oil feed—tachometer drive	AEC 687	35	1	See (1) foot of page	
Union—banjo—tachometer drive end	1K 21	36	1		
Union—banjo—crankcase end	11B 174	37	1		
Bolt—banjo union—tachometer drive end	AEC 796	38	1		
Washer—bolt	†6K 56	39	1		W.S.E. use 22A 136
Washer—bolt	†22A 136	39	1		
Bolt—banjo union—crankcase end	AEC 682	40	1		
Washer—bolt	11B 206	41	2		

NAMEPLATE

DESCRIPTION	Part No.	Illus. No.	Qty	Change Point	REMARKS
Nameplate—rocker cover	2A 263	42	1		For use with rocker cover AEC 2041
Nameplate—rocker cover	12A 1205	42A	1		For use with rocker cover 12B 1384
Plate—valve clearance instructions	12B 1386	47	1		

HEATER CONTROL TAP

DESCRIPTION	Part No.	Illus. No.	Qty	Change Point	REMARKS
Tap—heater control	2H 4933	43	1		
Washer—tap	88G 423	44	1		Was 1G 2342
Screw	HNS 0405	45	2		
Washer—spring	LWN 204	46	2		

CHANGE POINTS
(1) (E) 29F/H101 to 6188, (E) 29FF/H101 to 164
(2) (E) 29K/H101 on, (E) 29KF/H101 on, (E) 29KFA/H224 on
(3) (E) 29F/H101 to 6188, (E) 29FF/H101 to 164, (E) 29K/H101 to 10271, (E) 29KF/H101 to 223, (E) 29KFA/H224 to 326
(4) (E) 29K/H101 to 10271, (E) 29KF/H101 to 223, (E) 29KFA/H224 to 326
(5) (E) 29K/H10272 on, (E) 29KF/H224 on, (E) 29KFA/H327 on

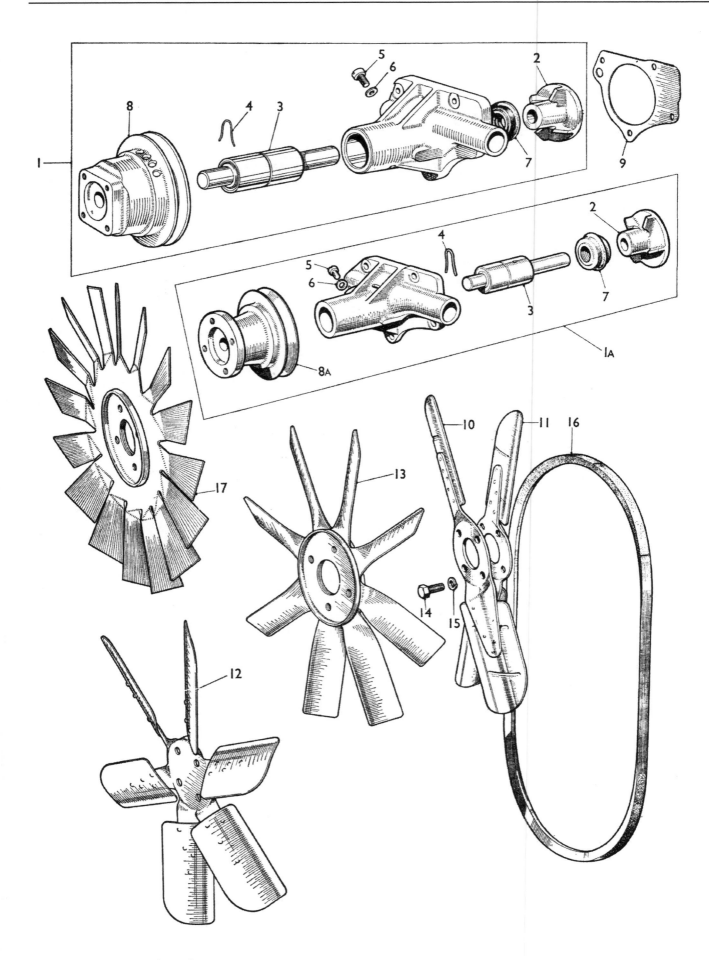

MECHANICAL SERVICE PARTS LIST   **AKD 3523**

DESCRIPTION	Part No.	Illus. No.	Quantity	Change Point	REMARKS

Engine Unit—*continued*

FAN BLADE—BELT

DESCRIPTION	Part No.	Illus. No.	Quantity	Change Point	REMARKS
Blade—fan—front	AEC 1025	10	1		
Blade—fan—rear	AEC 1024	11	1		
Fan					
6 bladed .... **Not UK**	AEC 76	12	1	(C) 17551 to 18208	
8 bladed .... **W. Germany**	AHB 7098	13	1	(C) 26705 on	Not available; use AHB 7109
16 bladed .... **W. Germany and Switzerland**	AHB 7109	17	1	(C) 26705 on	
Screw—blade to pulley	HNS 0507	14	4		
Washer—spring—screw	LWN 205	15	4		
Belt					
Fan—44″ (111·8 cm)	†AEC 932	16	1	(E) 29F/H101 to H6188 (E) 29FF/H101 to H164	Not available; use 13H 760
Fan—⅜″ × 44″ (95 cm × 111·8 cm)	†13H 760	16	1	(E) 29K/H101 to 10271 (E) 29KFA/H224 to 326 (E) 29KF/H101 to 223	
Fan—'V'-type—⅜″ (·95 cm)	†13H 848	16	1	(E) 29K/H10272 on (E) 29KFA/H327 on (E) 29KF/H224 on	

ENGINE SERVICE KITS

DESCRIPTION	Part No.	Illus. No.	Quantity	Change Point	REMARKS
Set—gasket—engine decarbonizing	8G 2291		1		W.S.E. use 8G 2407
Set—gasket—engine decarbonizing	8G 2407		1		Use together with 8G 2327 for engine complete overhaul
Gasket					
Cylinder head	AEC 875		1		
Valve rocker cover	AEC 1332		1		
Flange—exhaust pipe	ACC 5137		2		
Inlet and exhaust manifold	AEC 731		1		
Inlet manifold to exhaust manifold	AEC 950		2		
Carburetter to heat shield and heat shield to manifold	12B 561		4	(E) 29F/H101 to H6188 (E) 29FF/H101 to H164	
Carburetter to heat shield	12B 814		2	(E) 29K/H101 on (E) 29KFA/H224 on (E) 29KF/H101 on	
Grommet—valve stem	AEK 113		12		
Set—gasket—supplementary	†8G 2327		1		Use together with 8G 2407 for engine complete overhaul
Gasket					
Tap—drain	2K 4954		1		
Front plate to block	AEC 2033		1		
Rear plate to block	AEC 128		1		
Front cylinder cover to block	AEC 313		1		
Centre cylinder cover to block	12A 1139		1		
Rear cylinder cover to block	12A 1139		1		
Timing cover	AEC 202		1		
Chain tensioner to block	AEC 339		1		
Sump to block	AEC 205		1		
Sump drain to plug	AEC 699		1		
Oil pump to block	AEC 698		1		
Oil pump flange to block	AEC 315		1		
Oil filter flange to block	1B 1233		1		
Oil filter to flange	1B 1233		1		
Water pump to block	†AEC 216		1		
Water outlet elbow	1K 1056		1		
Seal—front and rear main bearing cap	AEC 108		2		
Plug—front and rear main bearing cap	AEC 888		4		

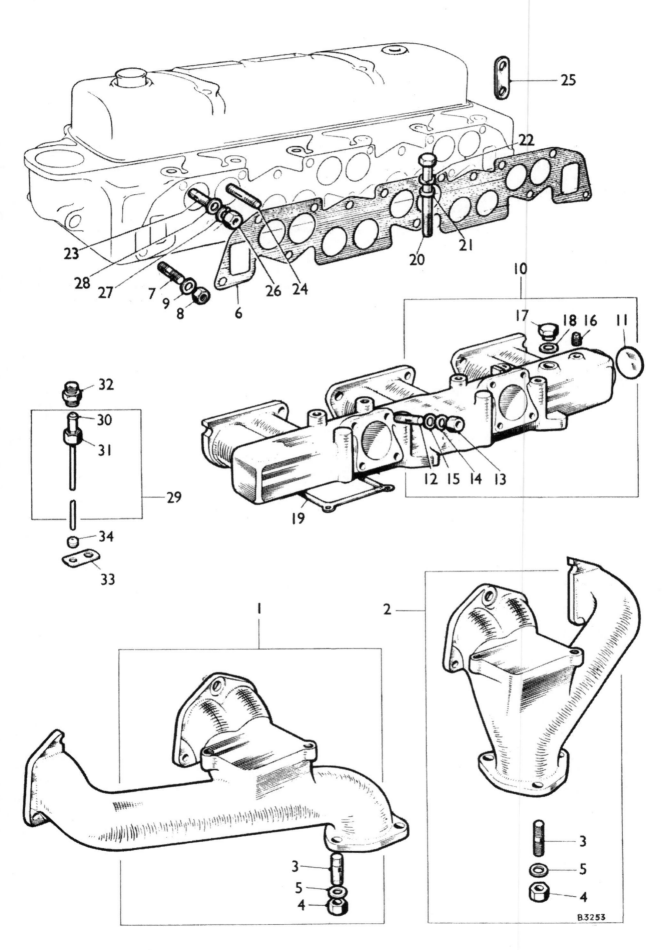

B.3253

	DESCRIPTION	Part No.	Illus. No.	Quantity	Stock recoms. DIST. Exp.	UK	D	Change Point	REMARKS
	INLET AND EXHAUST MANIFOLD								
	Manifold—exhaust—front	AEC 1877	1	1	★	★			
	Manifold—exhaust—rear	AEC 1878	2	1	★	★			
	Stud—outlet flange	53K 507	3	6					
	Nut	BNN 105	4	6					
	Washer—plain	PWZ 105	5	6					
	Joint—inlet and exhaust manifold to cylinder head	AEC 731	6	1	★	★	★		
	Stud—manifold to cylinder head	53K 564	7	10					
	Nut—stud	AEC 350	8	10					
	Washer—plain	PWZ 106	9	10					
	Manifold—inlet	68G 200	10	1	★	★			
	Plug—core	12H 736	11	1					
	Stud—carburetter to manifold	53K 1473	12	8					
	Nut	FNZ 105	13	8				(E) 29F/H101 to H6188	
	Washer—spring	LWZ 205	14	8				(E) 29FF/H101 to H164	
	Washer—plain	PWZ 105	15	8					
	Plug—vacuum take-off	AEC 479	16	1					
	Plug—servo boss	ADP 210	17	1					
	Washer—plug	1B 3664	18	1					
	Manifold—inlet	68G 270	10	1	★	★			
	Plug—core	†12H 736	11	1					Correction; was AEC 871
	Stud—carburetter to manifold	53K 1477	12	8					
	Nut	FNZ 105	13	8				(E) 29K/H101 on	
	Washer—spring	LWZ 205	14	8				†(E) 29KFA/H224 on	
	Washer—plain	PWZ 105	15	8				(E) 29KF/H101 on	
	Plug—servo boss	ADP 210	17	1					
	Washer—plug	1B 3664	18	1					
	Joint—inlet manifold to exhaust manifold	AEC 950	19	2	★	★	★		
	Bolt	HBZ 0526	20	4					
	Washer—plain	PWZ 105	21	4					
	Washer—spring	LWZ 205	22	4					
	Stud—inlet manifold to cylinder head—short	†53K 562	23	6					Correction; was 51K 562
	Stud—inlet manifold to cylinder head—long	53K 563	24	1					
	Clip—retainer—thermo capillary pipe	AHB 5397	25	2					
	Nut	FNZ 106	26	7					
	Washer—spring	LWZ 206	27	7					
	Washer—plain	PWZ 106	28	7					
	Pipe—drain—fuel	AEC 449	29	2					
	Nipple	2K 6192	30	2					
	Nut	2K 6193	31	2					
	Union—drain pipe	AEC 450	32	2					
	Clip—pipe	1A 2104	33	2					
	Ferrule—clip	2H 4935	34	2					

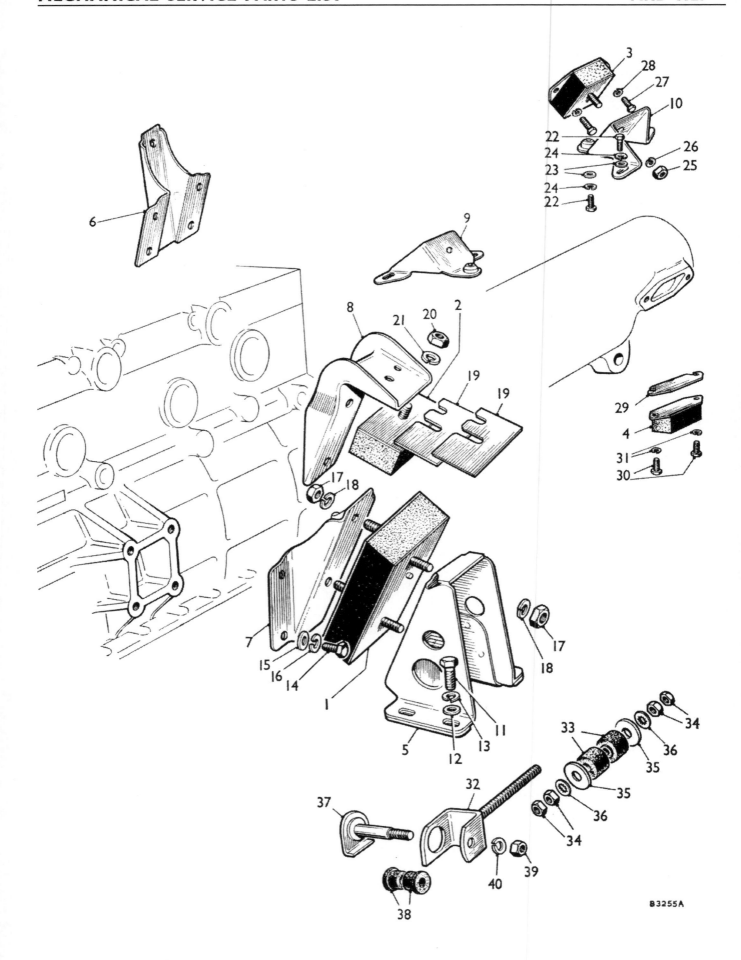

B3255A

	DESCRIPTION	Part No.	Illus. No.	Quantity	Change Point	REMARKS
	ENGINE MOUNTINGS					
	Rubber—engine mounting					
	Front	ACB 9407	1	2		
	Rebound—front	1B 4428	2	2		
	Rear	11B 5074	3	2		
	Rebound—rear	1A 9209	4	1		
	Bracket					
	Front mounting to side-member	11B 5188	5	2		
	Front mounting to crankcase—RH	AEC 889	6	1		
	Front mounting to crankcase—LH	AEC 890	7	1		
	Rebound buffer	1B 4422	8	2		
	Rear mounting—RH	11B 5113	9	1		
	Rear mounting—LH	11B 5115	10	1		
	Screw—front mounting bracket to side-member	HZS 0607	11	8		
	Washer—plain	PWZ 106	12	8		
	Washer—spring	†LWZ 206	13	8		Correction; was LWZ 806
	Screw—front mounting bracket to crankcase	HZS 0606	14	8		
	Washer—plain	PWZ 106	15	8		
	Washer—spring	LWZ 206	16	8		
	Nut	FNZ 107	17	8		
	Washer—spring	LWZ 207	18	8		
	Piece—packing—front rebound rubber	1B 1814	19	A/R		
	Piece—packing—front rebound rubber	1B 1815	19	A/R		
	Nut—rebound rubber to bracket	FNZ 105	20	2		
	Washer—spring	LWZ 205	21	2		
	Screw—rear mounting bracket to frame	HZS 0505	22	6		
	Washer—plain	PWZ 105	23	6		
	Washer—spring	LWZ 205	24	6		
	Nut	FNZ 105	25	2		
	Washer—spring	LWZ 205	26	2		
	Screw—rear mounting rubber to gearbox	HZS 0506	27	4		
	Washer—spring	LWZ 205	28	4		
	Shim—rear rebound rubber	1A 9211	29	A/R		
	Screw—rear rebound rubber to gearbox	HZS 0405	30	2		
	Washer—spring	LWZ 304	31	2		
	Tie-rod—engine	1G 9382	32	1		
	Bush—tie-rod (rubber)	1B 8882	33	2		
	Nut	FNZ 206	34	4		
	Washer—plain	†PWZ 206	35	2		Correction; was PWZ 106
	Washer—shakeproof	LWN 406	36	2		
	Pin—hinge—tie-rod to gearbox	1G 9384	37	1		
	Bush—gearbox (rubber)	1B 8847	38	2		
	Nut	FNZ 106	39	1		
	Washer—spring	LWZ 306	40	1		

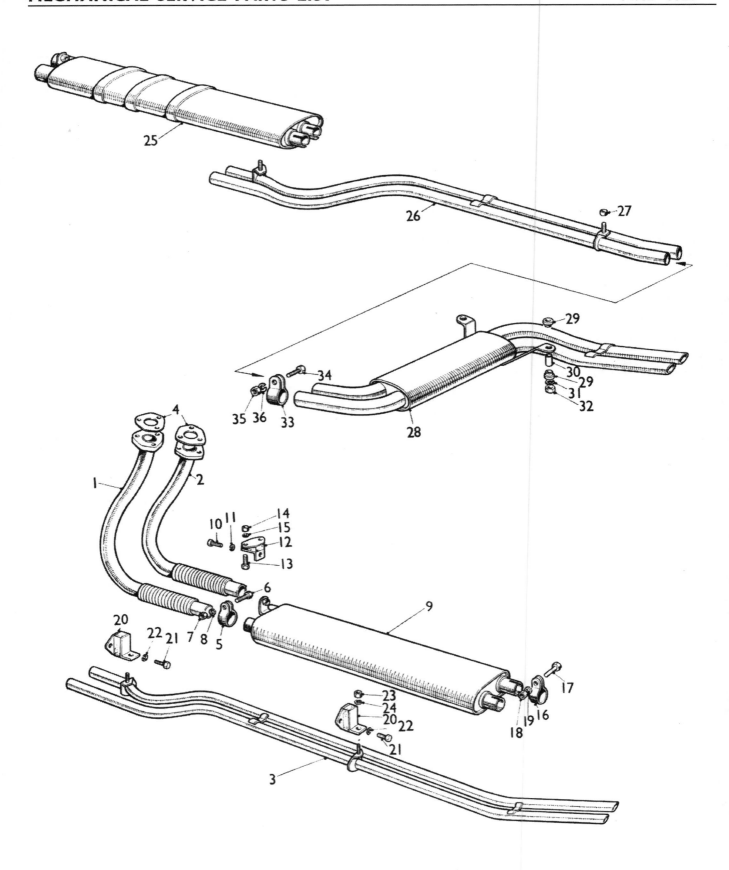

EXHAUST SYSTEM (BJ7)

Pipes

DESCRIPTION	Part No.	Illus. No.	Quantity	Exp.	UK	D	Change Point	REMARKS
Front—outer	11B 2120	1	1	★	★			
Front—inner	11B 2122	2	1	★	★			
Tail	11B 2357	3	1	★	★			
Gasket—front pipe to manifold	ACC 5137	4	2	★	★	★		
Clip—front pipe to silencer	1K 618	5	2					
Screw—clip	HZS 0507	6	2					
Nut—screw	FNZ 105	7	2					
Washer—spring—nut	LWZ 205	8	2					
Silencer	11B 2356	9	1	★	★			
Screw—silencer to mounting	HZS 0506	10	1					
Washer—spring—screw	LWZ 205	11	1					
Mounting—silencer—front	AHB 8993	12	1	★	★			
Screw—mounting to frame	PMZ 0510	13	2					
Nut—screw	FNZ 105	14	2					
Washer—spring—nut	LWZ 205	15	2					
Clip—tail pipe to silencer	DMK 5418	16	2					
Screw—clip	HZS 0607	17	2A				(C) 17551 to 25814	
Nut—screw	FNZ 106	18	2					
Washer—spring—nut	LWZ 306	19	2					
Mounting—silencer and tail pipe—rear	AHB 8993	20	2	★	★			
Screw—mounting to frame	HZS 0506	21	4					
Washer—spring—screw	LWZ 205	22	4					
Nut—tail pipe to mounting	FNZ 105	23	2					
Washer—spring—nut	LWZ 205	24	2					
Silencer—front	AHB 9389	25	1	★				
Pipe—front silencer to rear silencer	AHB 8976	26	1	★				
Distance piece—pipe to mounting	AHB 8996	27	1					
Silencer and tail pipe assembly—rear	AHB 8975	28	1	★				
Bush—rear silencer support (rubber) **Not U.K.**	AHA 5689	29	4	★				
Spacer—bush	AHA 5690	30	2					
Washer—plain	PWZ 205	31	2					
Locknut—rear silencer to boot floor	LNZ 205	32	2					
Clip—rear silencer to pipe	DMK 5418	33	2					
Screw—clip	HZS 0607	34	2					
Nut—screw	FNZ 106	35	2					
Washer—spring—nut	LWZ 306	36	2					

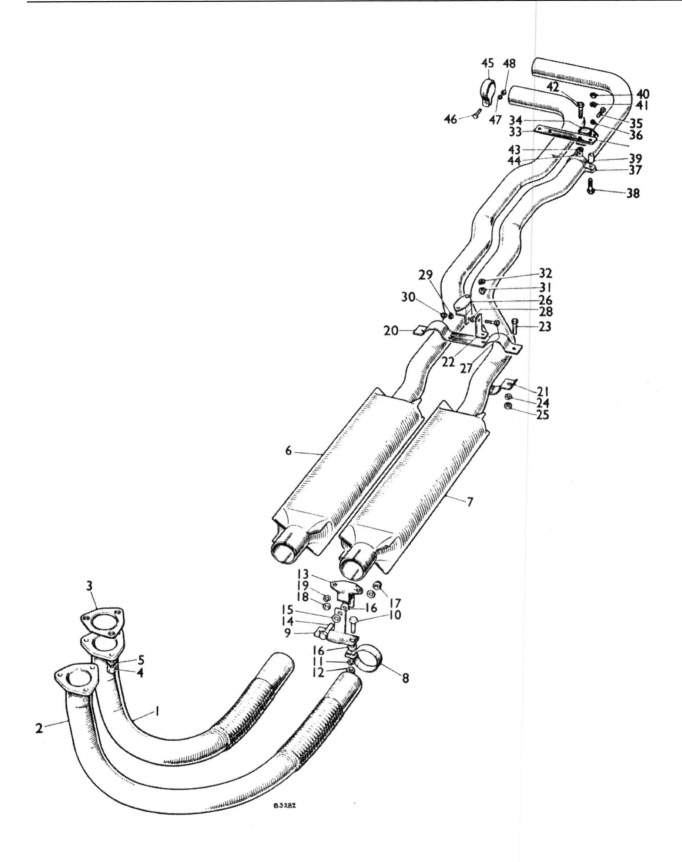

B3282

DESCRIPTION	Part No.	Illus. No.	Quantity	Stock recoms. DIST. Exp.	UK	D	Change Point	REMARKS
EXHAUST SYSTEM (BJ8)								
Pipe—front—inner	AHB 6009	1	1	★	★			
Pipe—front—outer	AHB 6006	2	1	★	★			
Gasket—pipe to manifold	ACC 5137	3	2	★	★	★		
Nut—pipe to manifold	BNN 105	4	6					
Washer—plain—nut	PWZ 105	5	6					
Front silencer and intermediate pipe—inner	ARB 97	6	1	★	★			
Front silencer and intermediate pipe—outer	ARB 98	7	1	★	★			
Clip—front pipe to silencer	AHB 6711	8	2					
Bracket—exhaust mounting—front	AHB 6220	9	1					
Screw—clip to bracket	HZS 0509	10	2					
Washer—spring—screw	LWZ 205	11	2					
Nut—screw	FNZ 105	12	2					
Mounting—exhaust	AHB 8993	13	1	★	★			
Bolt—bracket to mounting	HBZ 0511	14	1					
Washer—plain—bolt	PWZ 305	15	2					
Washer—insulating	AHB 6226	16	3					
Locknut—bolt	LNZ 205	17	2					
Nut—mounting to floor	FNZ 105	18	2					
Washer—spring—nut	LWZ 305	19	2					
Clip—upper—intermediate pipe—front	AHB 6224	20	1					
Clip—lower—intermediate pipe—front	AHB 6225	21	2					
Bracket—clip mounting	AHB 6223	22	2					
Screw—clip	HZS 0508	23	4				(C) 25315 on.	
Washer—spring—screw	LWZ 205	24	4					
Nut—screw	FNZ 105	25	4					
Mounting—exhaust	AHB 8993	26	2	★	★			
Bolt—bracket to mounting	HBZ 0511	27	2					
Washer—insulating	AHB 6226	28	6					
Washer—plain—bolt	PWZ 305	29	4					
Nut—bolt	LNZ 205	30	2					
Nut—mounting to floor	FNZ 105	31	4					
Washer—spring—nut	LWZ 205	32	4					
Strap—mounting—intermediate pipe	AHB 6105	33	1					
Mounting—intermediate	AHB 8993	34	2					
Screw—mounting to frame	HZS 0506	35	4					
Washer—spring—screw	LWZ 205	36	4					
Clip—pipe to strap	AHA 6173	37	2					
Bolt—clip	HBZ 0518	38	2					
Spacer—clip to strap	AHB 6106	39	2					
Washer—spring—bolt	LWZ 205	40	2					
Nut—bolt	FNZ 105	41	2					
Screw—strap to mounting	HZS 0506	42	2					
Washer—spring—screw	LWZ 205	43	2					
Nut—screw	FNZ 105	44	2					
Clip—intermediate pipe to rear silencer	1K 618	45	2					
Screw—clip	HZS 0508	46	2					
Washer—spring—screw	LWZ 205	47	2					
Nut—screw	FNZ 105	48	2					

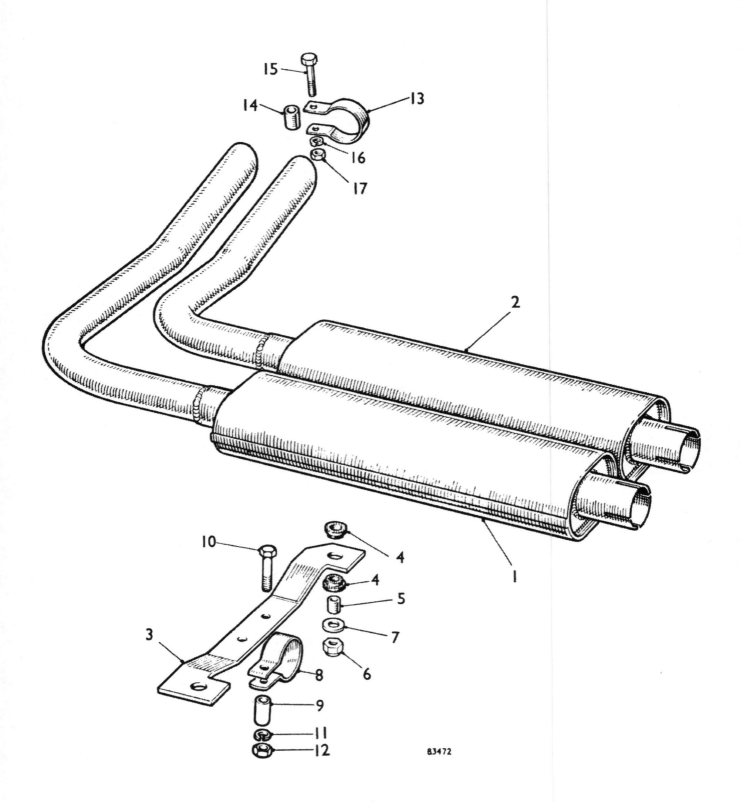

83472

		DESCRIPTION	Part No.	Illus. No.	Quantity	Stock recoms. DIST. Exp.	UK	D	Change Point	REMARKS

Exhaust system (BJ8)—*continued*

DESCRIPTION	Part No.	Illus. No.	Quantity	Exp.	UK	D	Change Point	REMARKS
Rear silencer and tail pipe—inner	ARB 99	1	1	★	★			
Rear silencer and tail pipe—outer	ARB 100	2	1	★	★			
Bracket—tail pipe mounting	AHB 6022	3	1					
Bush (rubber)	AHA 5689	4	4	★	★			
Spacer—bush	AHA 5690	5	2					
Nut—bracket	LNZ 205	6	2					
Washer—plain—nut	PWZ 205	7	2					
Clip—pipe to bracket	AHA 5450	8	2				(C) 25815 on	
Distance piece—clip to bracket	AHB 6023	9	2					
Bolt—clip	HBZ 0516	10	2					
Washer—spring—bolt	LWZ 205	11	2					
Nut—bolt	FNZ 105	12	2					
Clip—tail pipe	AHB 6126	13	2					
Spacer—clip	AHB 6127	14	1					
Bolt—clip	HBZ 0518	15	1					
Washer—spring—bolt	LWZ 205	16	1					
Nut—bolt	FNZ 105	17	1					

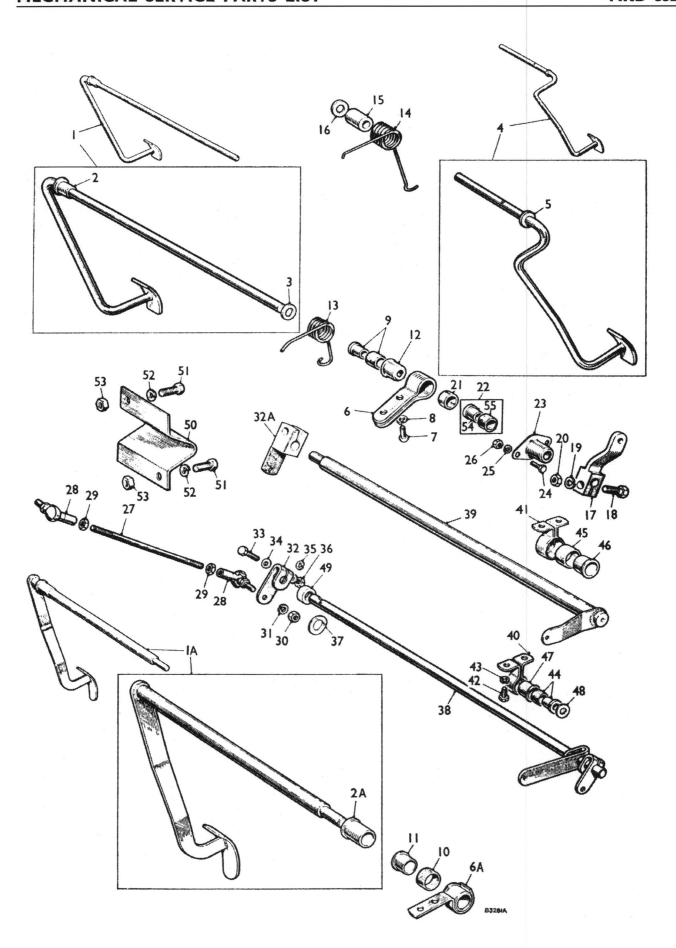

B3281A

PLATE 15   Issue 1   58

		DESCRIPTION	Part No.	Illus. No.	Quantity	Stock recoms. DIST. Exp.	UK	D	Change Point	REMARKS
		ENGINE CONTROLS								
		Pedal—accelerator	AHB 9190	1	1					
		Collar—pedal rod	11 B 2207	2	1				(C) H–BJ7–17551 to 25314	
		Washer—collar **RHD**	6K 467	3	1					
		Pedal—accelerator	AHB 9969	1A	1				(C) H–BJ8–25315 on	
		Collar—pedal rod	AHB 9961	2A	1					
		Pedal—accelerator **LHD**	AHB 9188	4	1					
		Washer—pedal rod	PWZ 106	5	1					
		Stop—pedal	†AHH 6503	50	1					
		Screw **RHD**	†PMZ 0412	51	2					
		Washer—spring	†LWZ 204	52	2					
		Nut	†FNZ 104	53	2					
		Support—pedal shaft								
		RHD	1F 657	6	1				(C) H–BJ7–17551 to 25314	
		RHD	AHB 9963	6A	1				(C) H–BJ8–25315 on	
		LHD	1F 657	6	1					
		Screw	PMZ 0410	7	2					
		Washer—spring	LWZ 304	8	2					
		Bush and housing—pedal shaft	AHB 8950	9	1				(C) H–BJ7–17551 to 25314	
		Bush—pedal shaft **RHD**	AHB 9957	10	1				(C) H–BJ8–25315 on	
		Housing—bush	AHB 6228	11	1					
		Cup—bush	1H 55	12	1				(C) H–BJ7–17551 to 25314	
		Bush and housing—pedal shaft **LHD**	AHB 8950	9	1					
		Cup—bush	1H 55	12	1					
		Spring—pedal return **RHD**	1G 2697	13	1	★				
		Spring—pedal return	11B 2146	14	1	★				
		Collar—return spring location **LHD**	1F 1293	15	1					
		Washer—return spring location	6K 467	16	1					
		Lever—pedal shaft	AHB 9795	17	1					
		Screw	HZS 0508	18	1					
		Washer—spring	LWZ 205	19	1					
		Nut	FNZ 105	20	1					
		Washer—plain	PWZ 106	21	1					
		Bush and housing—pedal shaft	AHB 9021	22	1					Not available; use component parts
		Bush	†AHB 9022	54	1					
		Housing	†AHB 8049	55	1					
		Cup—bush	21B 670	23	1					
		Screw	53K 124	24	2					
		Washer—spring	LWZ 303	25	2					
		Nut	FNZ 103	26	2					
		Rod—control—pedal shaft lever to relay shaft lever **RHD**	AHB 9866	27	1					
		Rod—control—pedal shaft lever to relay shaft lever **LHD**	AHB 9769	27	1					
		Joint—ball	ACB 5311	28	2	★	★			
		Nut	FNZ 103	29	2					
		Nut	FNZ 103	30	2					
		Washer—spring	LWZ 203	31	1					
		Lever—relay shaft	11B 2156	32	1				(C) H–BJ7–17551 to 25314	
		Lever—relay shaft	AHB 6853	32A	1				(C) H–BJ8–25315 on	
		Screw	HZS 0509	33	1					
		Washer—plain **RHD**	PWZ 105	34	2				(C) H–BJ7–17551 to 25314	
		Washer—spring	LWZ 205	35	1				(C) H–BJ8–25315 on	
		Nut	FNZ 105	36	1					
		Washer—anti-rattle	AWZ 109	37	1				(C) H–BJ8–25315 on	
		Shaft—relay								
		RHD	AHB 9204	38	1				(C) H–BJ7–17551 to 25314	
		RHD	AHB 9965	39	1				(C) H–BJ8–25315 on	
		LHD	AHB 9204	38	1					
		Bracket—relay shaft mounting								
		RHD	11B 2159	40	2				(C) H–BJ7–17551 to 25314	
		RHD	AHB 9958	41	2				(C) H–BJ8–25315 on	
		LHD	11B 2159	40	2					
		Screw	HZS 0405	42	4					
		Washer—spring	LWZ 304	43	4					
		Bush and housing—relay shaft	AHB 8950	44	2				(C) H–BJ7–17551 to 25314	
		Bush—relay shaft **RHD**	AHB 9957	45	2				(C) H–BJ8–25315 on	
		Housing—bush	AHB 6228	46	2					
		Cup—bush	1H 55	47	2				(C) H–BJ7–17551 to 25314	
		Bush and housing—relay shaft **LHD**	AHB 8950	44	2					
		Cup—bush	1H 55	47	2					
		Washer—plain	PWZ 106	48	2					
		Collar—relay shaft **LHD**	1A 9	49	1					

† Revised Information.

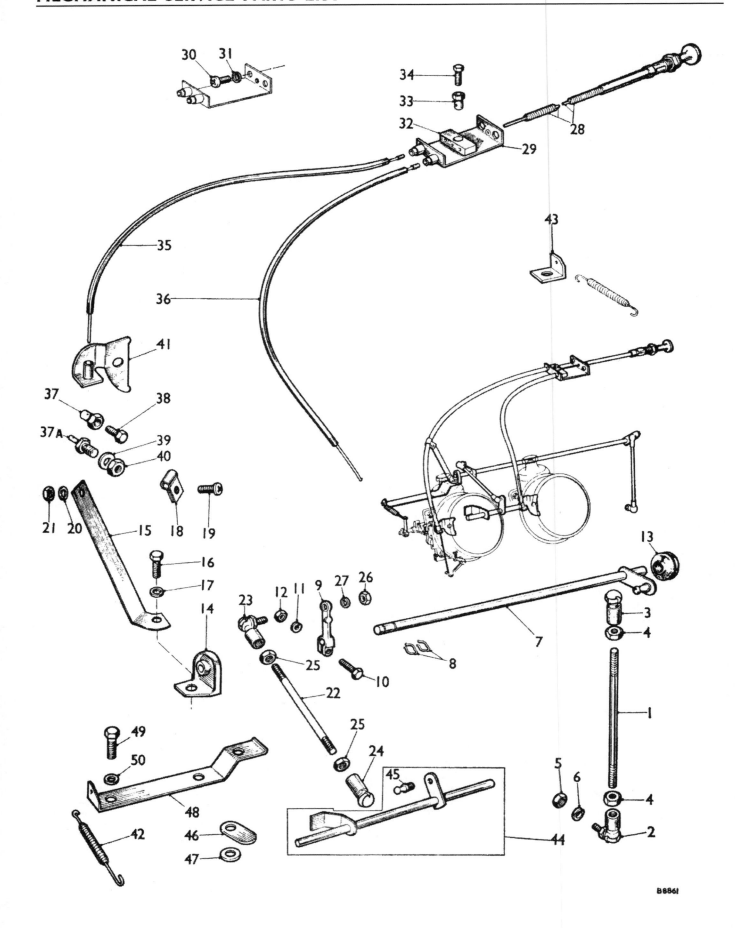

	DESCRIPTION	Part No.	Illus. No.	Quantity	Change Point	REMARKS
	Engine Controls—*continued*					
	Rod—control—relay shaft to accelerator spindle	AHB 9771	1	1		
	Joint—ball	ACB 5311	2	1		
	Housing—ball	AHB 9898	3	1		
	Nut—ball joint and ball housing to control rod	FNZ 103	4	2		
	Nut—ball joint to relay shaft lever	FNZ 103	5	1		
	Washer—spring	LWZ 303	6	1		
	Spindle—accelerator	AHB 9798	7	1		
	Circlip	11B 2350	8	2		
	Lever	88G 298	9	1		Part No. change; was AUC 3481. W.S.E. use AUC 4454
	Lever	AUC 4454	9	1		
	Screw—lever to spindle	53K 128	10	1		
	Washer—spring	LWZ 303	11	1		
	Nut	FNZ 103	12	1		
	Bearing—spindle in dash	AHB 8944	13	1		
	Bracket—spindle bearing	11B 2348	14	1		
	Bracket—reinforcement	12B 567	15	1		
	Screw	HZS 0506	16	1		
	Washer—plain	PWZ 105		1		
	Washer—spring	LWZ 205	17	1		
	Clip—front carburetter cable	PCR 0507	18	1		
	Screw—clip to reinforcement bracket	PMZ 0306	19	1		
	Washer—spring	LWZ 203	20	1		
	Nut	FNZ 103	21	1		
	Rod—control—spindle lever to carburetter	AHB 9800	22	1	(C) H–BJ7–17551 to 25314	
	Rod—control—spindle lever to carburetter	AHB 6114	22	1	(C) H–BJ8–25315 on	
	Joint—ball	ACB 5311	23	1		
	Housing—ball	AHB 9898	24	1		
	Nut—ball joint and ball housing to control rod	FNZ 103	25	2		
	Nut—ball joint to spindle lever	FNZ 103	26	1		
	Washer—spring	LWZ 303	37	1		
	Spring—throttle return	AEC 2127	42	2	(C) H–BJ7–17551 to 25314	
	Spring—throttle return	AEC 2075	42	2	(C) H–BJ8–25315 on	
	Bracket	12B 574	43	1		
	Shaft assembly—carburetter coupling	12B 568	44	1	(C) H–BJ7–17551 to 25314	
	Shaft assembly—carburetter coupling	12B 815	44	1	(C) H–BJ8–25315 on	
	Ball end	AEC 2091	45	1		
	Bracket—stop—throttle lever	12B 571	46	1		
	Washer—packing—bracket—·036″ (·91 mm) thick	2K 5976	47	A/R		
	Washer—packing—bracket—·006″ (·15 mm) thick	2K 5090	47	A/R		
	Bracket—mounting—accelerator spindle bearing bracket and reinforcement bracket	12B 572	48	1		
	Screw—bracket to manifold	HZS 0508	49	2		
	Washer—spring	LWZ 205	50	2		
	Control—choke **RHD**	AHB 9905	28	1	⎤ (C) H–BJ7–17551 to 25314	
	LHD	AHB 9840	28	1	⎦	W.S.E. use AHB 9905
	RHD or LHD	AHB 6021	28	1	(C) H–BJ8–25315 on	
	Body—choke control	AHB 9848	29	1		
	Screw—body to dash front panel	PMZ 0307	30	2		
	Washer—spring	LWZ 203	31	2		
	Block—remote control cable	AHB 9839	32	1		
	Trunnion—choke control cable to block	24G 1482	33	1		
	Screw—trunnion to cable	53K 1016	34	1		
	Cable					
	Block to front carburetter	AHB 9801	35	1	(C) H–BJ7–17551 to 25314	
	Block to front carburetter	AHB 6013	35	1	(C) H–BJ8–25315 on	
	Block to rear carburetter	AHB 9802	36	1	(C) H–BJ7–17551 to 25314	
	Block to rear carburetter	AHB 6014	36	1	(C) H–BJ8–25315 on	
	Pin—cable to carburetter	ACH 9042	37	2	(C) H–BJ7–17551 to 20721	
		AHA 6367	37	2	(C) H–BJ7–20722 to 25314	
		ACC 5062	37A	2	(C) H–BJ8–25315 on	
	Screw—pin to cable	†ACA 5453	38	2	(C) H–BJ7–17551 to 25314	W.S.E. use 53K 3503
	Screw—pin to cable	†53K 3503	38	2		
	Washer—plain	PWZ 104	39	4	⎤	
	Nut	FNZ 104	40	2	(C) H–BJ8–25315 on	
	Bracket—abutment	AHB 6018	41	2	⎦	

PLATE B 1

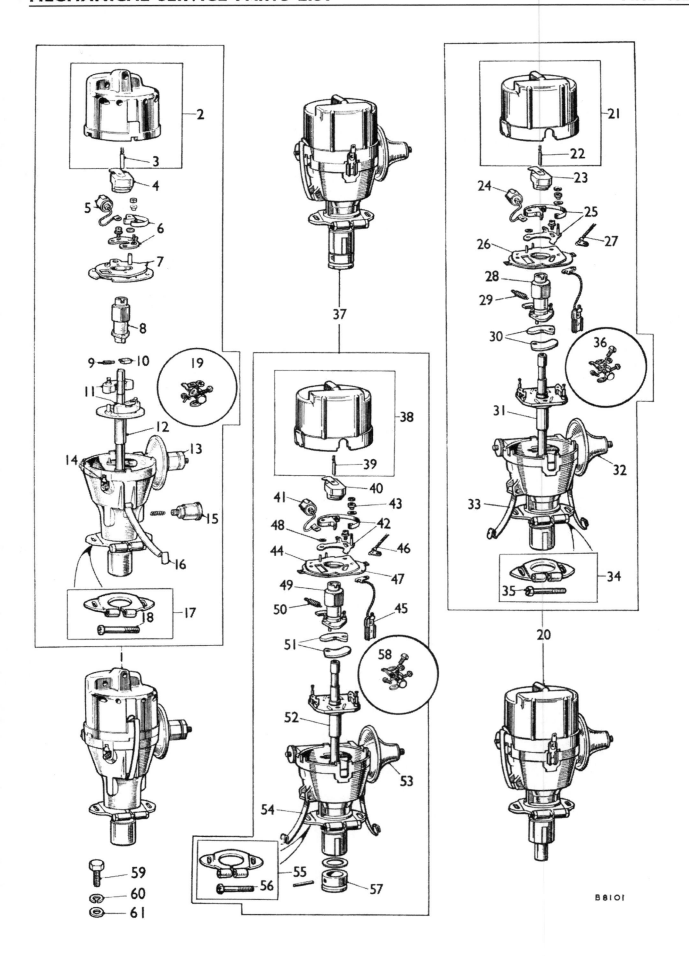

B 8101

	DESCRIPTION	Part No.	Illus. No.	Quantity	Change Point	REMARKS

†IGNITION EQUIPMENT

				Page	Plate
†CABLES—IGNITION	...	...	...	...	...	MB 2	B 2
†COIL—IGNITION	...	...	...	...	...	MB 2	B 2
†DISTRIBUTOR	...	...	...	...	...	MB 1·1	B 1
†FERRULES—IDENTIFICATION—IGNITION CABLES				MB 2	B 2
†PIPE—IGNITION CONTROL	...	...	...	...	MB 2	B 2
†SCREEN—DISTRIBUTOR	...	...	...	...	MB 2	B 2

IGNITION EQUIPMENT

DISTRIBUTOR

Description	Part No.	Illus. No.	Quantity	Change Point	REMARKS
Distributor	†AEJ 25	1	1		W.S.E. use 12B 823
Cover	17H 5158	2	1		
Brush and spring	17H 5065	3	1		
Arm—rotor	17H 5110	4	1		
Condenser	47H 5250	5	1		
Contact	17H 5243	6	1 set		
Plate—contact breaker base	17H 5437	7	1		
Cam	17H 5113	8	1		
Spring—auto advance	27H 5316	9	1 set	(E) 29F/H101 to H3562	
Toggle—spring	17H 5069	10	2		
Weight	17H 5095	11	2		
Shaft and action plate	17H 5166	12	1		
Unit—vacuum	57H 5241	13	1		
Connector—Lucar—14-amp	AUA 692	14	1		
Lubricator	AJC 5095	15	1		
Clip—cover	37H 5445	16	2		
Plate—fixing	3H 2138	17	1		
Screw—clamping	†NSP	18	1		Was 37H 5063
Sundry parts	17H 5117	19	1 set		
Distributor	12B 684	20	1		Use 12B 823 for 12B 684 for this application
Distributor	12B 823	20	1		
Cover	57H 5489	21	1		Use 17H 8844 for 57H 5489 for this application
Cover	17H 8844	21	1		
Brush and spring	17H 5065	22	1		
Arm—rotor	17H 5110	23	1		
Condenser	47H 5250	24	1		
Contact	17H 5423	25	1 set	(E) 29F/H3563 to H6188	
Plate—contact breaker base	17H 5469	26	1	(E) 29FF/H101 to H164	
Lead—earth	17H 5531	27	1		
Cam	57H 5488	28	1		
Spring—auto advance	57H 5490	29	1 set		
Weight	57H 5420	30	2		
Shaft and action plate	57H 5050	31	1		
Unit—vacuum	17H 6865	32	1		
Clip—cover	17H 2392	33	2		
Plate—fixing	3H 2138	34	1		
Screw—clamping	†NSP	35	1		Was 37H 5063
Sundry parts	17H 5117	36	1 set		
Distributor	12B 825	37	1		
Cover	17H 8844	38	1		
Brush and spring	17H 5065	39	1		
Arm—rotor	17H 5110	40	1		
Condenser	47H 5250	41	1		
Contact	17H 5423	42	1 set		
Bush—insulating	17H 5527	43	1		
Plate—contact breaker base	17H 5469	44	1		
Terminal—bush and lead	57H 5478	45	1		
Lead—earth	17H 5531	46	1	(E) 29K/H101 on	
Plate—bearing—contact breaker	NSP	47	1	(E) 29KFA/H224 on	W.S.E. 17H 8041
Washer—insulating—terminal	NSP	48	1	(E) 29KF/H101 on	Was 7H 6946
Cam	17H 6965	49	1		
Spring—automatic advance	27H 2122	50	1 set		
Weight	57H 5420	51	2		
Shaft and action plate	57H 5050	52	1		
Unit—vacuum	17H 6865	53	1		
Clip—cover retaining	17H 2392	54	2		
Plate—clamping	3H 2138	55	1		
Screw—clamping	†NSP	56	1		Was 37H 5063
Dog—driving	47H 5249	57	1		
Sundry parts	17H 5117	58	1 set		
Screw	HZS 0404	59	2		
Washer—spring	LWZ 204	60	2		
Washer—plain	PWZ 140	61	2		

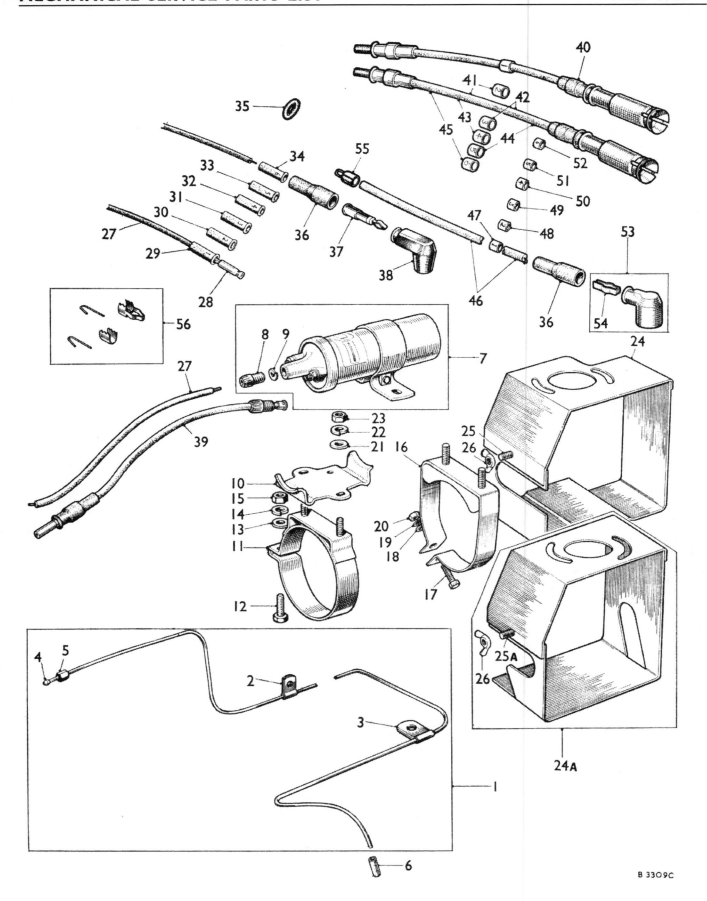

B 3309C

DESCRIPTION	Part No.	Illus. No.	Quantity	Change Point	REMARKS
Ignition Equipment—*continued*					
VACUUM CONTROL PIPES					
Pipe—Ignition control	12B 592	1	1	(E) 29F/H101 to 6188	
				(E) 29FF/H101 to 164	
Pipe—Ignition control	12B 834	1	1	(E) 29K/H 101 on	
				(E) 29KFA/H224 on	
				(E) 29KF/H101 to 223	
Clip—small	2H 3271	2	1		
Clip—large	1K 204	3	1		
Olive	6K 649	4	1		
Nut	6K 650	5	1		
Connection (Rubber)	ACH 9041	6	1		
IGNITION COIL					
Coil—ignition	†BCA 4309	7	1		Not available; use AJR 211
Coil—ignition	†AJR 211	7	1		
Nut—H.T. terminal	3H 2695	8	1		
Washer—H.T. terminal	3H 2696	9	1		
Plate—Steady—coil	11G 221	10	1		
Bracket—coil to dynamo	AEC 496	11	1	(E) 29F/H101 to 6188	
Bolt	HZS 0408	12	1	(E) 129FF/H101 to 164	
Washer—plain	PWN 204	13	3		
Washer—spring	LWN 204	14	3		
Nut	FNZ 104	15	3		
Bracket—Coil to dynamo	12H 51	16	1		
Bolt	HZS 0420	17	1		
Washer—plain	PWZ 204	18	1	(E) 29K/H101 on	
Washer—spring	LWZ 304	19	1	(E) 129KF/H101 to 223	
Nut	FNZ 104	20	1	(E) 129KFA/H224 on	
Washer—plain	PWZ 205	21	2		
Washer—spring	LWZ 305	22	2		
Nut	FNZ 105	23	2		
DISTRIBUTOR SCREEN					
Screen—distributor	†12B 776	24	1		Not available; use 12B 903
Screw	PWZ 0305	25	1	(E) 29FF/H101 to 264	
Nut—wing **France**	WNZ 103	26	1		
Screen—distributor	12B 903	24A	1	(E) 29KF/H101 to 223	
Screw	PMZ 0307	25A	1	(E) 29KFA/H224 on	
Nut—wing	WNZ 103	26	1		

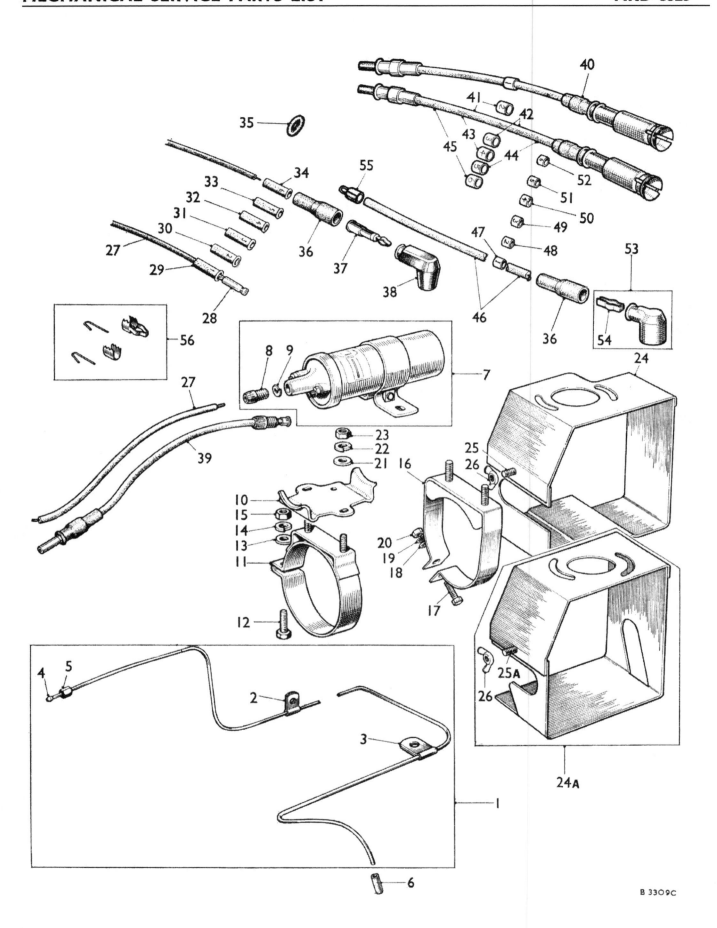

B 3309C

DESCRIPTION	Part No.	Illus. No.	Quantity	Change Point	REMARKS
Ignition Equipment—*continued*					
IGNITION CABLES					
Cable—ignition	AAA 5981	27	A/R		Supplied in 100 ft. (30·4 m) reels
Coil to distributor—11″ (28 cm)		27	1		
No. 1 plug—13½″ (35 cm)		27	1		
No. 2 plug—12″ (31 cm)		27	1	(E) 29F/H101 to 6188	
No. 3 plug—9″ (23 cm)		27	1		
No. 4 plug—11″ (28 cm)		27	1		
No. 5 plug—11½″ (30 cm)		27	1		
No. 6 plug—16″ (41 cm)		27	1		
Terminal—sparking plug	8G 616	28	6		
Sleeve—plug lead identification					
No. 1	3H 1655	29	1		
No. 2	3H 1656	30	1		
No. 3	3H 1657	31	1		
No. 4	3H 1658	32	1		
No. 5	3H 1659	33	1		
No. 6	3H 1660	34	1		
Ring—cable (rubber)	2H 35	35	2		
Sleeve—waterproof	8G 728	36	6		
Cable—ignition	AAA 5981	27	A/R		Supplied in 100 ft. (30·4 m) reels
Coil to distributor—9″ (23 cm)		27	1		
No. 1 plug—10″ (26 cm)		27	1		
No. 2 plug—9″ (23 cm)		27	1		
No. 3 plug—5½″ (14 cm)		27	1	(E) 29K/H101 on	
No. 4 plug—9″ (23 cm)		27	1		
No. 5 plug—11″ (28 cm)		27	1		
No. 6 plug—15½″ (40 cm)		27	1		
Suppressor—ignition (with clip)	13H 1953	37	6		
Cap—sparking plug	13H 1950	37	6		
Lead—screened (with fittings)					
Coil to distributor	12G 350	39	1		
No. 1 plug	12B 779	40	1		
No. 2 plug	12B 780	41	1	(E) 29FF/H101 to 264	
No. 3 plug	12B 786	42	1	(E) 29KF/H101 to 223	
No. 4 plug **France†**	12B 787	43	1	(E) 29KFA/H224 on	W.S.E. use 12B 956
No. 4 plug	12B 956	43	1		
No. 5 plug	†12B 783	44	1		W.S.E. use 12B 957
No. 5 plug	12B 957	44	1		
No. 6 plug	12B 784	45	1		
Cable—ignition—suppressed	AJA 11	46	A/R		Supplied in 100 ft. (30·4 m) reels
No. 1 plug—12″ (31 cm)		46	1		
No. 2 plug—9¾″ (25 cm)		46	1		
No. 3 plug—8½″ (22 cm)		46	1		
No. 4 plug—8½″ (22 cm)		46	1		
No. 5 plug—9⅝″ (25 cm) **Norway, Hong Kong,**		46	1		
No. 6 plug—13″ (34 cm) **Denmark, and**			1		
Sleeve—plug lead identification					
No. 1 **Germany**	2H 4243	47	1		
No. 2	2H 4244	48	1		
No. 3	2H 4245	49	1		
No. 4	2H 4246	50	1		
No. 5	NSP	51	1		
No. 6	†NSP	52	1		Was 2H 4672
Cap—sparking plug—weatherproof	8G 576	53	6		
Clip—cable end	7H 6894	54	6		
Insert—wire (copper)	NSP		A/R		
Ferrule (brass)	37H 1342	55	6		W.S.E. use 8G 2565
Terminal set—ignition cable	8G 2565	56	1		
Clip—cable end	NSP		6		
Ferrule (brass)	NSP		6		
Insert wire	NSP		12		

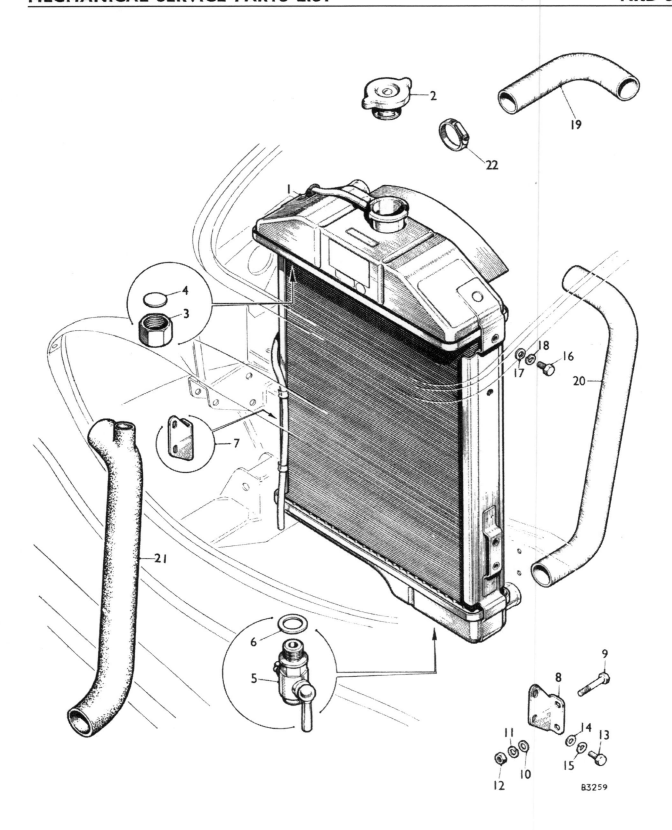

B3259

	DESCRIPTION	Part No.	Illus. No.	Quantity	Change Point	REMARKS

RADIATOR AND FITTINGS

					Page	Plate
HOSE—WATER					MC 2	C 1
RADIATOR					MC 2	C 1

RADIATOR AND FITTINGS

DESCRIPTION	Part No.	Illus. No.	Quantity	REMARKS
Radiator	AHB 8946	1	1	
Cap—filler	†ARH 1542	2	1	W.S.E. use ARH 1662
Cap—filler	†ARH 1662	2	1	
Plug—header tank	AHB 5401	3	1	
Washer (fibre)	AHB 5402	4	1	
Tap—drain	2H 10	5	1	
Washer—tap	2K 4954	6	1	⎤ Alternatives; use as required
Washer—tap	2K 4975	6	1	⎦ to align drain tap
Bracket—radiator support—RH	11B 2118	7	1	
Bracket—radiator support—LH	11B 2119	8	1	
Bolt—bracket to front suspension support	HBZ 0516	9	4	
Washer—plain	PWZ 105	10	4	
Washer—spring	LWZ 205	11	4	
Nut	FNZ 105	12	4	
Screw—radiator to support bracket	HZS 0505	13	4	
Washer—plain	PWZ 105	14	4	
Washer—spring	LWZ 205	15	2	
Screw—radiator to top fixing bracket	HZS 0505	16	2	
Washer—plain	PWZ 205	17	2	
Washer—spring	LWZ 205	18	2	
Hose—radiator				
Top	11B 2115	19	1	
Bottom	AHB 8970	20	1	When heater is not fitted
Bottom	AHB 8971	21	1	When heater is fitted
Clip—hose	HCS 1217	22	4	

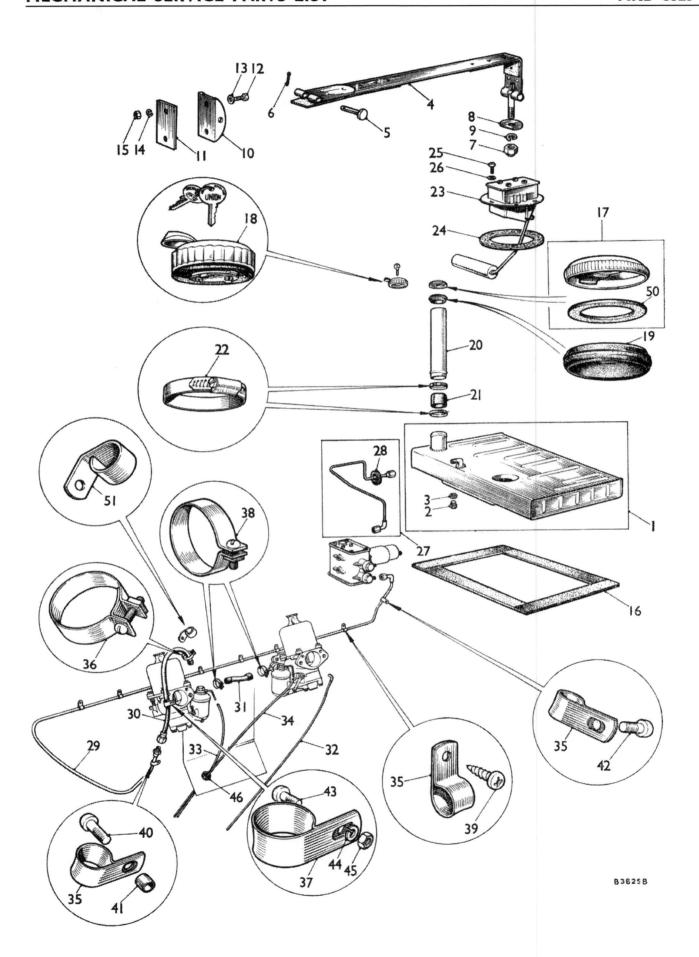

B3825B

	DESCRIPTION	Part No.	Illus. No.	Quantity	Change Point	REMARKS

FUEL SYSTEM

				Page	Plate
CLEANERS—AIR	... ...	MD 3	D 3
PIPES—FUEL	... ...	MD 1-1	D 1
PUMP—FUEL	... ...	MD 2, MD 2-1	D 2, D 2-1
SHIELD—HEAT	... ...	MD 3	D 3
TANK—FUEL	... ...	MD 1-1	D 1

† FOR CARBURETTER DETAILS USE THE S.U. CARBURETTER
SERVICE PARTS LIST NUMBER AKD 5036.

FUEL SYSTEM

FUEL TANK AND FUEL PIPES

DESCRIPTION	Part No.	Illus. No.	Quantity	Change Point	REMARKS
Tank assembly—fuel	11B 2375	1	1		
Plug—drain	88G 257	2	1		Part No. change; was 2A 380
Washer—plug	6K 638	3	1		
Strap—tank to body	11B 2137	4	2		
Pin—joint—strap	†53K 3061	5	2		W.S.E. use CLZ 0523
Pin—joint—strap	†CLZ 0523	5	2		
Pin—split	ZPS 0306	6	2		
Nut—lock	FNZ 205	7	4		
Washer—plain	14B 2036	8	2		
Washer—spring	LWZ 205	9	2		
Bracket—strap	14B 1884	10	2		
Plate—stiffening—bracket	14B 2531	11	2		
Screw	HZS 0405	12	4		
Washer—plain	PWZ 104	13	4		
Washer—spring	LWZ 204	14	4		
Nut	FNZ 104	15	4		
Rubber—sealing	14B 6632	16	1		
Cap assembly—filler	8G 654	17	1		
Seal—filler—cap	27H 3573	50	1		
Cap—filler—locking	2A 504	18	1		W.S.E. use AKF 1439 ⎫ Optional
Cap—filler—locking	AKF 1439	18	1		⎭ extra
Collar—filler tube	11G 2100	19	1		
Tube—filler	AHB 8315	20	1		
Connection—tube to tank	11B 2011	21	1		
Clip—connection	HCS 2228	22	2		
Unit—fuel gauge	1B 2736	23	1	(C) H–BJ7–17551 to 25314	
Unit—fuel gauge	BHA 4435	23	1	(C) H–BJ8–25315 on	
Washer—joint—unit	2H 1082	24	1		
Screw	53K 165	25	6		
Washer (copper)	2A 2088	26	6		
Pipe assembly—tank to pump	AHB 9383	27	1		
Grommet	8D 5768	28	1		
Pipe Pump to flexible pipe	AHB 9386	29	1		
Flexible	12B 564	30	1	(C) H–BJ7–17551 to 25314	
Flexible	AHB 6715	30	1	(C) H–BJ8–25315 on	
Flexible **Benelux and France**	AHB 7194	30	1	(C) H–BJ8–41930 on	W.S.E. use AHB 6715
Front to rear carburetter	BRT 2405	31	1	(E) 29F/H101 to H6188	
Front to rear carburetter	12B 883	31	1	(E) 29K/H101 on (E) 29KFA/H224 on	
Overflow—front and rear carburetters	AEC 2133	32	2	(E) 29F/H101 to H6188	
Overflow—front carburetter	AEC 981	33	1	⎤ (E) 29K/H101 on	
Overflow—rear carburetter	AEC 982	34	1	⎦ (E) 29KFA/H224 on	
Clip Pipe to body	PCR 0507	35	10		
Flexible pipe to carburetter	ACH 5854	36	1		
Flexible pipe to carburetter mounting bolt **Benelux and France**	12H 1001	51	1	(C) H–BJ8–41930 on	
Flexible pipe to bonnet surround	PCR 1007	37	1	(E) 29K/H101 on (E) 29KFA/H224 on	
Carburetter connecting pipe	12B 566	38	2		
Screw	PTZ 1003	39	6		
Screw	PMZ 0310	40	1		
Spacer—wheel arch clip	AHH 5297	41	1		
Screw	PMZ 0308	42	1		
Screw	PMZ 0305	43	1	(E) 29K/H101 on (E) 29KFA/H224 on	
Washer—spring	LWZ 203	44	2/3		⎤ Quantity increased at
Nut	FNZ 103	45	2/3		⎦ (E) 29K/H101
Ferrule—overflow pipe	11B 425	46	1	(E) 29K/H101 on (E) 29KFA/H224 on	
Union—banjo—fuel pump	AUC 1833	47	2	⎤	
Bolt—union	AUC 2698	48	2	⎬ (C) H–BJ8–28225 on	
Washer (fibre)	AUC 2141	49	4	⎦	

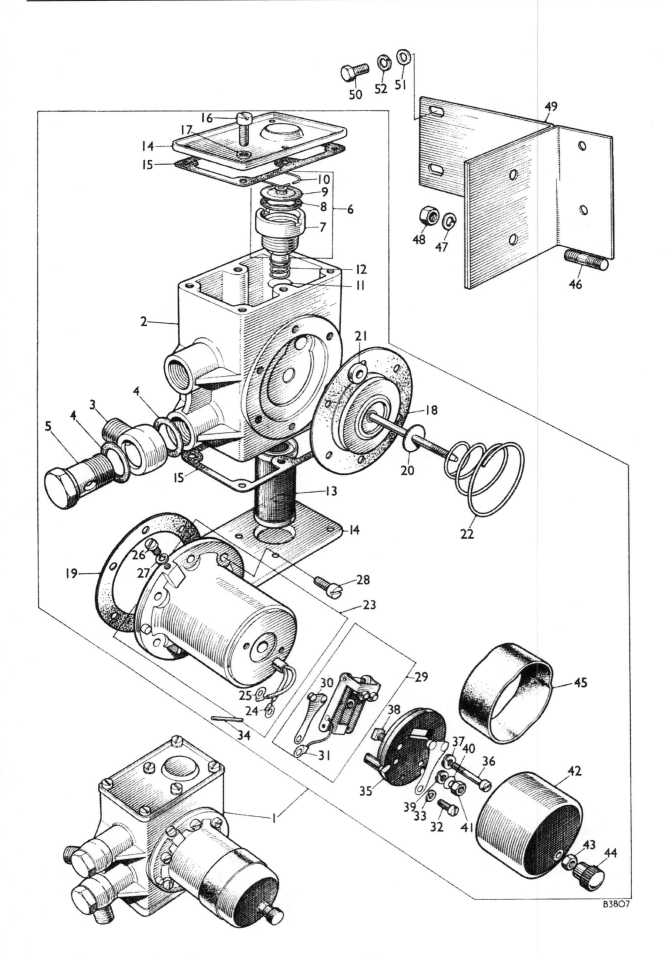

B3807

DESCRIPTION	Part No.	Illus. No.	Quantity	Stock recoms. DIST. Exp.	UK	D	Change Point	REMARKS
FUEL PUMP								
Pump—fuel	AUA 178	1	1	★	★			
Body	AUA 6058	2	1					
Connection—banjo	AUC 1833	3	2					
Washer—connection (fibre)	AUC 2141	4	4					
Bolt—connection	AUC 2098	5	2					
Cage assembly—valve	AUE 88	6	1					
Cage	AUB 624	7	1					
Washer	AUB 625	8	1					
Valve	AUB 6003	9	1					
Circlip	AUB 579	10	1					
Disc—valve	AUA 4611	11	1					
Spring—disc	AUB 581	12	1					
Filter	AUA 4647	13	1					
Lid—body	AUA 4645	14	2					
Washer—lid	AUA 4646	15	2					
Screw—lid to body	AUA 4083	16	12					
Washer—shakeproof	LWN 403	17	12					
Diaphragm	AUB 6025	18	1	★	★			⎤ Alter- ⎤ Not available; use AUB 6071
Diaphragm	AUB 6015	18	1					⎦ natives ⎦
Washer—joint	AUB 593	19	1					For use with AUB 6025 and AUB 6015
Washer—impact	AUB 582	20	1					For use with AUB 6015
Diaphragm	†AUB 6071		1					Not available; use AUB 6097
Diaphragm	†AUB 6097		1				†(C) H–BJ7–17551 to 25314	
Washer—joint	AUB 706		1					
Roller	AUA 1433	21	11				(C) H–BJ8–25315 to 28224	
Spring	AUB 521	22	1					
Housing—coil	88G 235	23	1					Part No. change; was AUB 6007 and AUB 6045
Tag—5BA terminal	AUA 1455	24	1					
Tag—2BA terminal	AUA 1456	25	1					
Screw—earth	AUA 699	26	1					
Washer—spring	AUA 585	27	1					
Screw—housing to body	AUA 1453	28	6					
Rocker and blade	†AUA 6021	29	1	★	★			⎤ Alter- ⎤ Correction; was 88 G286
Rocker and blade	†AUB 6022	29	1					⎦ natives ⎦
Blade	AUA 6036	30	1					
Tag—2BA terminal	AUA 1456	31	1					
Screw—blade	AUA 565	32	1					
Washer—spring	AUA 566	33	1					
Spindle—contact breaker	AUA 1435	34	1					
Pedestal	AUB 6034	35	1					
Screw—pedestal to housing	AUA 1459	36	2					
Washer—spring	AUA 1863	37	2					
Screw—terminal	AUA 1468	38	1					
Washer—spring	AUA 1863	39	1					
Washer (lead)	AUA 1662	40	1					
Nut	AUA 1661	41	1					
Cover—end	AUA 1466	42	1					
Nut—cover	AUA 878	43	1					
Knob—terminal	AUA 869	44	1					
Sleeve (rubber)	AUA 504	45	1					
Stud—pump to bracket	AUA 1500	46	2					
Washer—spring	LWZ 305	47	2					
Nut	FNZ 105	48	2					
Bracket—pump mounting	AHB 9378	49	1					
Screw	HZS 0404	50	4					
Washer—plain	PWZ 104	51	4					
Washer—spring	LWZ 204	52	4					

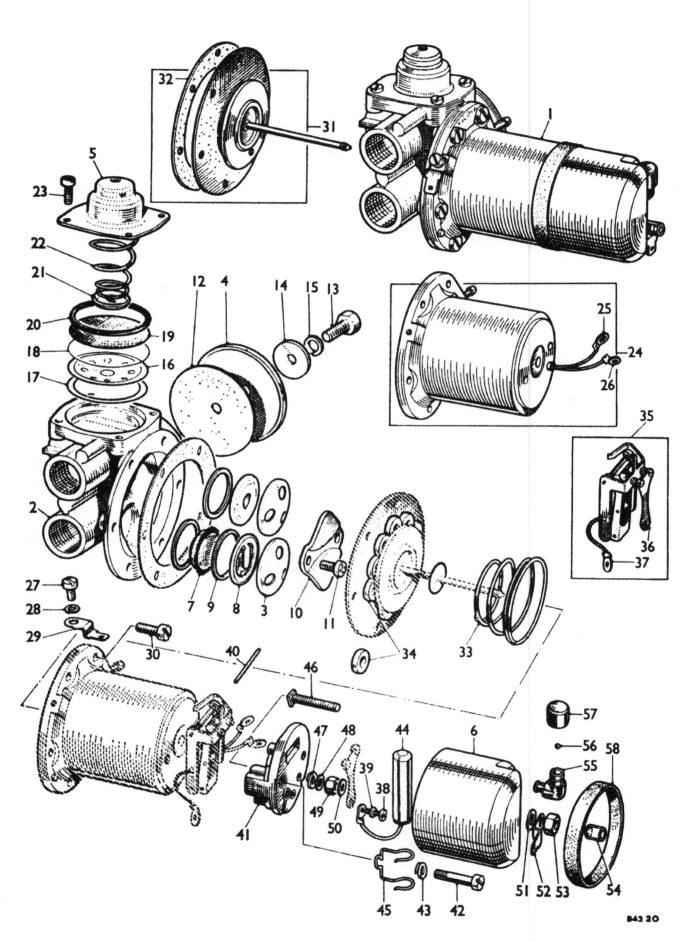

B43 20

DESCRIPTION	Part No.	Illus. No.	Quantity	Stock recoms. DIST.			Change Point	REMARKS
				Exp.	UK	D		

Fuel System—*continued*

Fuel pump—*continued*

DESCRIPTION	Part No.	Illus. No.	Quantity	Exp.	UK	D	Change Point	REMARKS
Pump—fuel	AUF 801	1	1	★	★	★		
Body	AUB 662	2	1					
Cover								
Valve	AUB 652	3	2					
Side—dished	AUA 574	4	1					
Air bottle	AUB 695	5	1					
End	AUB 707	6	1					
Filter	AUB 617	7	1					
Valve	†AUB 6061	8	2					Not available; use AUB 6062
Valve	†AUB 6062	8	2					
Washer—sealing	†AUB 618	9	8					Use AUB 676 for this application
Washer—sealing	†AUB 676	9	8					
Plate—valve cover clamp	AUB 653	10	1					
Screw—plate	AUB 597	11	2					
Washer—joint—side cover	AUA 578	12	1					
Bolt—side cover	AJD 1042	13	1					
Washer—dished	AUA 575	14	1					
Washer—spring	LWZ 303	15	1					
Plate—support	AUB 694	16	1					
Washer—joint—plate	AUB 675	17	1	★				
Diaphragm (nylon)	AUB 696	18	1	★				
Support—diaphragm	AUB 693	19	1					
Ring—sealing	AUB 711	20	1					
Cap—spring	AUB 698	21	1					
Spring—diaphragm	AUB 697	22	1					
Screw—air bottle cover	AUC 2588	23	4					
Housing—coil	AUB 6080	24	1					
Tag—5BA terminal	AUA 1455	25	1					
Tag—2BA terminal	AUA 1456	26	1					
Screw—earth	AUA 699	27	1					
Washer—spring	AUA 585	28	1					
Connector—Lucar	AUA 692	29	1					
Screw—coil housing to body	AUB 660	30	6					
Diaphragm	AUB 6097	31	1	★				†(C) H–BJ8–28225 on
Washer—joint	AUB 706	32	1					
Spring—armature	AUB 759	33	1					
Roller	AUA 1433	34	1					
Rocker and blade	†AUA 6021	35	1	★				Alternatives — Correction; was 88G 286
Rocker and blade	†AUB 6022	35	1	★				
Blade	AUB 6036	36	1					
Tag—2BA terminal	AUA 1456	37	1					
Screw—blade	AUA 565	38	1					
Washer—dished	AUA 566	39	1					
Spindle—contact breaker	AUA 1435	40	1					
Pedestal	AUB 6034	41	1					
Screw—pedestal to coil housing	AUA 1459	42	2					
Washer—spring	AUA 1863	43	2					
Condenser	AUA 5060	44	1					
Clip—condenser	AUA 5059	45	1					
Screw—terminal	AUA 1468	46	1					
Washer—spring	AUA 1863	47	1					
Washer (lead)	AUA 1662	48	1					
Nut	AUA 1661	49	1					
Washer—plain	AUB 609	50	1					
Washer—shakeproof	LWN 408	51	1					
Connector—Lucar	AUA 692	52	1					
Nut—end cover	AUA 878	53	1					
Sleeve—insulating	AUB 611	54	1					
Valve—ventilator	AUB 702	55	1					
Ball—valve	AUB 704	56	1					
Cap—valve	AUB 708	57	1					
Ring—sealing	AUB 716	58	1					
Knob—terminal	AUA 869		1					
Stud—pump to bracket								For details see page MD 2
Washer—spring								
Nut								
Bracket—pump mounting								
Screw								
Washer—plain								
Washer—spring								

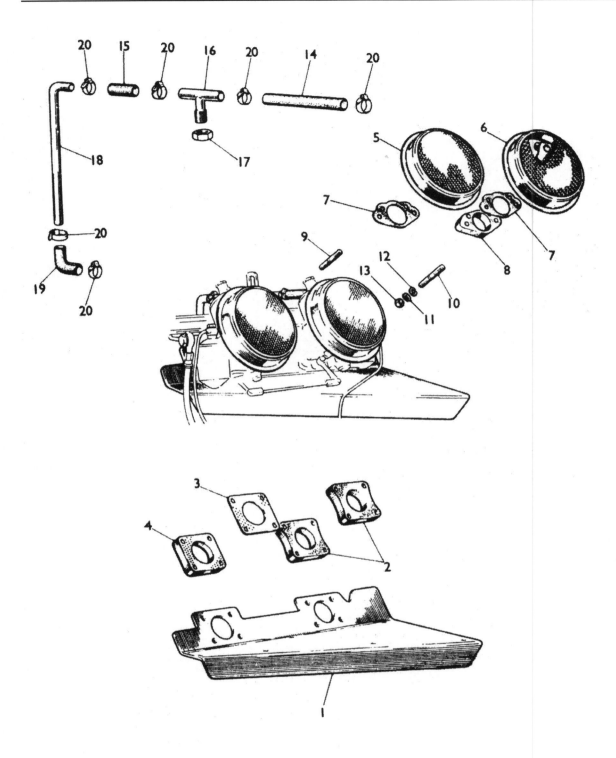

	DESCRIPTION	Part No.	Illus. No.	Quantity	Stock recoms. DIST. Exp.	UK	D	Change Point	REMARKS
	HEAT SHIELD								
	Shield—heat	12B 562	1	1				(E) 29F/H101 to H6188	
	Shield—heat	12B 812	1	1				(E) 29K/H101 on	
								†(E) 29KFA/H224 on	
	Joint								
	Carburetter to heat shield and heat shield to manifold	12B 561	2	4	★	★		(E) 29F/H101 to H6188	
	Carburetter to heat shield	12B 814	3	4	★	★		] (E) 29K/H101 on	
	Heat shield to manifold	12B 811	4	2	★	★		(E) 29KFA/H224 on	
	AIR CLEANERS								
	Cleaner—air								
	Front	88G 333	5	1				(C) H–BJ7–17551 to 25314	Part No. change; was 11B 621
	Front	AHB 6002	5	1				(C) H–BJ8–25315 on	
	Rear	11B 622	6	1				(C) H–BJ7–17551 to 25314	] Not available; use AHB 9909
	Rear] **USA**	11B 622	6	1				(C) H–BJ7–17551 to 23520	
	Rear]	AHB 9909	6	1				(C) H–BJ7–23521 to 25314	
	Rear	AHB 6003	6	1				(C) H–BJ8–25315 on	
	Washer—joint—cleaner to carburetter	AEC 375	7	3	★	★		(C) H–BJ7–17551 to 25314	
	Washer—joint—cleaner to carburetter	AHB 6019	7	2	★	★		(C) H–BJ8–25315 on	
	Piece-packing—rear cleaner to carburetter	AHB 9766	8	1				] (C) H–BJ7–17551 to 25314	
	Stud								
	Front cleaner to carburetter	FHS 2512	9	2				]	
	Rear cleaner to carburetter	FHS 2516	10	2					
	Cleaner to carburetter	FHS 2511	9	4				(C) H–BJ8–25315 on	
	Washer—plain	PWZ 105	11	4					
	Washer—spring	LWZ 205	12	4					
	Nut	FNZ 105	13	4					
	Hose								
	Cleaner to rocker cover	1G 2268	14	1	★	★		(C) H–BJ7–17551 to 25314	Not available; use 12B 702
	Cleaner to rocker cover	12B 702	14	1	★	★		(C) H–BJ7–25315 on	
	Cleaner to rocker cover] **USA**	1G 2268	14	1	★			(C) H–BJ7–17551 to 23730	Not available; use 12B 702
	Cleaner to rocker cover]	12B 702	14	1	★			(C) H–BJ7–23730 to 25314 (C) H–BJ8–25315 on	
	Rocker cover to breather pipe	AEC 441	15	1	★	★			Not available; use 12B 703
	Rocker cover to breather pipe **USA**	12B 703	15	1	★				
	Pipe—breather—rocker cover	AEC 703	16	1					
	Nut—lock—breather pipe	1B 2261	17	1					
	Pipe—breather—crankcase	AEC 702	18	1					
	Elbow—breather hose to side cover	AEC 440	19	1					Not available; use 12B 704
	Elbow—breather hose to side cover **USA**	12B 704	19	1					
	Clip	HCS 0709	20	6					

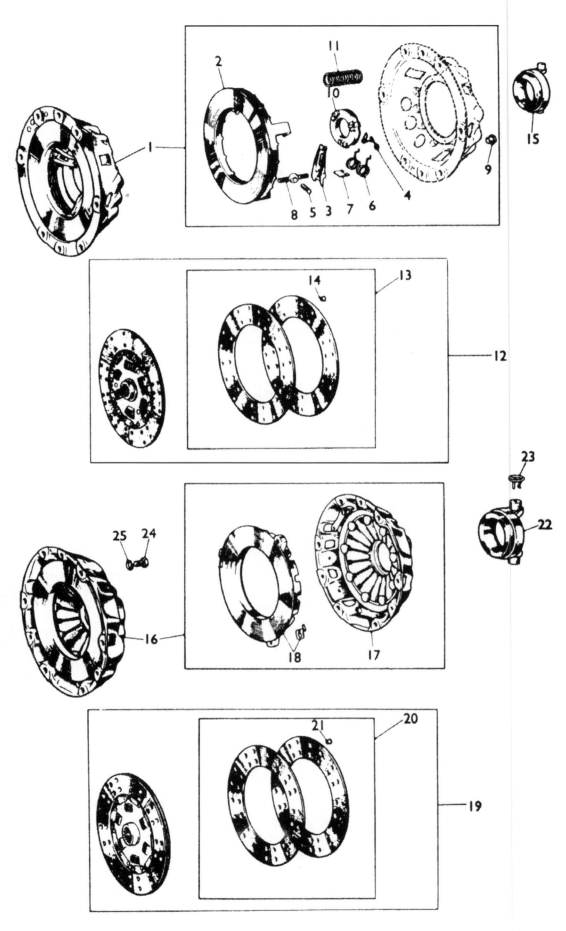

	DESCRIPTION	Part No.	Illus. No.	Quantity	Change Point	REMARKS

†CLUTCH

	Page	Plate
†COVER—CLUTCH	ME 1·1	E 1
†CYLINDERS—CLUTCH OPERATING	ME 2	E 2
†HOSE—CLUTCH	ME 3	E 2
†LEVER—CLUTCH PEDAL	ME 2	E 2
†PIPES—CLUTCH	ME 3	E 2
†PLATES—CLUTCH	ME 1·1	E 1

CLUTCH AND CONTROLS

CLUTCH

Description	Part No.	Illus. No.	Quantity	Change Point	Remarks
Cover assembly—clutch	AEJ 30	1	1		
Cover	NSP		1		
Plate—pressure	27H 3234	2	1		
Lever—release	7H 3239	3	3		
Retainer—lever	7H 3001	4	3		
Pin—lever	7H 3067	5	3		
Spring—anti-rattle	7H 3092	6	3		
Strut—release lever	7H 3069	7	3	(E) 29F/H101 to 4878	
Eyebolt	†7H 3195	8	3	(E) 29FF/H101 to 149	W.S.E. use 37H 2151
Eyebolt	†37H 2151	8	3		
Nut—eyebolt	17H 2724	9	3		
Plate—thrust	7H 3042	10	1		
Spring—pressure plate	7H 3082	11	12		
Plate assembly—driven—10″ (25 cm)	AEJ 17	12	1		
Lining assembly (with rivets)	8G 8355	13	1 set		
Rivet	7H 3078	14	42		
Bearing—release	7H 3120	15	1		
Cover assembly—clutch	†13H 1581	16	1		
	†13H 1739	16	1		
	†13H 3910	16	1		W.S.E. use 13H 4757
	13H 3747	16	1		
	†13H 4757	16	1		
Cover (with straps, diaphragm spring, and release plate)	NSP	17	1		Was 27H 2318
Plate—pressure (with clips)	NSP	18	1	(E) 29F/H4979 on	Was 17H 8799
Plate assembly—driven—9½″ (24·13 cm)	†13H 818	19	1	(E) 28FF/H150 on	W.S.E. use 13H 2127
Lining assembly (with rivets)	†8G 8811	20	1		
Rivets	†7H 3078	21	32		
Plate assembly—driven—9″ (22·86 cm)	13H 2127	19	1		
Lining assembly (with rivets)	8G 8354	20	1		
Rivets	†7H 3078	21	32		
Bearing—release	13H 1583	22	1		
Retainer—release bearing to clutch withdrawal fork	7H 3048	23	2		
Screw	HNS 0607	24	6	(E) 29F/H101 to 4878	
Washer—spring	LWN 206	25	6	(E) 29FF/H101 to 149	
Screw	HNS 0506	24	6	(E) 29F/H4879 on	
Washer—spring	LWN 205	25	6	(E) 29FF/H150 on	

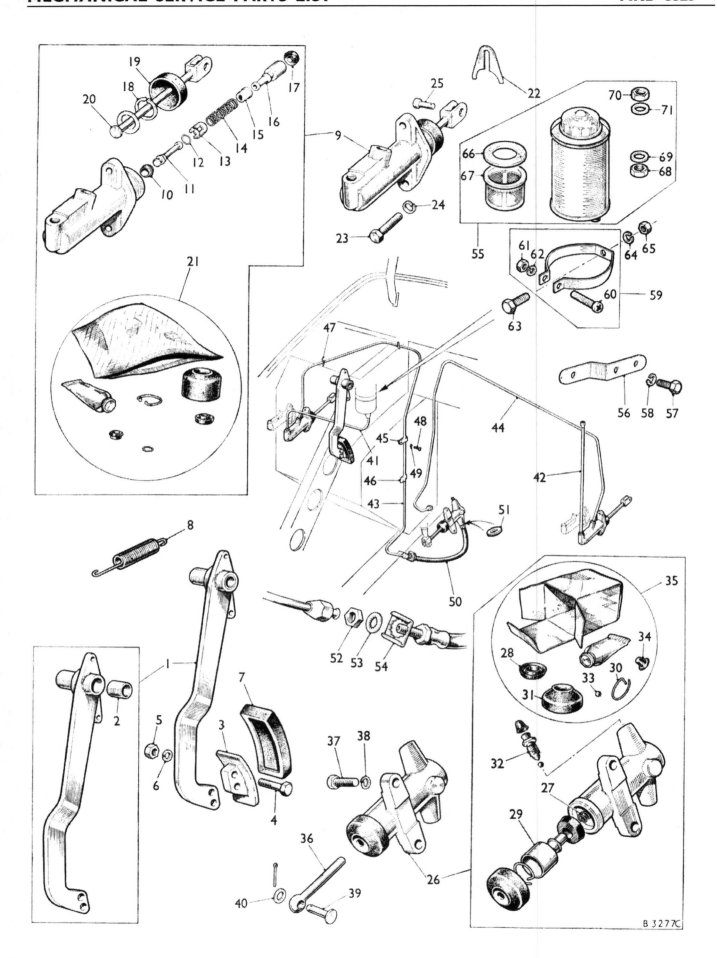

B 3277C

DESCRIPTION	Part No.	Illus. No.	Quantity	Change Point	REMARKS
Clutch and Controls—*continued*					
CLUTCH CONTROLS					
Lever assembly—pedal	AHB 9183	1	1		
Bush	1G 9310	2	1		
Pad—pedal	1B 8817	3	1		
Bolt—pad to lever	HBZ 0411	4	2		
Nut	FNZ 104	5	2		
Washer—spring	LWZ 304	6	2		
Rubber—pedal pad	1B 8751	7	1		
Spring—pedal return	11B 5283	8	1		
Shaft—brake and clutch pedal					
Bracket—pedal levers					
Screw—bracket to pedal box					
Washer—plain					See page MM 1·1
Washer—spring					
Sleeve—pedal shaft					
Piece—distance—pedal levers					
Nut					
Tank assembly—supply—clutch fluid	BHA 4647	55	1		
Gasket—filler cap	†7H 4726	66	1		
Filter (Nylon)	†17H 4743	67	1		
Adaptor	†17H 4946	68	1		
Gasket—adaptor to body	†17H 4635	69	1		
Nut—adaptor fixing	†7H 4867	70	1		
Washer—plain **Benelux**	†PWZ 108	71	1		
Bracket—tank **and**	11B 5521	56	1	(E) H–BJ8–41930 on	
Screw—bracket **France**	HZS 0403	57	2		
Washer—spring	LWZ 204	58	2		
Clip assembly—tank to bracket	13H 297	59	1		
Screw—clip	PMZ 0314	60	1		
Nut	FNZ 103	61	1		
Washer—spring	LWZ 203	62	1		
Screw	HZS 0404	63	1		
Nut	FNZ 104	64	1		
Washer—spring	LWZ 204	65	1		
Cylinder assembly—master	11B 5510	9	1		
Body	NSP		1		
Stem—valve	7H 4751	11	1		
Spacer—valve	17H 4132	13	1		
Spring	7H 4944	14	1		
Retainer—spring	17H 4827	15	1		
Plunger	17H 8113	16	1		
Circlip	†7H 4451	18	1		Also included in repair kit 8G 8807
Push-rod	17H 4513	20	1		
Kit—master cylinder repair	8G 8807	21	1		
Seal—valve	17H 4561	10	1		
Washer—valve	7H 4752	12	1		
Seal—plunger	17H 8112	17	1		
Circlip	†7H 4451	18	1		
Cover—dust	17H 4831	19	1		
Tube of grease	NSP		1		
Piece—packing—master cylinder	11B 5138	22	A/R		
Screw	HZS 0508	23	2		
Washer—spring	LWZ 205	24	2		
Pin—push-rod to pedal lever	CLZ 0518	25	1		

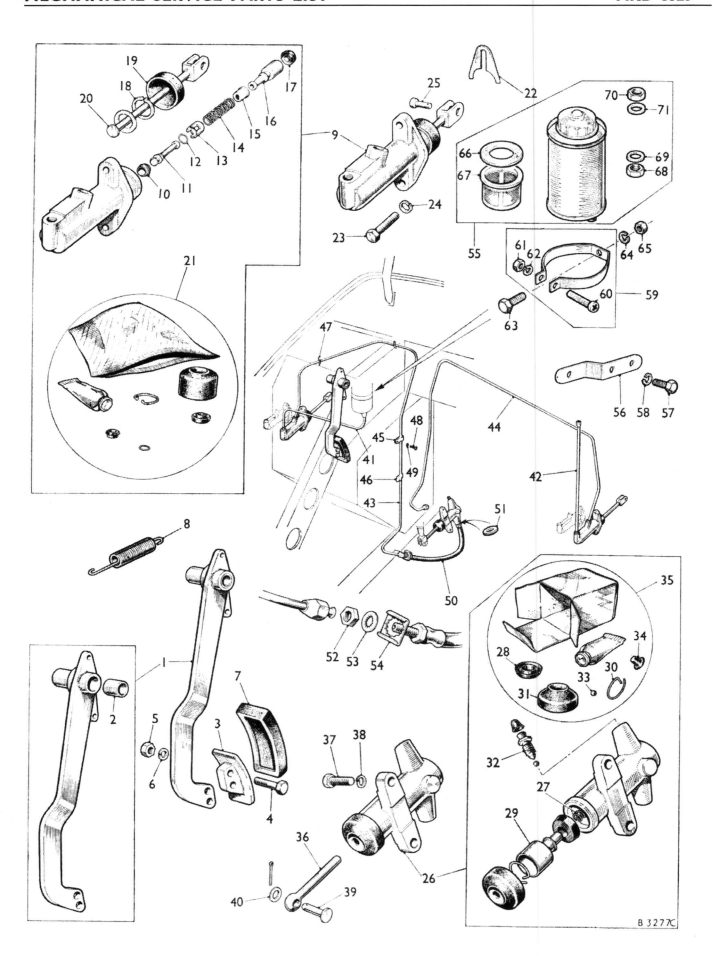

B 3277C

PLATE 2   Issue 4   82

		DESCRIPTION	Part No.	Illus. No.	Quantity	Stock recoms. DIST. Exp.	UK	D	Change Point	REMARKS

Clutch Controls—*continued*

DESCRIPTION	Part No.	Illus. No.	Quantity	Exp.	UK	D	Change Point	REMARKS
Cylinder assembly—clutch operating	†BHA 4112	26	1	★	★			
Body	N.S.P.		1					
Spring	7H 4970	27	1					
Plunger	17H 4554	29	1					
Screw—bleeder	7H 4973	32	1					
Kit—clutch operating cylinder repair	†8G 8249	35	1	★	★	★		
Seal—plunger	17H 4712	28	1					
Circlip	17H 4011	80	1					
Cover—dust	17H 4010	31	1					
Ball—bleeder screw	BLS 106	33	1					
Cover—dust—bleeder screw	7H 4419	84	1					
Tube of grease	†NSP		1					
Push-rod—clutch operating cylinder	BHA 4134	36	1					
Screw—clutch operating cylinder	HZS 0608	37	2					
Washer—spring	LWZ 306	38	2					
Pin—push-rod to clutch withdrawal fork	2K 5622	39	1					
Washer—plain	PWZ 105	40	1					
Pipe								
Supply tank to master cylinder **RHD**	17H 4517	41	1					
Supply tank to master cylinder **LHD**	17H 4516	42	1					
Master cylinder to flexible hose **RHD**	AHB 8939	43	1					
Master cylinder to flexible hose **LHD**	11B 5298	44	1					
Clip								
Pipe to pedal box	PCR 0307	45	2/1					Quantity reduced for LHD
Pipe to pedal box	1G 9529	46	1					
Pipe to dash **LHD**	6K 35	47	2					
Screw—clip to pedal box	PMZ 0306	48	1					
Washer—spring	LWZ 203	49	1					
Hose—flexible	1G 9516	50	1					
Gasket—hose to clutch operating cylinder	3H 2287	51	1	★	★			
Locknut—hose	FNZ 206	52	1	★	★			
Washer—shakeproof	LWN 406	53	1					
Plate—locking—hose	1G 9622	54	1					

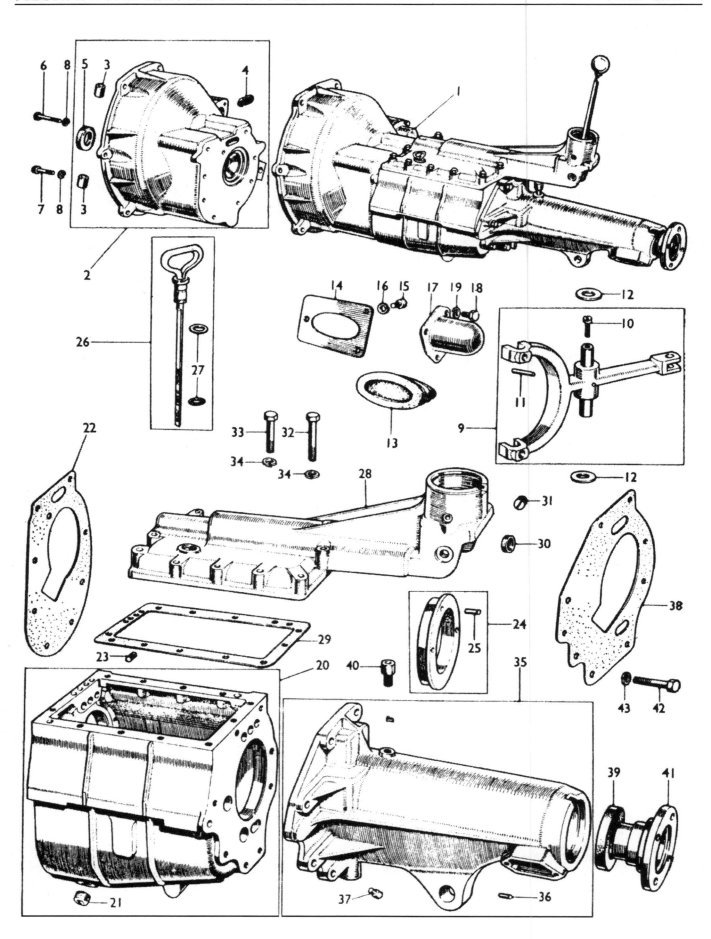

	DESCRIPTION	Part No.	Illus. No.	Quantity	Change Point	REMARKS

†GEARBOX

GEARBOX (BJ7)

Description	Part No.	Illus. No.	Quantity	Change Point	REMARKS
Gearbox assembly	AEC 3555	1	1		
Housing—clutch	AEC 3559	2	1		
Bush—fork and shaft	AEC 3102	3	2		
Pad—buffer	AEC 3298	4			
Seal—oil	10K 7089	5	1		
Bolt—2¼″ (5·71 cm)	HBN 0518	6	1		
Screw—1⅛″ (2·85 cm)	HNS 0509	7	8		
Washer—spring	LWN 205	8	9		
Fork and shaft assembly—clutch withdrawal	AEC 3088	9	1		
Screw—shaft blanking	AEC 3221	10	1		
Pin—taper	TPS 0610	11	1		
Washer—thrust—fork and shaft	AEC 3105	12	2		
Seal—fork and shaft	AEC 3106	13	1		
Plate—seal retaining	AEC 3168	14	1		
Screw	53K 1435	15	3		
Washer—spring	LWN 204	16	3		
Cover—starter end	1B 3346	17	1		
Screw—cover to housing	AEC 3207	18	3		
Washer—spring	LWN 204	19	3		
Casing—gearbox	AEC 3547	20	1		
Plug—oil drain	6K 499	21	1		
Gasket—casing to clutch housing	†AEC 3601	22	1		
Plug—interlock ball hole	AEC 479	23	1		
Housing—mainshaft bearing	AEC 3533	24	1		
Peg—locating	AEC 3112	25	1		
Indicator—oil level	AEC 3683	26	1		
Grommet (rubber)	AEC 3461	27	2		
Cover—gearbox top	AEC 3657	28	1		
Gasket—cover to gearbox	†AEC 3492	29	1		
Seal—oil—cover	AEJ 51	30	1		
Plug—overdrive switch hole	AEC 385	31	1		
Bolt—1⅞″ (4·76 cm)	HBN 0515	32	2		
Bolt—1½″ (3·81 cm)	HBN 0512	33	10		
Washer—spring	LWN 205	34	12		
Casing—gearbox extension	AEC 3620	35	1		
Plug—taper	2K 1345	36	1		
Button—thrust—speedometer pinion	1A 3073	37	1		
Gasket—casing to gearbox	†AEC 3605	38	1		
Seal—oil	88G 320	39	1		
Breather—gearbox	1H 3364	40	1		Part No. change; was ATA 7047
Flange—coupling	ATC 7100	41	1		
Bolt	HBN 0510	42	8		
Washer—spring	LWN 205	43	8		

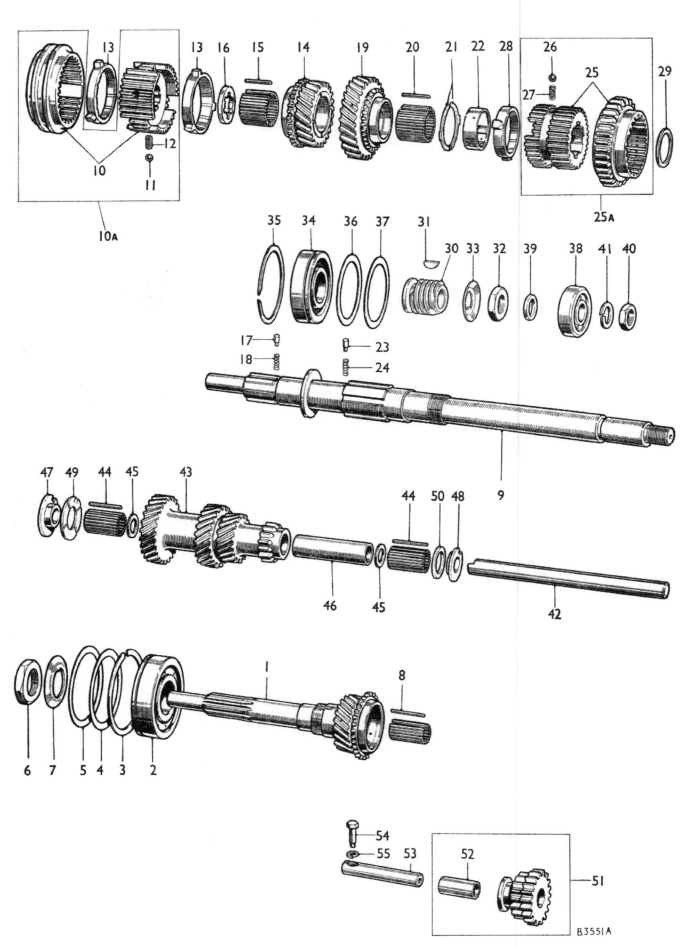

	DESCRIPTION	Part No.	Illus. No.	Quantity	Change Point	REMARKS

Gearbox (BJ7)—*continued*

DESCRIPTION	Part No.	Illus. No.	Quantity	Change Point	REMARKS
Gear—drive	AEC 3472	1	1		
Bearing—drive gear	6K 777	2	1		
Circlip—bearing	6K 780	3	1		
Plate—bearing	AEC 3184	4	1		
Plate—spring—bearing	AEC 3183	5	1		
Nut—bearing to drive gear	AEB 3124	6	1		
Washer—locknut	AEC 3185	7	1		
Roller—needle—drive gear	AEC 3186	8	18		
Mainshaft	AEC 3417	9	1		
Coupling sleeve and synchronizer — 3rd and 4th speed	AEC 3072	10	1		W.S.E. use 8G 3028
Ball—3rd and 4th speed synchronizer	BLS 110	11	3		
Spring—ball	AEC 3208	12	3		
Synchronizer assembly—3rd and 4th speed (with coupling sleeve)	8G 3028	10A	1		
Ball	BLS 110	11	3		
Spring	AEC 3208	12	3		
Ring—baulk—3rd and 4th speed	AEC 3481	13	2		
Gear—3rd speed	AEC 3468	14	1		
Roller—needle—gear	AEC 3180	15	32		
Plate—locking	†AEC 3193	16	1		W.S.E. use 22B 187
Plate—locking	†22B 187	16	1		
Plunger—gear	AEC 3181	17	1		
Spring—plunger	AEC 3182	18	1		
Gear—2nd speed	AEC 3469	19	1		
Roller—needle—gear	AEC 3180	20	33		
Washer—gear	AEB 3111	21	2		
Plate—locking	AEB 3112	22	1		
Plunger—gear	AEC 3181	23	1		
Spring—plunger	AEC 3182	24	1		
1st speed gear and 2nd speed synchronizer	†8G 3013	25	1		W.S.E. use 8G 3027
Ball—2nd speed synchronizer	BLS 110	26	3		
Spring—ball	AEC 3208	27	3		
Gear assembly—1st speed (with 2nd speed synchronizer)	†8G 3027	25A	1		
Ball	BLS 110	26	3		
Spring	AEC 3208	27	3		
Ring—baulk—2nd speed	AEC 3482	28	1		
Collar—distance—mainshaft	AEB 3115	29	1		
Gear—speedometer	AEC 3418	30	1		
Key—gear	WKN 305	31	1		
Locknut—gear	AEB 3162	32	1		
Washer—lock—gear	AEB 3163	33	1		
Bearing—mainshaft—gearbox casing	6K 681	34	1		
Circlip—bearing	1K 8055	35	1		
Plate—bearing	AEB 3105	36	1		
Plate—spring—bearing	AEC 3178	37	1		
Bearing—mainshaft—rear extension	2K 5505	38	1		
Washer—bearing	1B 3766	39	1		
Nut—flange to mainshaft	FNZ 612	40	1		
Washer—spring	LWZ 212	41	1		
Layshaft	AEB 3208	42	1		
Laygear	AEC 3649	43	1		
Roller—needle—laygear	AEB 3212	44	46		
Washer—roller	AEB 3204	45	2		
Spacer—roller	AEC 3393	46	1		
Plate—thrust—laygear—front	AEC 3115	47	1		
Plate—thrust—laygear—rear	AEC 3116	48	1		
Washer—thrust—laygear—front	AEC 3679	49	1		
Washer—thrust—laygear—rear	AEC 3681	50	1		
Gear—reverse	AEC 3565	51	1		W.S.E. use 22B 233
Gear—reverse	22B 233	51	1		
Bush—gear	AEC 3119	52	1		
Shaft—gear	AEC 3340	53	1		
Screw—shaft retaining	AEC 3121	54	1		
Washer—spring	LWN 305	55	1		

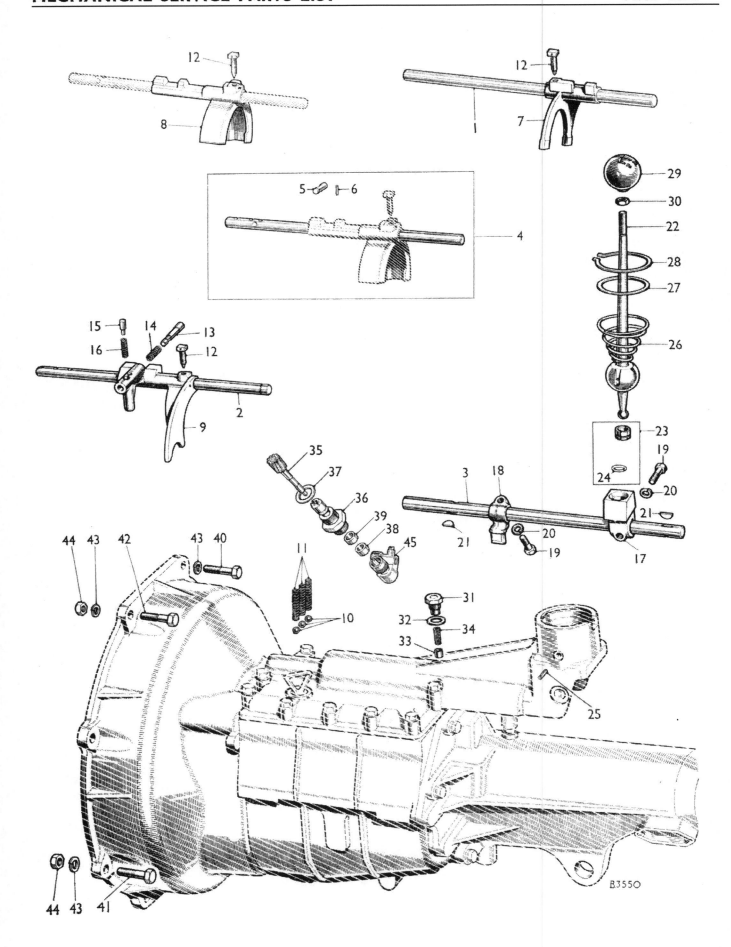

	DESCRIPTION	Part No.	Illus. No.	Quantity	Change Point	REMARKS
	Gearbox (BJ7)—*continued*					
	Shaft					
	3rd and 4th shifter	AEC 3342	1	1		
	Reverse shifter	AEC 3343	2	1		
	Remote control	AEC 3656	3	1		
	Shaft—1st and 2nd shifter	AEC 3557	4	1		
	Pin—shaft interlocking	AEC 3187	5	1		
	Rivet—pin	AEC 3188	6	1		
	Fork—striking					
	3rd and 4th	AEC 3625	7	1		
	1st and 2nd	AEC 3624	8	1		
	Reverse	†AEC 3626	9	1		W.S.E. use 22B 162
	Reverse	22B 162	9	1		
	Ball—interlock—shifter shaft	BLS 110	10	5		
	Spring—ball	AEC 3189	11	3		
	Screw—fork to shifter shaft	AEB 3130	12	3		
	Plunger—reverse selector	1B 3710	13	1		
	Spring—plunger	2F 3198	14	1		
	Plunger—detent	1B 3836	15	1		
	Spring—plunger	22A 75	16	1		
	Socket—change speed lever	AEC 3654	17	1		
	Lever—selector	AEC 3636	18	1		
	Bolt—selector lever and socket	AEC 3689	19	2		
	Washer—spring—bolt	LWN 205	20	2		
	Key—selector lever and socket	WKN 404	21	2		
	Lever—change speed	AEC 3658	22	1		
	Bush—lever	AEC 3520	23	1 pr		
	Circlip—bush	1G 3709	24	1		
	Rollpin	†RPS 1210	25	2		Correction; was AEA 558
	Spring—ball end retaining	AEC 3671	26	1		
	Washer—spring	AEC 3659	27	1		
	Circlip	1H 3087	28	1		
	Knob—change speed lever	1B 3736	29	1		
	Locknut—knob	54K 1723	30	1		
	Plug—plunger retaining	AEG 3113	31	1		
	Washer—plug	AEG 3122	32	1		
	Plunger	AEG 3124	33	1		
	Spring—plunger	AEG 3123	34	1		
	Pinion—speedometer	AEC 3419	35	1		
	Bearing—pinion	AEC 3198	36	1		
	Washer—bearing	2K 7500	37	1		
	Collar—distance—pinion	AEB 3202	38	1		
	Seal—oil—pinion	2A 3254	39	1		
	Bolt—clutch housing to rear plate—1½″ (3·81 cm)	HBZ 0612	40	1		
	Bolt—clutch housing to rear plate—1⅜″ (3·50 cm)	HBZ 0611	41	4		
	Bolt—dowel—clutch housing to rear plate	AEC 3487	42	2		
	Washer—spring—bolt	LWZ 206	43	7		
	Nut—bolt	FNZ 106	44	6		
	Adaptor box—speedometer drive	†1H 3131	45	1		W.S.E. use 13H 2567
	Adaptor box—speedometer drive	†13H 2567	45	1		

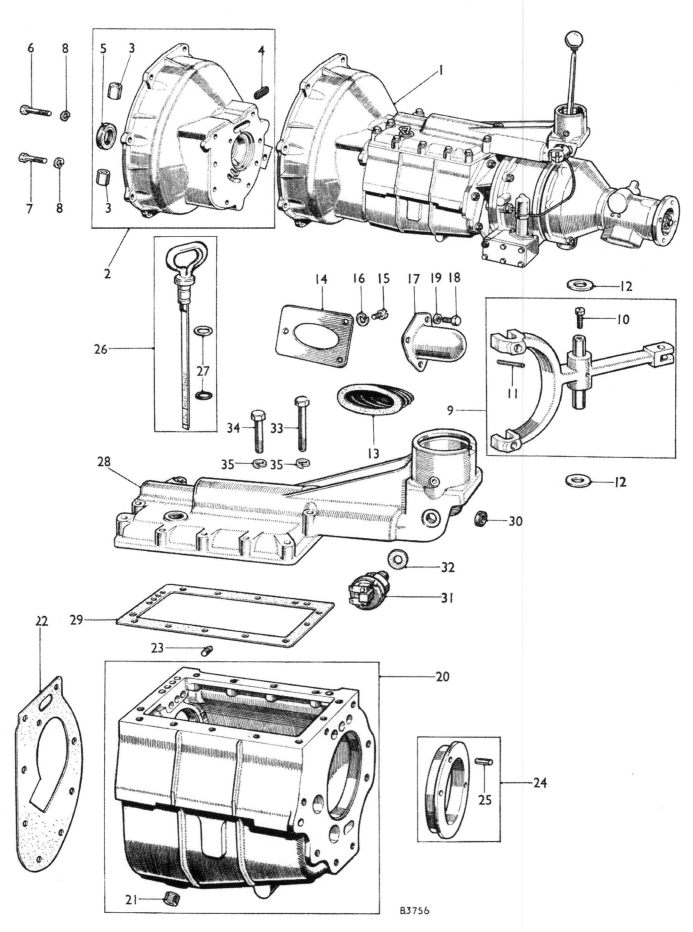

B.3756

	DESCRIPTION	Part No.	Illus. No.	Quantity	Change Point	REMARKS
	GEARBOX WITH OVERDRIVE **(Optional Extra)** **(BJ7)**					
	Gearbox assembly	AEC 3554	1	1		
	Housing—clutch	AEC 3559	2	1		
	Bush—fork and shaft	AEC 3102	3	2		
	Pad—buffer	AEC 3298	4	1		
	Seal—oil	10K 7089	5	1		
	Bolt—housing to gearbox—2¼″ (5·71 cm)	HBN 0518	6	1		
	Screw—housing to gearbox—1⅛″ (2·85 cm)	HNS 0509	7	8		
	Washer—spring—bolt and screw	LWN 205	8	9		
	Fork and shaft assembly—clutch withdrawal	AEC 3088	9	1		
	Screw—shaft blanking	AEC 3221	10	1		
	Pin—taper—shaft to fork	TPS 0610	11	1		
	Washer—thrust—fork and shaft	AEC 3105	12	2		
	Seal—fork and shaft	AEC 3106	13	1		
	Plate—seal retaining	AEC 3168	14	1		
	Screw—plate	53K 1435	15	3		
	Washer—spring—screw	LWN 204	16	3		
	Cover—starter end	1B 3346	17	1		
	Screw—cover to housing	AEC 3207	18	3		
	Washer—spring—screw	LWN 204	19	3		
	Casing—gearbox	AEC 3547	20	1		
	Plug—oil drain	6K 499	21	1		
	Gasket—casing to clutch housing	AEC 3601	22	1		
	Plug—interlock ball hole	AEC 479	23	1		
	Housing—mainshaft bearing	AEC 3533	24	1		
	Peg—locating	AEC 3112	25	1		
	Indicator—oil level	AEC 3683	26	1		
	Grommet (rubber)	AEC 3461	27	2		
	Cover—gearbox top	AEC 3657	28	1		
	Gasket—cover to gearbox	AEC 3492	29	1		
	Seal—oil—cover	AEJ 51	30	1		
	Switch—overdrive	†AEJ 20	31	1		
	Gasket—switch	2K 7914	32	1		
	Bolt—cover to gearbox—1⅞″ (4·76 cm)	HBN 0515	33	2		
	Bolt—cover to gearbox—1½″ (3·81 cm)	HBN 0512	34	10		
	Washer—spring—bolt	LWN 205	35	12		

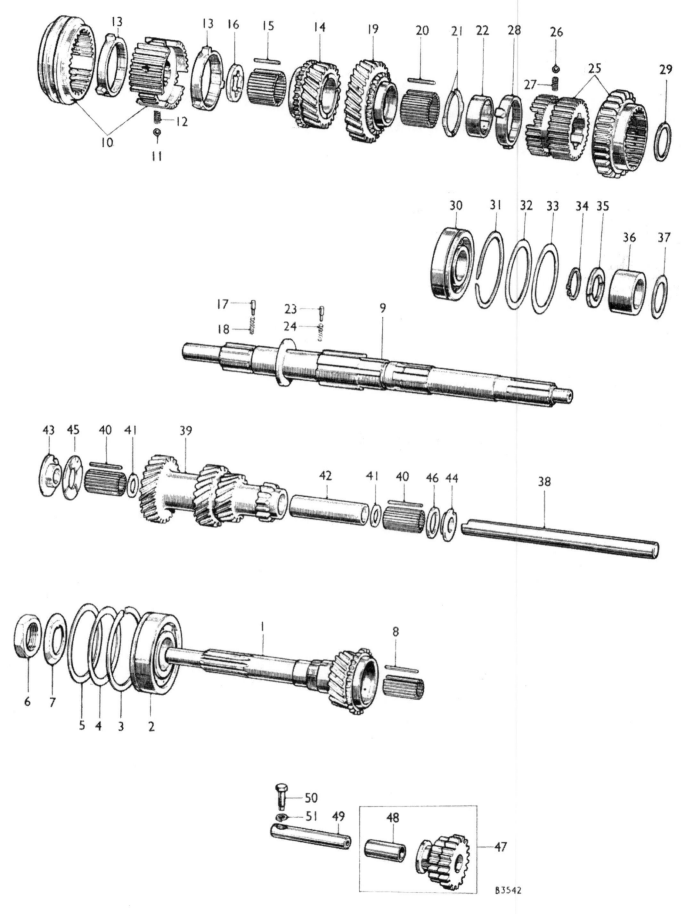

B3542

	DESCRIPTION	Part No.	Illus. No.	Quantity	Change Point	REMARKS
	Gearbox with Overdrive (BJ7)—*continued*					
	Gear—drive	AEC 3472	1	1		
	Bearing—drive gear	6K 777	2	1		
	Circlip—bearing	6K 780	3	1		
	Plate—bearing	AEC 3184	4	1		
	Plate—spring—bearing	AEC 3183	5	1		
	Nut—bearing to drive gear	AEB 3124	6	1		
	Washer—lock—nut	AEC 3185	7	1		
	Roller—needle—drive gear	AEC 3186	8	18		
	Mainshaft	AEC 3486	9	1		
	Coupling sleeve and synchronizer—3rd and 4th speed	AEC 3072	10	1		W.S.E. use 8G 3028
	Ball—3rd and 4th speed synchronizer	BLS 110	11	3		
	Spring—ball	AEC 3208	12	3		
	Synchronizer assembly—3rd and 4th speed (with coupling sleeve)	8G 3028	10A	1		
	Ball	BLS 110	11	3		
	Spring	AEC 3208	12	3		
	Ring—baulk—3rd and 4th speed	AEC 3481	13	2		
	Gear—3rd speed	AEC 3468	14	1		
	Roller—needle—gear	AEC 3180	15	32		
	Plate—locking	†AEC 3193	16	1		W.S.E. use 22B 187
	Plunger—gear	AEC 3181	17	1		
	Spring—plunger	AEC 3182	18	1		
	Gear—2nd speed	AEC 3469	19	1		
	Roller—needle—gear	AEC 3180	20	33		
	Washer—gear	AEB 3111	21	2		
	Plate—locking	AEB 3112	22	1		
	Plunger—gear	AEC 3181	23	1		
	Spring—plunger	AEC 3182	24	1		
	Gear—1st speed and 2nd speed synchronizer	8G 3013	25	1		W.S.E. use 8G 3027
	Ball—2nd speed synchronizer	BLS 110	26	3		
	Spring—ball	AEC 3208	27	3		
	Gear assembly—1st speed (with 2nd speed synchronizer)	8G 3027	25A	1		
	Ball	BLS 110	26	1		
	Spring	AEC 3208	27	1		
	Ring—baulk—2nd speed	AEC 3482	28	1		
	Collar—distance—mainshaft	AEB 3115	29	1		
	Bearing—mainshaft	6K 681	30	1		
	Circlip—bearing	1K 3055	31	1		
	Plate—bearing	AEB 3105	32	1		
	Plate—spring—bearing	AEC 3178	33	1		
	Circlip—mainshaft	CCN 120	34	1		
	Collar—abutment—bearing					
	·187″ (4·749 mm) thick	AEC 3484	35	A/R		
	·190″ (4·826 mm) thick	AEC 3484 03	35	A/R		
	·193″ (4·902 mm) thick	AEC 3484 06	35	A/R		
	Ring—abutment collar retaining	AEC 3485	36	1		
	Shim	1B 3655	37	A/R		
	Layshaft	AEB 3203	38	1		
	Laygear	AEC 3649	39	1		
	Roller—needle—laygear	AEB 3212	40	46		
	Washer—roller	AEB 3204	41	2		
	Spacer—roller	AEC 3393	42	1		
	Plate—thrust—laygear—front	AEC 3115	43	1		
	Plate—thrust—laygear—rear	AEC 3116	44	1		
	Washer—thrust—laygear—front	AEC 3679	45	1		
	Washer—thrust—laygear—rear	AEC 3681	46	1		
	Gear—reverse	AEC 3565	47	1		W.S.E. use 22B 233
	Gear—reverse	22B 233	47	1		
	Bush—gear	AEC 3119	48	1		
	Shaft—gear	AEC 3340	49	1		
	Screw—shaft retaining	AEC 3121	50	1		
	Washer—spring	LWN 305	51	1		

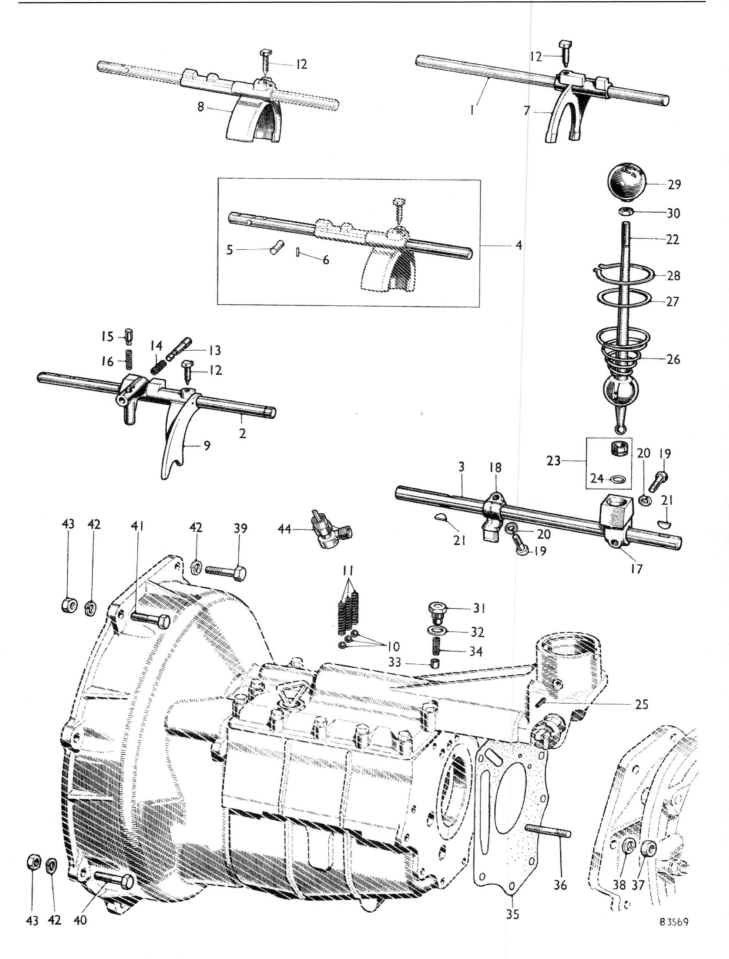

B 3569

DESCRIPTION	Part No.	Illus. No.	Quantity	Change Point	REMARKS
Gearbox with Overdrive (BJ7)—*continued*					
Shaft					
3rd and 4th shifter	AEC 3342	1	1		
Reverse shifter	AEC 3343	2	1		
Remote control	AEC 3656	3	1		
Shaft—1st and 2nd shifter	AEC 3557	4	1		
Pin—shaft interlocking	AEC 3187	5	1		
Rivet—pin	AEC 3188	6	1		
Fork—striking					
3rd and 4th	AEC 3625	7	1		
1st and 2nd	AEC 3624	8	1		
Reverse	AEC 3626	9	1		W.S.E. use 22B 162
Reverse	22B 162	9	1		
Ball	BLS 110	10	5		
Spring—ball	AEC 3189	11	3		
Screw—fork to shifter shaft	AEB 3130	12	3		
Plunger—reverse selector	1B 3710	13	1		
Spring—plunger	2F 8198	14	1		
Plunger—detent	1B 3836	15	1		
Spring—plunger	22A 75	16	1		
Socket—change speed lever	AEC 3654	17	1		
Lever—selector	AEC 3636	18	1		
Bolt—selector lever and socket	AEC 3689	19	2		
Washer—spring	LWN 205	20	2		
Key	WKN 404	21	2		
Lever—change speed	AEC 3658	22	1		
Bush—lever	AEC 3520	23	1 pr		
Circlip—bush	1G 3709	24	1		
Rollpin	†RPS 1210	25	2		Correction; was AEA 558
Spring—ball end retaining	AEC 3671	26	1		
Washer—spring	AEC 3659	27	1		
Circlip	1H 3087	28	1		
Knob—change speed lever	1B 3736	29	1		
Locknut—knob	54K 1723	30	1		
Plug—plunger retaining	AEG 3113	31	1		
Washer—plug	AEG 3122	32	1		
Plunger	AEG 3124	33	1		
Spring—plunger	AEG 3123	34	1		
Unit—overdrive assembly					For details see Page MF 13
Gasket—overdrive unit to gearbox	AEC 3605	35	1		
Stud—overdrive unit to gearbox	51K 505	36	8		
Nut	FNN 505	37	8		
Washer—spring	LWN 205	38	8		
Bolt—1½″ (3·81 cm)	HBZ 0612	39	1		
Bolt—1⅜″ (3·50 cm)	HBZ 0611	40	4		
Bolt—dowel	AEC 3487	41	2		
Washer—spring	LWZ 206	42	7		
Nut	FNZ 106	43	6		
Box adaptor—speedometer drive	†1H 3131	44	1		W.S.E. use 13H 2567
Box adaptor—speedometer drive	†13H 2567	44	1		

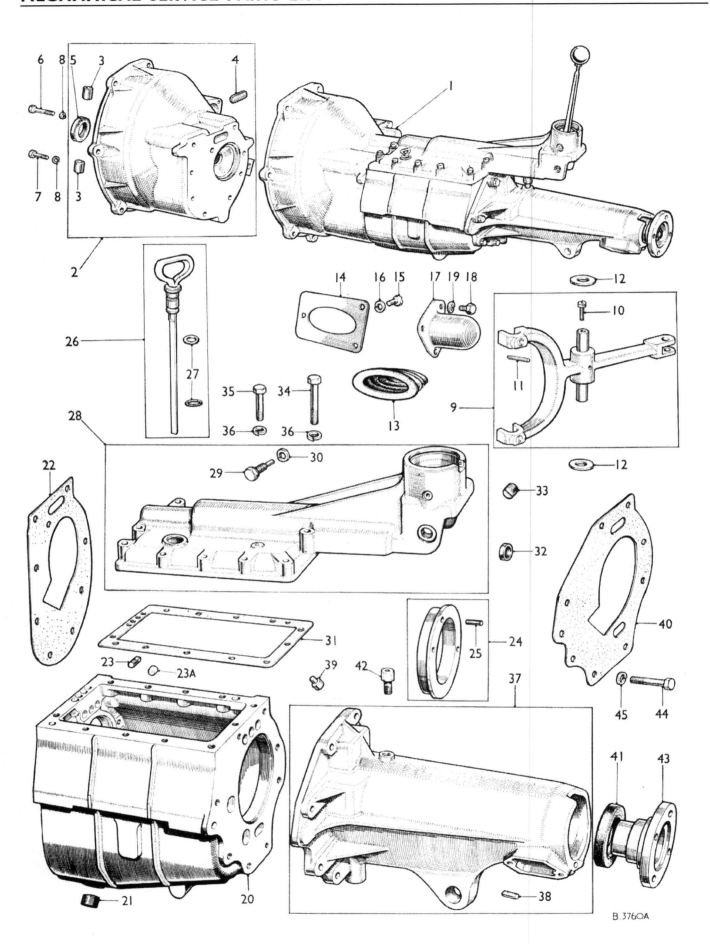

B.3760A

DESCRIPTION	Part No.	Illus. No.	Quantity	Change Point	REMARKS
GEARBOX (BJ8)					
Gearbox assembly	22B 176	1	1		
Housing—clutch	†22B 172	2	1		W.S.E. use 22B 237
Housing—clutch	22B 237	2	1		
Bush—fork and shaft	AEC 3102	3	2		
Pad—buffer	AEC 3298	4	1		For use with 22B 172 only
Seal—oil	10K 7089	5	1		
Bolt—2¼″ (5·71 cm)	HBN 0518	6	1		
Bolt—1⅛″ (2·85 cm)	HBN 0509	7	8		
Washer—spring	LWN 205	8	9		
Fork and shaft assembly—clutch withdrawal	AEC 3088	9	1		
Screw—shaft blanking	AEC 3221	10	1		
Pin—taper	TPS 0610	11	1		
Washer—thrust—fork and shaft	AEC 3105	12	2		
Seal—fork and shaft	AEC 3106	13	1		
Plate—seal retaining	AEC 3168	14	1		
Screw	53K 1435	15	3		
Washer—spring	LWN 204	16	3		
Cover—starter end	1B 3346	17	1		
Screw—cover to housing	AEC 3207	18	3		
Washer—spring	LWN 204	19	3		
Casing—gearbox	22B 138	20	1		
Plug—oil drain	6K 499	21	1		
Gasket—casing to clutch housing	AEC 3601	22	1		
Plug—interlock ball hole—screwed	AEC 479	23	1	(E) 29K/H101 to H5793 (E) 29KF/H101 to H223	
Plug—interlock ball hole—plain	2K 1351	23A	1	(E) 29K/H5794 on (E) 29KF/H224 on	
Housing—mainshaft bearing	AEC 3533	24	1		
Peg—locating	AEC 3112	25	1		
Indicator—oil level	AEC 3683	26	1		
Grommet (rubber)	AEC 3461	27	2		
Cover—gearbox top	†22B 197	1		(G) 101–118	W.S.E. use 8G 3016
Cover assembly—gearbox top	8G 3016	28	1	(G) 119 on	
Pin—locating—change speed lever	2A 3602	29	2		
Washer—spring	LWZ 304	30	2		
Gasket—cover to gearbox	AEC 3492	31	1		
Seal—oil—cover	AEJ 51	32	1		
Plug—overdrive switch hole	AEC 385	33	1		
Bolt—1⅞″ (4·76 cm)	HBN 0515	34	2		
Bolt—1½″ (3·81 cm)	HBN 0512	35	10		
Washer—spring	LWN 205	36	12		
Casing—gearbox extension	22B 179	37	1		
Plug—taper	2K 1345	38	1		
Button—thrust—speedometer pinion	1A 3073	39	1		
Gasket—casing to gearbox	AEC 3605	40	1		
Seal—oil	88G 320	41	1		
Breather—gearbox	1H 3364	42	1		
Flange—coupling	ATC 7100	43	1		
Bolt	HBN 0510	44	8		
Washer—spring	LWN 205	45	8		

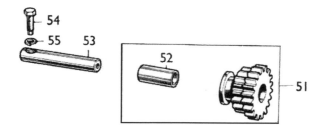

B 3646C

DESCRIPTION	Part No.	Illus. No.	Quantity	Change Point	REMARKS
Gearbox (BJ8)—*continued*					
Gear—drive	22B 140	1	1		
Bearing—drive gear	6K 777	2	1		Part No. change; was 6K 830
Circlip—bearing	6K 780	3	1		
Shim—packing—bearing	22B 152	4	A/R		
Shim—packing—bearing	22B 153	4	A/R		
Nut—bearing to drive gear	AEB 3124	6	1		
Washer—locknut	AEC 3185	7	1		
Bearing—pilot—drive gear	13H 1565	8	1		
Mainshaft	22B 177	9	1		
Coupling sleeve and synchronizer—3rd and 4th speed	†8G 3015	10	1		⎫ W.S.E. use 8G 3024
	†8G 3023	10	1		⎬
	†8G 3024	10	1		⎭ W.S.E. use 8G 3026
Plunger—3rd and 4th speed synchronizer	22B 155	11	2		
Ball	BLS 110	12	3		
Spring—ball	AEC 3208	13	3		
Coupling sleeve and synchronizer assembly —3rd and 4th speed	†8G 3026	10A	1		
Sleeve—coupling	†NSP		1		
Synchronizer	†NSP		1		
Ball—synchronizer	†BLS 110	12	3		
Spring—ball	†AEC 3208	13	3		
Ring—baulk—3rd and 4th speed	22B 159	14	2		
Gear—3rd speed	22B 144	15	1		
Roller—needle—gear	AEC 3180	16	32		
Plate—locking	22B 187	17	1		
Plunger—gear	AEC 3181	18	1		
Spring—plunger	AEC 3182	19	1		
Gear—2nd speed	22B 145	20	1		
Roller—needle—gear	AEC 3180	21	33		
Washer—gear	AEB 3111	22	2		
Plate—locking	22B 188	23	1		
Plunger—gear	AEC 3181	24	1		
Spring—plunger	AEC 3182	25	1		
Gear — 1st speed and 2nd speed synchronizer	†8G 3014	26	1		W.S.E. use 8G 3025
Gear — 1st speed and 2nd speed synchronizer assembly	8G 3025	26A	1		
Gear—1st speed	NSP		1		
Synchronizer—2nd speed	NSP		1		
Ball—synchronizer	BLS 110	28	3		
Spring—ball	AEC 3208	29	3		
Plunger—2nd speed synchronizer	22B 158	27	1		
Ring—baulk—2nd speed	22B 149	30	1		
Collar—distance—mainshaft	AEB 3115	31	1		
Gear—speedometer	AEC 3418	32	1		
Key	WKN 305	33	1		
Locknut—gear	AEB 3162	34	1		
Washer—lock—gear	AEB 3163	35	1		
Bearing—mainshaft—gearbox casing	6K 681	36	1		
Circlip—bearing	1K 3055	37	1		
Shim—packing—bearing	†1B 3668	38	A/R		⎫ Alternatives
Shim—packing—bearing	†1B 3669	38	A/R		⎬
Bearing—mainshaft—rear extension	†2K 5505	39	1		⎭
Washer—bearing	1B 3766	40	1		
Nut	FNZ 612	41	1		
Washer—spring	LWZ 212	42	1		
Layshaft	22B 142	43	1		
Laygear	22B 141	44	1		
Bearing—laygear	13H 1564	45	2 prs		
Spacer—bearing	22B 196	46	1		
Plate—thrust—laygear—front	22B 182	47	1		
Plate—thrust—laygear—rear	22B 181	48	1		
Washer—thrust—laygear					
Front	AEC 3679	49	1		
Rear	22B 183	50	1		⎫
Rear	22B 184	50	1		⎟
Rear	22B 185	50	1		⎬ Alternatives
Rear	22B 186	50	1		⎟
Rear	AEC 3681	50	1		⎭
Gear—reverse	22B 233	51	1		
Bush—gear	AEC 3119	52	1		
Shaft—gear	AEC 3340	53	1		
Screw—shaft retaining	AEC 3121	54	1		
Washer—spring	LWN 305	55	1		

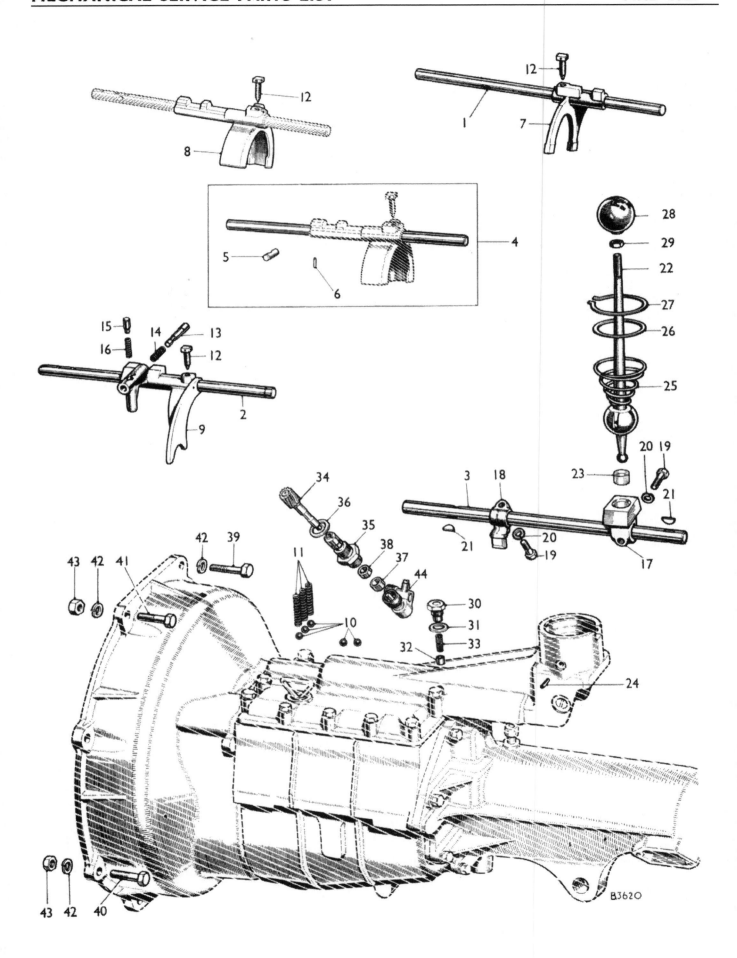

B3620

DESCRIPTION	Part No.	Illus. No.	Quantity	Change Point	REMARKS
Gearbox (BJ8)—*continued*					
Shaft					
3rd and 4th shifter	AEC 3342	1	1		
Reverse shifter	AEC 3343	2	1		
Remote control	AEC 3656	3	1		
Shaft—1st and 2nd shifter	AEC 3557	4	1		
Pin—shaft interlocking	AEC 3187	5	1		
Rivet—pin	AEC 3188	6	1		
Fork—striking					
3rd and 4th	AEC 3625	7	1		
1st and 2nd	22B 146	8	1		
Reverse	†AEC 3626	9	1		W.S.E. use 225 162
Reverse	22B 162	9	1		
Ball—interlock—shifter shaft	BLS 110	10	5		
Spring—ball	AEC 3189	11	3		
Screw—fork to shifter shaft	AEB 3130	12	3		
Plunger—reverse selector	1B 3710	13	1		
Spring—plunger	2F 3198	14	1		
Plunger—detent	1B 3836	15	1		
Spring—plunger	22A 75	16	1		
Socket—change speed lever	22B 361	17	1		Part No. change; was 22B 192
Lever—selector	AEC 3636	18	1		
Bolt—selector lever and socket	AEC 3689	19	2		
Washer—spring—bolt	LWN 205	20	2		
Key—selector lever and socket	WKN 404	21	2		
Lever—change speed	22B 195	22	1		
Bush—lever	22B 191	23	1		
Rollpin	†RPS 1210	24	2	(G) 101–118	Correction; was AEA 558
Spring—ball end retaining	AEC 3671	25	1		
Washer—spring	AEC 3659	26	1		
Circlip	1H 3087	27	1		
Knob—change speed lever	1B 3736	28	1		
Locknut—knob	54K 1723	29	1		
Plug—plunger retaining	AEG 3113	30	1		
Washer—plug	AEG 3122	31	1		
Plunger	AEG 3124	32	1		
Spring—plunger	AEG 3123	33	1		
Pinion—speedometer	AEC 3419	34	1		
Bearing—pinion	AEC 3198	35	1		
Washer—bearing	2K 7500	36	1		
Collar—distance—pinion	AEB 3202	37	1		
Seal—oil—pinion	2A 3254	38	1		
Bolt—clutch housing to rear plate—1½″ (3·81 cm)	HBZ 0612	39	1		
Bolt—clutch housing to rear plate—1⅜″ (3·50 cm)	HBZ 0611	40	4		
Bolt—dowel—clutch housing to rear plate	AEC 3487	41	2		
Washer—spring—bolt	LWZ 206	42	7		
Nut—bolt	FNZ 106	43	6		
Adaptor box—speedometer drive	†1H 3131	44	1		W.S.E. use 13H 2567
Adaptor box—speedometer drive	†13H 2567	44	1		

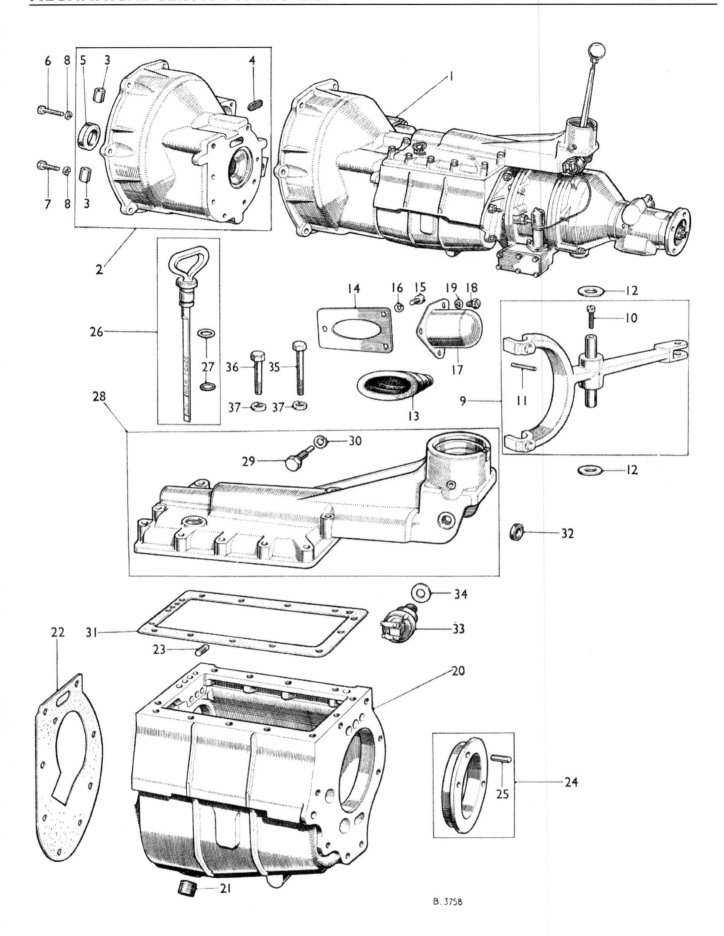

B. 3758

DESCRIPTION	Part No.	Illus. No.	Quantity	Change Point	REMARKS
GEARBOX WITH OVERDRIVE **(Optional Extra)** **(BJ8)**					
Gearbox assembly	22B 170	1	1		
Housing—clutch	22B 172	2	1		W.S.E. use 22B 237
Housing—clutch	22B 237	2	1		
Bush—fork and shaft	AEC 3102	3	2		
Pad—buffer	AEC 3298	4	1		For use with 22B 172 only
Seal—oil	10K 7089	5	1		
Bolt—2¼″ (5·71 cm)	HBN 0518	6	1		
Bolt—1⅛″ (2·85 cm)	HNS 0509	7	8		
Washer—spring	LWN 205	8	9		
Fork and shaft assembly—clutch withdrawal	AEC 3088	9	1		
Screw—shaft blanking	AEC 3221	10	1		
Pin—taper	TPS 0610	11	1		
Washer—thrust—fork and shaft	AEC 3105	12	2		
Seal—fork and shaft	AEC 3106	13	1		
Plate—seal retaining	AEC 3168	14	1		
Screw	53K 1435	15	3		
Washer—spring	LWN 204	16	3		
Cover—starter end	1B 3346	17	1		
Screw—cover to housing	AEC 3207	18	3		
Washer—spring	LWN 204	19	3		
Casing—gearbox	22B 138	20	1		
Plug—oil drain	6K 499	21	1		
Gasket—casing to clutch housing	AEC 3601	22	1		
Plug—interlock ball hole—screwed	AEC 479	23	1	(E) 29K/H101 to H5793 (E) 29KF/H101 to H223	
Plug—interlock ball hole—plain	2K 1351	23A	1	(E) 29K/H5794 on (E) 29KF/H224 on	
Housing—mainshaft bearing	AEC 3533	24	1		
Peg—locating	AEC 3112	25	1		
Indicator—oil level	AEC 3683	26	1		
Grommet (rubber)	AEC 3461	27	2		
Cover—gearbox top	†22B 197	28	1	(G) 101–1441	W.S.E. use 8G 3016
Cover assembly—gearbox top	8G 3016	28	1	(G) 1442 on	
Pin—locating—change speed lever	2A 3602	29	2		
Washer—spring	LWZ 304	30	2		
Gasket—cover to gearbox	AEC 3492	31	1		
Seal—oil—cover	AEJ 51	32	1		
Switch—overdrive	AEJ 20	33	1		
Gasket—switch	2K 7914	34	1		
Bolt—1⅞″ (4·76 cm)	HBN 0515	35	2		
Bolt—1½″ (3·81 cm)	HBN 0512	36	10		
Washer—spring	LWN 205	37	12		

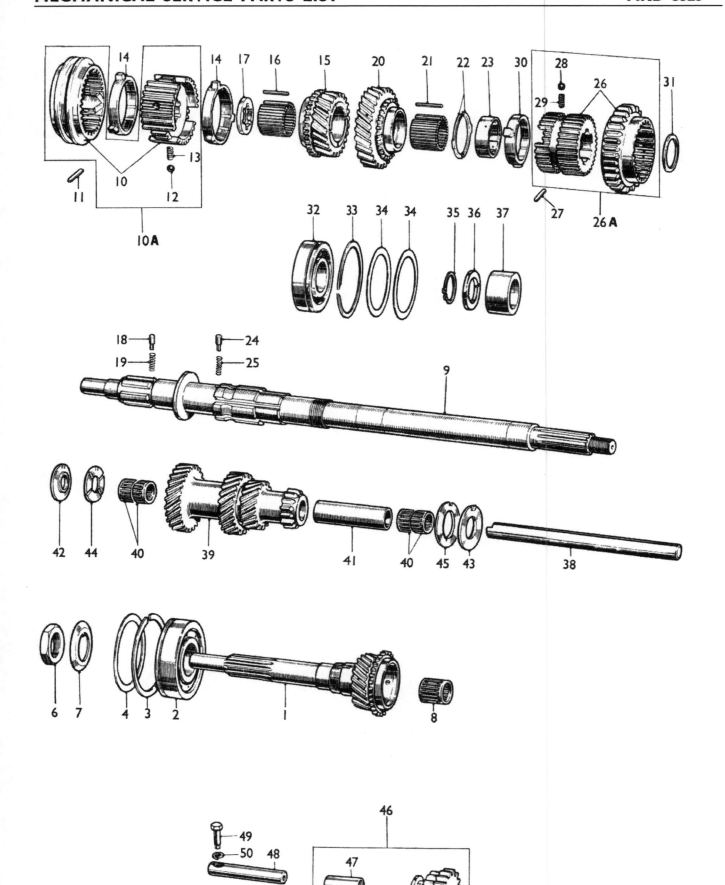

E 2 4 39

DESCRIPTION	Part No.	Illus. No.	Quantity	Change Point	REMARKS
Gearbox with Overdrive (BJ8)—*continued*					
Gear—drive	22B 140	1	1		
Bearing—drive gear	6K 777	2	1		Part No. change; was 6K 830
Circlip—bearing	6K 780	3	1		
Shim—packing—bearing	22B 152	4	A/R		
Shim—packing—bearing	22B 153	4	A/R		
Nut—bearing to drive gear	AEB 3124	6	1		
Washer—locknut	AEC 3185	7	1		
Bearing—pilot—drive gear	13H 1565	8	1		
Mainshaft	22B 171	9	1		
Coupling sleeve and synchronizer—3rd and 4th speed	†8G 3015	10	1		
	†8G 3023	10	1		] W.S.E. use 8G 3024
	†8G 3024	10	1		W.S.E. use 8G 3026
Plunger—3rd and 4th speed synchronizer	22B 155	11	2		
Ball	BLS 110	12	3		
Spring—ball	AEC 3208	13	3		
Coupling sleeve and synchronizer assembly —3rd and 4th speed	†8G 3026	10A	1		
Sleeve—coupling	†NSP		1		
Synchronizer	†NSP		1		
Ball—synchronizer	†BLS 110	12	3		
Spring—ball	†AEC 3208	13	3		
Ring—baulk—3rd and 4th speed	22B 159	14	2		
Gear—3rd speed	22B 144	15	1		
Roller—needle—gear	AEC 3180	16	32		
Plate—locking	22B 187	17	1		
Plunger—gear	AEC 3181	18	1		
Spring—plunger	AEC 3182	19	1		
Gear—2nd speed	22B 145	20	1		
Roller—needle—gear	AEC 3180	21	33		
Washer—gear	AEB 3111	22	2		
Plate—locking	22B 188	23	1		
Plunger—gear	AEC 3181	24	1		
Spring—plunger	AEC 3182	25	1		
Gear—1st speed and 2nd speed synchronizer	8G 3014	26	1		W.S.E. use 8G 3025
Gear—1st speed and 2nd speed synchronizer assembly	8G 3025	26A	1		
Gear—1st speed	NSP		1		
Synchronizer—2nd speed	NSP		1		
Ball—synchronizer	BLS 110	28	3		
Spring—ball	AEC 3208	29	3		
Plunger—2nd speed synchronizer	22B 158	27	1		
Ring—baulk—2nd speed	22B 149	30	1		
Collar—distance—mainshaft	AEB 3115	31	1		
Bearing—mainshaft	6K 681	32	1		
Circlip—bearing	1K 3055	33	1		
Shim—packing—bearing	†1B 3668	34	A/R		] Alternatives
Shim—packing—bearing	†1B 3669	34	A/R		
Circlip—mainshaft	CCN 120	35	1		
Collar—abutment—bearing					
·187″ (4·749 mm) thick	AEC 3484	36	A/R		
·190″ (4·826 mm) thick	AEC 3484 03	36	A/R		
·193″ (4·902 mm) thick	AEC 3484 06	36	A/R		
Ring—abutment collar retaining	AEC 3485	37	1		
Layshaft	22B 142	38	1		
Laygear	22B 141	39	1		
Bearing—laygear	13H 1564	40	2 prs.		
Spacer—bearing	22B 196	41	1		
Plate—thrust—laygear—front	22B 182	42	1		
Plate—thrust—laygear—rear	22B 181	43	1		
Washer—thrust—laygear					
Front	AEC 3679	44	1		
Rear	22B 183	45	1		]
Rear	22B 184	45	1		
Rear	22B 185	45	1		Alternatives
Rear	22B 186	45	1		
Rear	AEC 3681	45	1		]
Gear—reverse	22B 233	46	1		
Bush—gear	AEC 3119	47	1		
Shaft—gear	AEC 3340	48	1		
Screw—shaft retaining	AEC 3121	49	1		
Washer—spring	LWN 305	50	1		

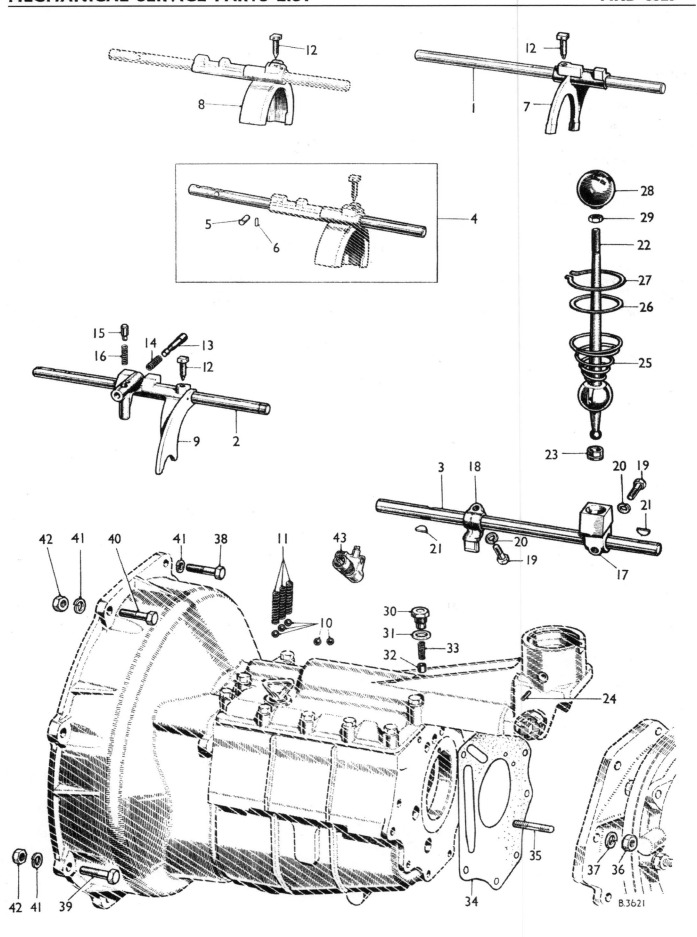

B.3621

DESCRIPTION	Part No.	Illus. No.	Quantity	Change Point	REMARKS
Gearbox with Overdrive (BJ8)—*continued*					
Shaft					
3rd and 4th shifter	AEC 3342	1	1		
Reverse shifter	AEC 3343	2	1		
Remote control	AEC 3656	3	1		
Shaft—1st and 2nd shifter	AEC 3557	4	1		
Pin—shaft interlocking	AEC 3187	5	1		
Rivet—pin	AEC 3188	6	1		
Forks—striking					
3rd and 4th	AEC 3625	7	1		
1st and 2nd	22B 146	8	1		
Reverse	AEC 3626	9	1		W.S.E. use 22B 162
Reverse	22B 162	9	1		
Ball—interlock—shifter shaft	BLS 110	10	5		
Spring—ball	AEC 3189	11	3		
Screw—fork to shifter shaft	AEB 3130	12	3		
Plunger—reverse selector	1B 3710	13	1		
Spring—plunger	2F 3198	14	1		
Plunger—detent	1B 3836	15	1		
Spring—plunger	22A 75	16	1		
Socket—change speed lever	22B 361	17	1		Part No. change; was 22B 192
Lever—selector	AEC 3636	18	1		
Bolt—selector lever and socket	AEC 3689	19	2		
Washer—spring—bolt	LWN 205	20	2		
Key—selector lever and socket	WKN 404	21	2		
Lever—change speed	22B 195	22	1		
Bush—lever	22B 191	23	1		
Rollpin	†RPS 1210	24	2	(G) 101–1441	Correction; was AEA 558
Spring—ball end retaining	AEC 3671	25	1		
Washer—spring	AEC 3659	26	1		
Circlip	1H 3087	27	1		
Knob—change speed lever	1B 3736	28	1		
Locknut—knob	54K 1723	29	1		
Plug—plunger retaining	AEG 3113	30	1		
Washer—plug	AEG 3122	31	1		
Plunger	AEG 3124	32	1		
Spring—plunger	AEG 3123	33	1		
Overdrive unit assembly					For details see page MF 13
Gasket—overdrive unit to gearbox	AEC 3605	34	1		
Stud—overdrive unit to gearbox	51K 505	35	8		
Nut—stud	FNN 505	36	8		
Washer—spring—nut	LWN 205	37	8		
Bolt—clutch housing to rear plate—1½" (3·81 cm)	HBZ 0612	38	1		
Bolt—clutch housing to rear plate—1⅜" (3·50 cm)	HBZ 0611	39	4		
Bolt—dowel—clutch housing to rear plate	AEC 3487	40	2		
Washer—spring—bolt	LWZ 206	41	7		
Nut—bolt	FNZ 106	42	6		
Adaptor box—speedometer drive	†1H 3131	43	1		W.S.E. use 13H 2567
Adaptor box—speedometer drive	†13H 2567	43	1		

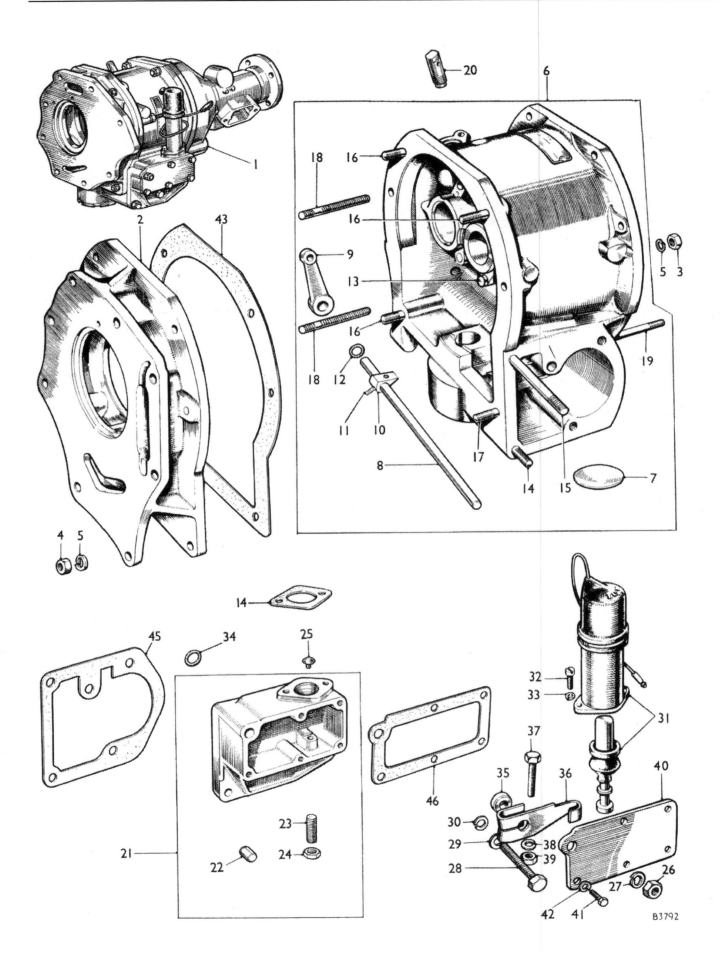

DESCRIPTION	Part No.	Illus. No.	Quantity	Change Point	REMARKS
OVERDRIVE UNIT					
Overdrive unit assembly	AEC 3661	1	1	(E) 29F–H101 to 6188	
Overdrive unit assembly	22B 190	1	1	(E) 29K–H101 on	
Plate—adaptor	AEC 3623	2	1	(E) 29F–H101 to 6188	
Plate—adaptor	22B 204	2	1	(E) 29K–H101 on	
Nut—plate to casing	FNZ 105	3	2		
Nut—plate to casing	FNZ 205	4	4		
Washer—spring—nut	LWZ 205	5	6		
Casing—front	17H 5862	6	1		
Plug—Welch	7H 5897	7	1		
Shaft—valve operating	17H 5875	8	1		
Lever—shaft	7H 5822	9	1		
Cam—valve operating	7H 5827	10	1		
Pin—taper—cam and lever to shaft	TPS 0405	11	2		
Seal—oil—shaft	17H 5815	12	1		
Peg—guide—oil pump plunger	7H 5851	13	1		
Stud					
Solenoid bracket	FHS 0511	14	1		
Solenoid bracket	17H 5856	15	1		
Adaptor plate	FHS 0510	16	3		
Adaptor plate	7H 5881	17	1		
Adaptor plate	7H 5829	18	2		
Front casing to rear casing	7H 5833	19	2		
Breather	17H 5825	20	1		
Bracket—solenoid	27H 2315	21	1		
Dowel	27H 2412	22	1		
Screw—adjusting	27H 2418	23	1		
Locknut	†27H 2414	24	1		Not available; use FNN 204
Locknut	†FNN 204	24	1		
Stop (rubber)	17H 5811	25	1		
Nut—bracket to casing	FNZ 105	26	2		
Washer—spring—nut	LWZ 205	27	2		
Screw—bracket to casing	HNS 0514	28	2		
Washer—plain—screw	PWZ 105	29	2		
Washer—spring—screw	LWZ 205	30	2		
Solenoid	AEJ 42	31	1		
Screw—solenoid to bracket	PMZ 0308	32	2		
Washer—spring—screw	LWZ 203	33	2		
Seal—oil—valve operating shaft	17H 5815	34	1		
Collar—distance—valve operating shaft	17H 5809	35	1		
Lever—solenoid	17H 5808	36	1		
Screw—lever to valve operating shaft	HZS 0406	37	1		
Washer—spring—screw	LWZ 204	38	1		
Nut—screw	FNZ 104	39	1		
Plate—cover—bracket	17H 5857	40	1		
Screw—plate to bracket	53K 126	41	5		
Washer—spring—screw	LWZ 203	42	5		
Joint					
Adaptor plate to casing	7H 5825	43	1		
Solenoid to bracket	7H 8196	44	1		
Solenoid bracket to casing	7H 5852	45	1		
Solenoid bracket cover plate	17H 5858	46	1		

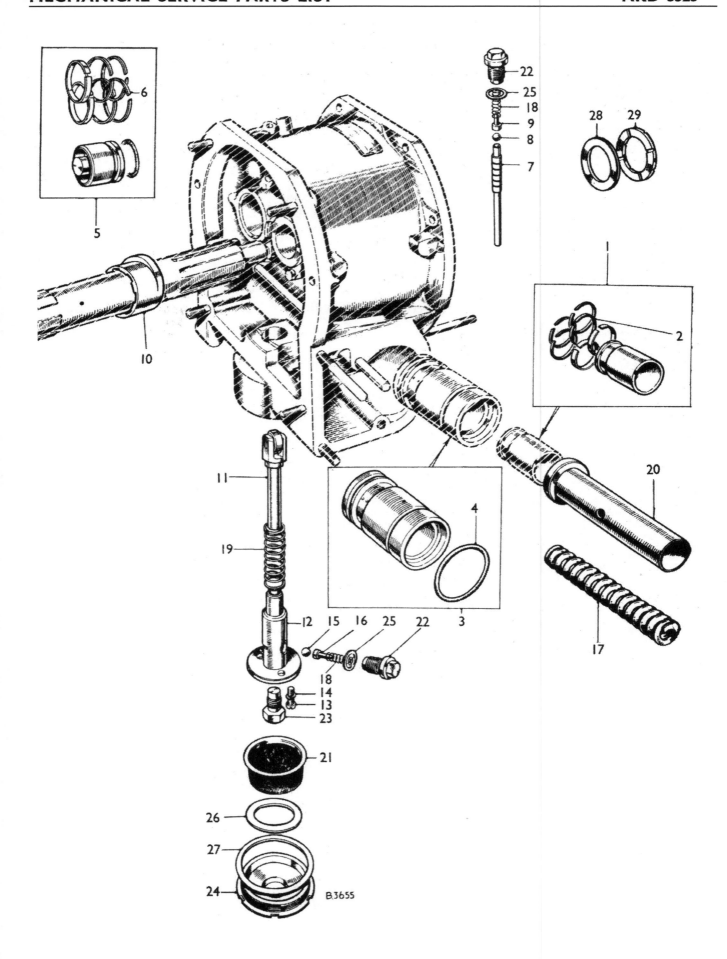

B.3655

	DESCRIPTION	Part No.	Illus. No.	Quantity	Exp.	UK	D	Change Point	REMARKS
					Stock recoms. DIST.				

Overdrive Unit—*continued*

DESCRIPTION	Part No.	Illus. No.	Quantity	Exp.	UK	D	Change Point	REMARKS
Piston assembly—accumulator	17H 5847	1	1					
Ring—piston	7H 5849	2	2 sets					
Housing assembly—accumulator	17H 5848	3	1					
Ring (rubber)	7H 5846	4	1	★	★			
Piston assembly—operating	17H 5873	5	1					
Ring—piston	17H 5874	6	2					
Valve—operating	17H 5827	7	1	★	★			
Ball—valve plunger	BLS 110	8	1	★	★			
Plunger—valve	7H 5837	9	1	★	★			
Cam—oil pump	1B 3650	10	1					
Plunger—oil pump	17H 5077	11	1					
Body—oil pump	7H 5840	12	1					
Screw—body to casing	PMZ 0308	13	2					
Washer—spring—screw	LWZ 203	14	2					
Ball—oil pump valve plunger	BLS 108	15	1	★	★			
Plunger—ball	7H 5837	16	1	★	★			
Springs								
Accumulator pressure	17H 5838	17	1	★	★			
Valve plungers	7H 5836	18	2	★	★			
Oil pump plunger	7H 5839	19	1	★	★			
Tube—accumulator pressure spring	7H 5845	20	1					
Strainer—oil pump	17H 5878	21	1					
Plugs								
Valve	17H 5876	22	2					
Oil pump body	7H 5841	23	1					
Oil drain	17H 5879	24	1					
Washer—valve plug (copper)	7H 5898	25	2					
Magnet—oil drain plug	17H 8157	26	1					
Washer—oil drain plug	7H 5857	27	1					
Washers—sunwheel adjusting—front								
·113″ to ·114″ (2·87 mm. to 2·89 mm.)	7H 5872A	28	A/R					
·107″ to ·108″ (2·71 mm. to 2·74 mm.)	7H 5872B	28	A/R					
·101″ to ·102″ (2·56 mm. to 2·59 mm.)	7H 5872C	28	A/R					
·095″ to ·096″ (2·40 mm. to 2·43 mm.)	7H 5872D	28	A/R					
·089″ to ·090″ (2·26 mm. to 2·28 mm.)	7H 5872E	28	A/R					
·083″ to ·084″ (2·10 mm. to 2·13 mm.)	7H 5872F	28	A/R					
·077″ to ·078″ (1·95 mm. to 1·98 mm.)	7H 5872G	28	A/R					
Washer—sunwheel thrust—front	7H 5873	29	1					

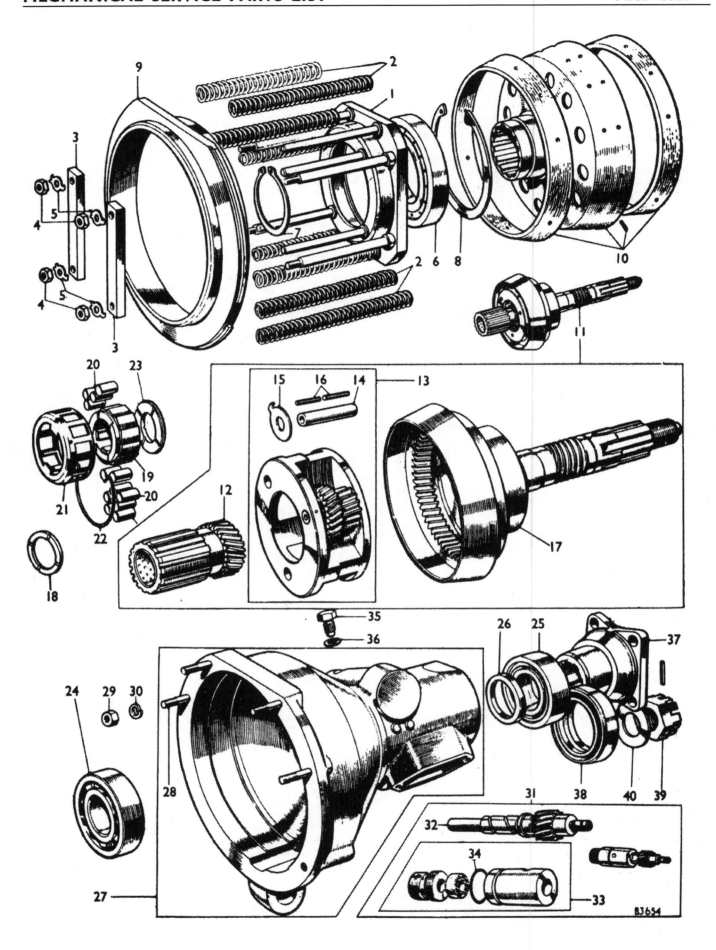

83654

					DESCRIPTION	Part No.	Illus. No.	Quantity	Exp.	UK	D	Change Point	REMARKS

Overdrive unit—*continued*

DESCRIPTION	Part No.	Illus. No.	Quantity	Exp.	UK	D	Change Point	REMARKS
Ring—clutch thrust	7H 5861	1	1					
Spring—clutch	17H 5804	2	1 set					
Bridge bar	7H 5862	3	2					
Nut—bridge bar	FNN 104	4	4					
Washer—tab—nut	7H 5863	5	4					
Bearing—thrust ring	7H 5866	6	1	★	★			
Circlip—bearing—small	7H 5867	7	1					
Circlip—bearing—large	7H 5868	8	1					
Ring—clutch brake	17H 5824	9	1					
Sliding member—clutch	7H 5870	10	1					
Sunwheel, planet carrier and annulus assembly	†N.S.P.	11	1	★	★			Was 17H 5861
Sunwheel	17H 5864	12	1					
Carrier assembly—planet	17H 5865	13	1					
Shaft—planet wheel	17H 5844	14	3					
Washer—thrust	17H 5859	15	3					
Roller—needle—planet wheel	17H 5846	16	6					
Annulus	17H 5867	17	1					
Washer—sunwheel thrust—rear	17H 5869	18	1					
Inner member—roller clutch	7H 5879	19	1					
Roller—clutch	17H 5823	20	1 set					
Cage—roller	7H 5881	21	1					
Ring—spring—clutch	7H 8273	22	1					
Washer—clutch thrust	7H 5883	23	1					
Bearing—annulus—front	2K 5507	24	1	★	★			
Bearing—annulus—rear	7H 5884	25	1	★	★			
Washers—annulus end float								
·146″ (3·70 mm.)	7H 5885E	26	A/R					
·151″ (3·83 mm.)	7H 5885F	26	A/R					
·156″ (3·96 mm.)	7H 5885G	26	A/R					
·161″ (4·08 mm.)	7H 5885H	26	A/R					
·166″ (4·21 mm.)	7H 5885J	26	A/R					
Casing—rear	17H 5822	27	1					
Stud—rear casing to front casing	FHS 0513	28	4					
Nut—stud	FNZ 105	29	6					
Washer—spring—nut	LWZ 205	30	6					
Pinion assembly—speedometer	17H 5863	31	1	★	★			
Pinion	17H 5855	32	1					
Bearing assembly	17H 5819	33	1					
'O' ring	17H 5818	34	1					
Seal—oil	N.S.P.		1					
Screw—Pinion locking	7H 5894	35	1					
Washer—spring—screw	LWZ 205	36	1					
Flange—coupling	17H 5821	37	1					
Seal—oil—flange	17H 5854	38	1	★	★			
Nut—flange to annulus	7H 5889	39	1					
Washer—plain—nut	PWN 112	40	1					

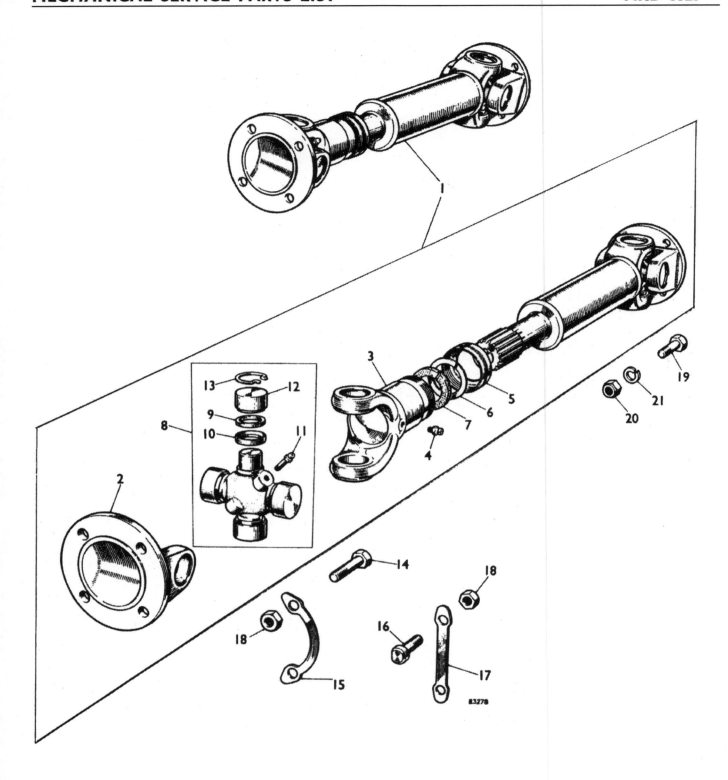

	DESCRIPTION	Part No.	Illus. No.	Quantity	Change Point	REMARKS

TRANSMISSION

	Page	Plate
† SHAFT—PROPELLER...	MG 2	G 1

PROPELLER SHAFT

DESCRIPTION	Part No.	Illus. No.	Quantity	Change Point	REMARKS
Shaft assembly—propeller	†1B 7489	1	1		
Yoke—flange	7H 3902	2	1		
Yoke—sleeve	7H 3905	3	1		
Lubricator—sleeve yoke	UHN 400	4	1		
Cap—dust—sleeve yoke	7H 3835	5	1		
Washer—dust cap (steel)	7H 3836	6	1		
Washer—dust cap (cork)	7H 3956	7	1		
Kit—journal repair	†8G 3001	8	2		W.S.E. use 8G 8981
Gasket	7H 3962	9	8		
Retainer—gasket	†NSP	10	8		Was 7H 3918
Lubricator	7H 3858	11	2		
Bearing—needle	7H 3912	12	8		
Circlip—bearing	7H 3913	13	8		
Kit—journal repair	†8G 8981		2		
Journal	†NSP		2		
Bearing—race	†NSP		8		
Circlip—bearing retaining	†NSP		8		
Bolt—flange to gearbox	ATC 7071	14	4		⎫ Required when overdrive
Washer—lock	1B 7386	15	4		⎬ is not fitted
Bolt—flange to overdrive unit	1B 7474	16	4		⎫ For use when overdrive is
Washer—lock	2K 5914	17	2		⎬ fitted
Nut	FNZ 106	18	4		
Bolt—flange to bevel pinion	53K 1048	19	4		
Locknut—bolt	LNZ 206	20	4		
Washer—spring	LWZ 306	21	4		

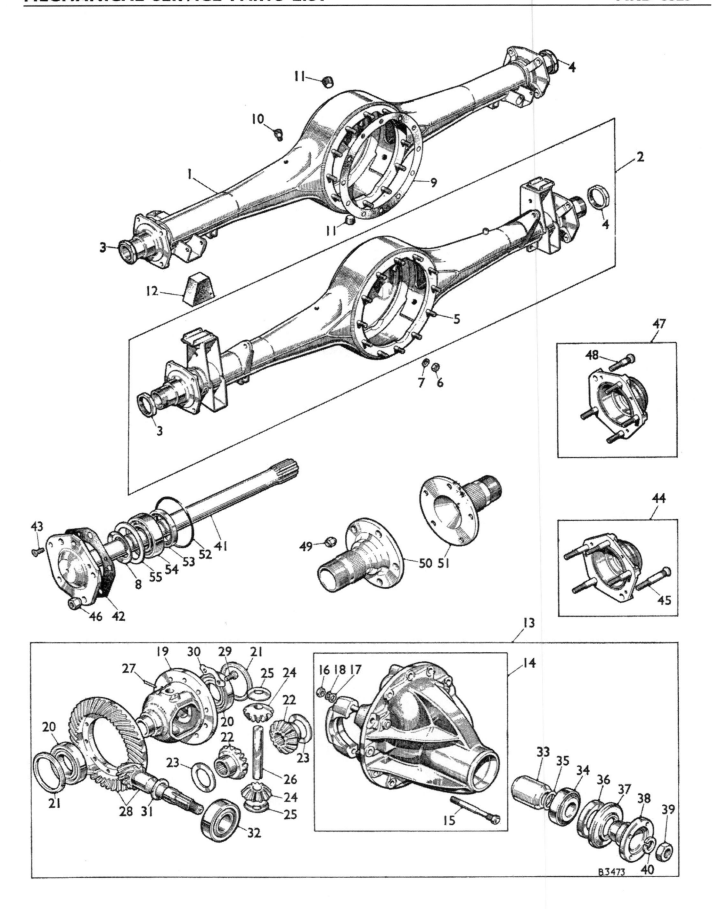

B.3473

	DESCRIPTION	Part No.	Illus. No.	Quantity	Exp.	UK	D	Change Point	REMARKS
						Stock recoms. DIST.			

REAR AXLE AND REAR SUSPENSION

				Page	Plate
†BRAKE—REAR	...	...	...	MH 3	H 2
CASE—REAR AXLE	...	...	...	MH 1·1	H 1
CROWN WHEEL AND PINION		...	...	MH 1·1	H 1
DIFFERENTIAL	...	...	...	MH 1·1	H 1
†HUB—REAR	...	...	...	MH 2	H 1
SHAFT—AXLE	...	...	...	MH 2	H 1
SPRING—ROAD—LEAF (BJ7)	...	...	...	MH 4	H 3
SPRING—ROAD—LEAF (BJ8)	...	...	...	MH 8	H 4

REAR AXLE AND REAR SUSPENSION

DESCRIPTION	Part No.	Illus. No.	Quantity	Exp.	UK	D	Change Point	REMARKS
Rear axle assembly	N.S.P.		1					
Case assembly	ATC 7815	1	1				(C) 17551 to 26704	
Case assembly	BTC 444	2	1				(C) 26705 on	
Nut—bearing retaining—RHT	ATC 7062	3	1	★	★			
Nut—bearing retaining—LHT	ATC 7309	4	1	★	★			
Bolt—to differential carrier	ATC 7125	5	12					
Nut	FNZ 106	6	12					
Washer—spring	†LWZ 306	7	12					
Washer—bearing retaining nut	†ATC 7810	8	2					
Joint—axle case	†ATC 7124	9	1					
Breather	1H 3864	10	1					
Plug—drain	6K 499	11	1					
Plug—filler	6K 499	11	1					
Bumper—axle (rubber)	2A 7142	12	2				(C) 26705 on	
Differential assembly—11/39 (3·545 to 1 ratio)	ATC 7568	13	1	★	★			
Differential assembly—11/43 (3·909 to 1 ratio)	ATC 7290	13	1					For use when overdrive is fitted
Carrier assembly	ATC 7288	14	1					
Bolt—serrated—cap	ATC 7083	15	4					
Nut	FNN 107	16	4					
Washer—plain	ATC 7084	17	4					
Washer—spring	LWN 307	18	4					
Cage—differential	ATC 7189	19	1					
Bearing—differential	2K 6541	20	2	★	★			
Washer—bearing packing								
·193″ (4·90 mm)	ATC 7268	21	2					
·191″ (4·85 mm)	ATC 7267	21	2					
·189″ (4·80 mm)	ATC 7266	21	2					
·187″ (4·74 mm)	ATC 7061	21	2					
·185″ (4·69 mm)	ATC 7111	21	2					Two used of selected size
·183″ (4·64 mm)	ATC 7112	21	2					
·181″ (4·59 mm)	ATC 7113	21	2					
·179″ (4·54 mm)	ATC 7114	21	2					
·177″ (4·49 mm)	ATC 7115	21	2					
·175″ (4·44 mm)	ATC 7116	21	2					
Wheel—differential	ATC 7262	22	2	★	★			
Washer—thrust—wheel	ATC 7106	23	2					
Pinion—differential	ATC 7263	24	2	★	★			W.S.E.; use BTC 451
Pinion—differential	BTC 451	24	2					
Washer—thrust—pinion	ATC 7104	25	2					
Pin—pinion	ATC 7107	26	1	★	★			
Peg—pinion pin	†ATC 7108	27	1					W.S.E.; use RPS 1222
Peg—pinion pin	†RPS 1222	27	1					Part No. change; was AEA 557
Crown wheel and pinion 11 × 39 teeth (3·545 to 1 ratio)	ATC 7564	28	1	★	★			
Crown wheel and pinion 11 × 43 teeth (3·909 to 1 ratio)	8G 7131	28	1					For use when overdrive is fitted
Bolt—cage	†ATA 7043	29	10					W.S.E.; use ATA 7232
Bolt—cage	†ATA 7232	29	10					
Washer—tab	ATC 7109	30	5					
Washer—pinion—thrust								
·222″ (5·638 mm)	ATC 7092	31	1					
·220″ (5·588 mm)	ATC 7093	31	1					
·218″ (5·537 mm)	ATC 7094	31	1					
·216″ (5·486 mm)	ATC 7095	31	1					
·214″ (5·435 mm)	ATC 7096	31	1					
·212″ (5·384 mm)	ATC 7097	31	1					
·210″ (5·334 mm)	ATC 7098	31	1					
·208″ (5·283 mm)	ATC 7099	31	1					

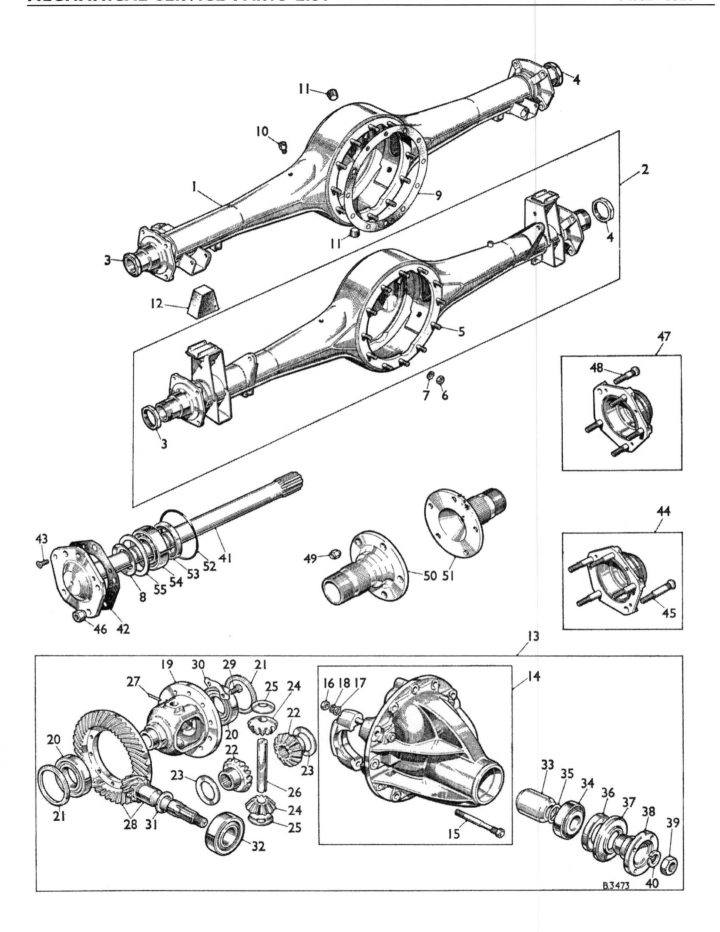

B.3473

	DESCRIPTION	Part No.	Illus. No.	Quantity	Change Point	REMARKS
	Rear Axle and Rear Suspension—*continued*					
	Bearing—pinion—inner	ATC 7089	32	1		
	Piece distance—bearing	ATC 7172	33	1		
	Bearing—pinion—outer	ATC 7091	34	1		
	Shim—outer bearing					
	·004″ (·101 mm)	ATC 7152	35	A/R		
	·006″ (·152 mm)	ATC 7153	35	A/R		
	·008″ (·203 mm)	ATC 7154	35	A/R		
	·010″ (·254 mm)	ATC 7155	35	A/R		
	·012″ (·304 mm)	ATC 7156	35	A/R		
	·020″ (·508 mm)	ATC 7157	35	A/R		
	·030″ (·762 mm)	ATC 7158	35	A/R		
	Seal—oil	ATC 7085	36	1		
	Cover—dust	ATC 7101	37	1		
	Flange—universal joint	ATC 7100	38	1		
	Nut	FNN 612	39	1		
	Washer—spring	LWZ 212	40	1		
	Shaft—axle	ATC 7394	41	2		
	Washer—joint—shaft to hub	ATC 7589	42	2		
	Screw	CMZ 0408	43	2		
	Hub assembly	ATC 7595	44	2		} Disc wheels only
	Stud—wheel	ATC 7344	45	10		
	Nut—wheel stud	88G 275	46	10	Part No. change; was ATB 7285 and 1G 8075	
	Hub assembly	ATC 7593	47	2		
	Stud—wheel	ATC 7257	48	10		
	Nut—stud—conical	ATB 7198	49	10		
	Extension—hub					Wire wheels only
	Right-hand	ATC 7236	50	1	(C) H-BJ7-17551 to 25314	
	Left-hand	ATC 7237	51	1	(C) H-BJ8-25315 to 26704	
	Right-hand	BTC 406	50	1	(C) H-BJ8-26705 on	
	Left-hand	BTC 407	51	1		
	Ring—oil seal	ATC 7588	52	2		
	Seal—oil	†3H 1589	53	2		
	Bearing	ATC 7060	54	2		
	Spacer—bearing	ATC 7569	55	2		

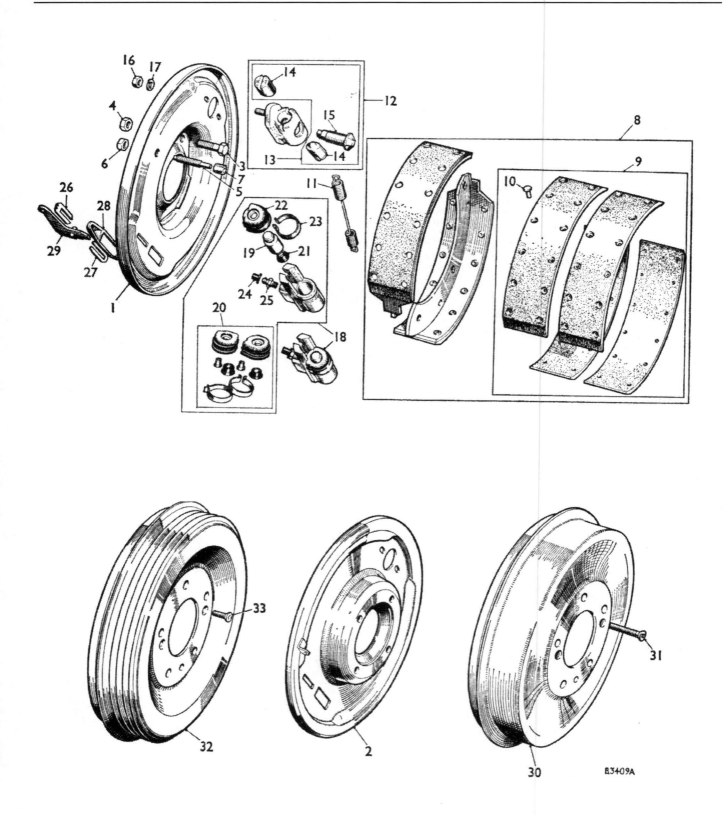

B3409A

	DESCRIPTION	Part No.	Illus. No.	Quantity	Change Point	REMARKS

Rear Axle and Rear Suspension—*continued*

DESCRIPTION	Part No.	Illus. No.	Quantity	Change Point	REMARKS
Plate—brake—RH	1B 7437	1	1		
Plate—brake—LH	1B 7438	2	1		
Bolt—brake plate to axle case	ATC 7071	3	8		
Nut	LNZ 206	4	8		
Post—steady	7H 4461	5	4		
Nut	FNZ 205	6	4		
Bush—steady post (felt)	7H 4429	7	4		
Shoe assembly—brake	8G 8282	8	2 sets	(C) H–BJ7–17551 to 25314	STD brakes
Lining assembly	8G 8281	9	1 box		
Rivet	†7H 4989	10	48		
Shoe assembly—brake	†8G 8649	8	2 sets		W.S.E. use 18G 8401 — Servo-assisted brakes
Lining assembly	8G 8650	9	1 box		W.S.E. use 18G 8402 — BJ7 optional extra
Rivet	7H 4989	10	48	(C) H–BJ8–25315 on	BJ8 standard fitting
Shoe assembly—brake	18G 8401	8	1 set		
Lining assembly USA	18G 8402	9	1 box		
Rivet	7H 4989	10	48		
Spring—brake shoe return	7H 4596	11	4		
Adjuster assembly	7H 4997	12	2		
Kit—repair—adjuster	8H 7070	13	2		
Tappet	7H 4998	14	4		
Wedge	†NSP		2		Was 1G 4116
Nut	FNZ 106	16	4		
Washer—spring	LWZ 206	17	4		
Cylinder assembly—wheel	†17H 4641	18	2		
Body	NSP		2		
Piston	17H 4690	19	2		
Kit—repair—wheel cylinder	8G 8280	20	1		
Seal—piston	17H 4507	21	2		W.S.E. use 27H 2576
Seal—piston	27H 2576	21	2		
Cover—dust—piston	17H 4546	22	2		
Retainer—dust cover	†NSP		2		Was 7H 4918
Cover—dust—bleed screw	7H 4419	24	2		
Screw—bleed	7H 4973	25	2		
Cover—dust—bleed screw	7H 4419	24	2		Also included in repair kit 8G 8280
Spring—wheel cylinder retaining	7H 4904	26	2		
Plate—locking—retaining spring	7H 4907	27	2		
Cover—dust—wheel cylinder	7H 4906	28	2		
Lever—hand brake	7H 4990	29	2		W.S.E. use 17H 4694
Lever—hand brake	17H 4694	29	2		
Drum—brake	1B 7490	30	2		Disc wheels only
Screw	CMZ 0428	31	4		
Drum—brake	1B 7526	82	2		Wire wheels only
Screw	CMZ 0414	83	4		

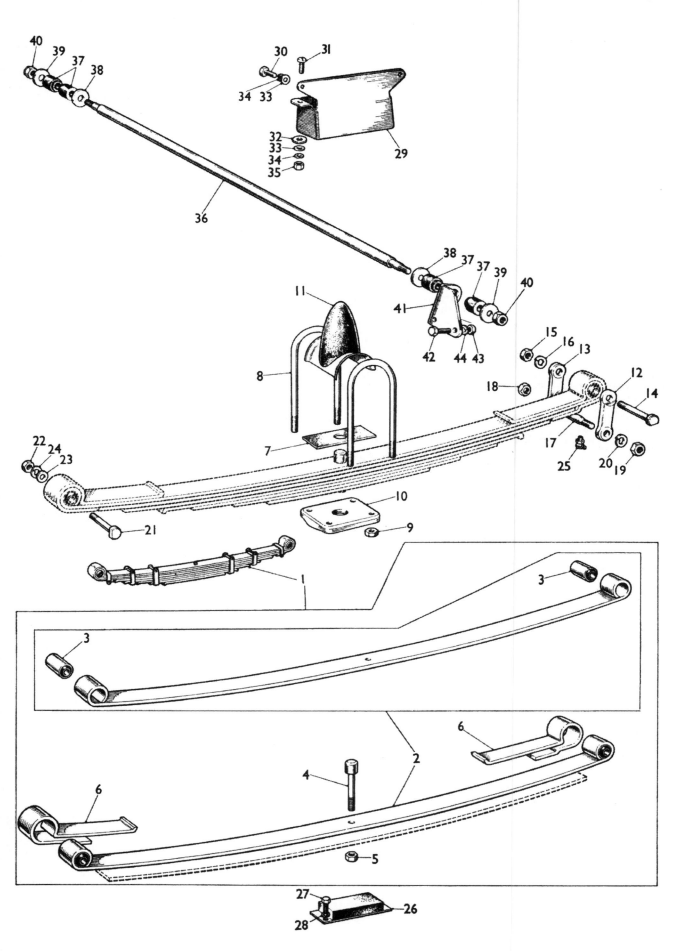

DESCRIPTION	Part No.	Illus. No.	Quantity	Exp.	UK	D	Change Point	REMARKS
Rear Axle and Rear Suspension—*continued*								
REAR SPRING								
Spring assembly	11 B 5266	1	2	★	★			
Leaf—main	1B 8930	2	2					
Bush	88G 278	3	4	★	★			Part No. change; was 1H 5286 and 2–4605
Leaf—second	N.S.P.		2					
Bolt—toe	2A 5006	4	2					
Nut	FNZ 104	5	2					
Reinforcement—spring eye	11B 5199	6	4					
Pad (fibre)	1G 5753	7	2					
Clip—spring	11B 5070	8	4					
Nut	LNZ 206	9	8					
Plate—clip	11B 5071	10	2					
Buffer—spring	11B 5068	11	2					
Shackle—outer	1A 9222	12	2	★	★			
Shackle—inner	1A 9223	13	2	★	★			
Pin—top—rear shackle	1G 9321	14	2	★	★			
Nut	FNZ 107	15	2					
Washer—spring	LWZ 207	16	2					
Pin—bottom—rear shackle	1G 9320	17	2	★	★			
Locknut	FNZ 206	18	4					
Nut	FNZ 106	19	2					
Washer—spring	LWZ 206	20	2	★	★			
Pin—front	1G 9321	21	2					
Nut	FNZ 107	22	2				(C) 17551 to 26704	
Washer—plain	PWZ 107	23	2					
Washer—spring	LWZ 207	24	2					
Lubricator	2A 5393	25	2					
Buffer—rebound	11B 5234	26	2					
Screw	HZS 0405	27	4					
Washer—spring	LWZ 304	28	4					
Bracket—bump	1B 7480	29	2					
Screw	HZS 0404	30	4					
Screw	PMZ 0412	31	4					
Washer								
Plain	PWZ 204	32	2					
Plain	PWZ 104	33	8					
Spring	LWZ 204	34	8					
Nut	FNZ 104	35	4					
Rod—tie	1B 7366	36	1					
Bush (rubber)	3H 3079	37	4	★	★			
Washer—plain	PWZ 207	38	2					
Washer—plain	PWZ 206	39	2					
Locknut	LNZ 206	40	2					
Bracket—tie rod	1B 7470	41	1					
Bolt	HZS 0607	42	2					
Nut	FNZ 106	43	2					
Washer—spring	LWZ 306	44	2					

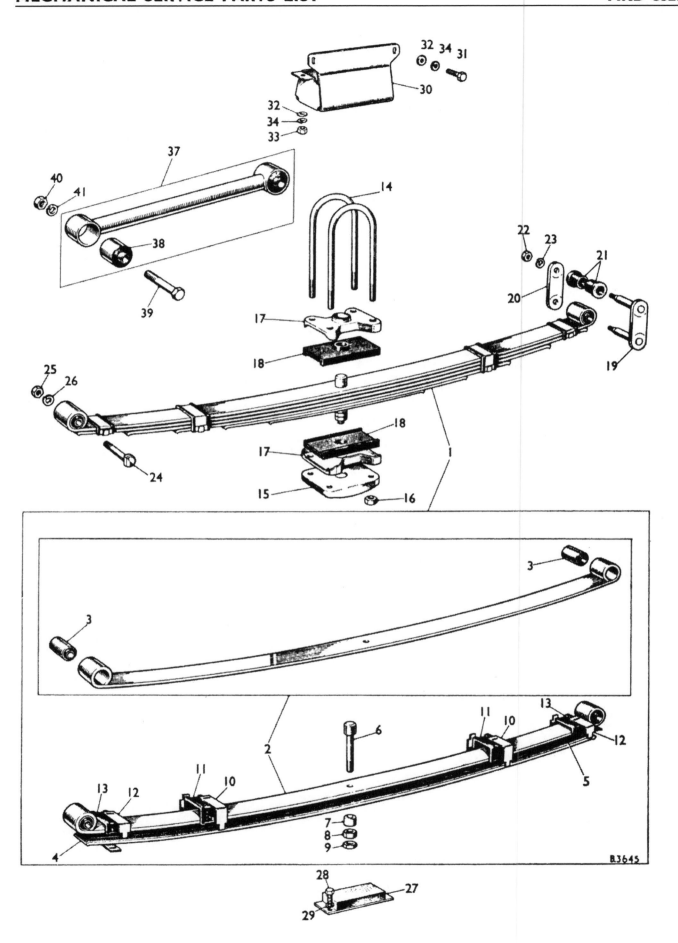

B.3645

DESCRIPTION	Part No.	Illus. No.	Quantity	Change Point	REMARKS
Rear Axle and Rear Suspension—*continued*					
Rear Spring—*continued*					
Spring assembly	AHB 9980	1	2		
Leaf assembly—main	AHB 6696	2	2		
Bush	88G 278	3	4		Part No. change; was 1H 5286 and 2H 4605
Strip—interleaf					
36″ (91·5 cm) long	AHH 7078	5	A/R		
29¾″ (75·6 cm) long	AHH 7078	5	A/R		Supplied in 25-yard (22·86 m) lengths
23½″ (59·7 cm) long	AHH 7078	5	A/R		
Bolt—toe	AHB 6703	6	2		
Piece distance—toe-bolt	ACA 5000	7	2		
Nut	FNZ 105	8	2		
Locknut	FNZ 205	9	2		
Clip—leaf—long	AHB 6706	10	8		
Pad—clip (rubber)	AHB 6707	11	4		
Clip—leaf—short	AHB 6704	12	8		
Pad—clip (rubber)	†AHB 6705	13	4		W.S.E. use AHB 6707
'U' bolt—spring	AHB 9982	14	4		
Plate—'U' bolt	AHB 9981	15	2		
Nut	LNZ 206	16	8		
Plate—locating	AHB 6660	17	4		
Pad—seating	ACG 5002	18	4		
Plate—shackle (with pins)	AHB 9977	19	2	(C) 26705 on	
Plate—shackle	AHB 9978	20	2		
Bush (rubber)	2A 5176	21	8		
Nut	FNZ 106	22	4		
Washer—spring	LWZ 206	23	4		
Pin—spring—front end	1G 9321	24	2		
Nut	FNZ 107	25	2		
Washer—spring	LWZ 207	26	2		
Buffer—rebound	11B 5234	27	2		
Screw	HZS 0405	28	4		
Washer—spring	LWZ 304	29	4		
Bracket—bump	AHB 9983	30	2		
Screw	HZS 0404	31	4		
Washer—plain	PWZ 104	32	8		
Nut	FNZ 104	33	4		
Washer—spring	LWZ 204	34	8		
Screw	PMZ 0412	35	4		
Washer—plain	PWZ 204	36	2		
Arm assembly—radius	AHB 9985	37	2		
Bush (rubber)	AHB 9984	38	4		
Bolt	HBZ 0722	39	4		
Nut	FNZ 107	40	4		
Washer—spring	LWZ 207	41	4		

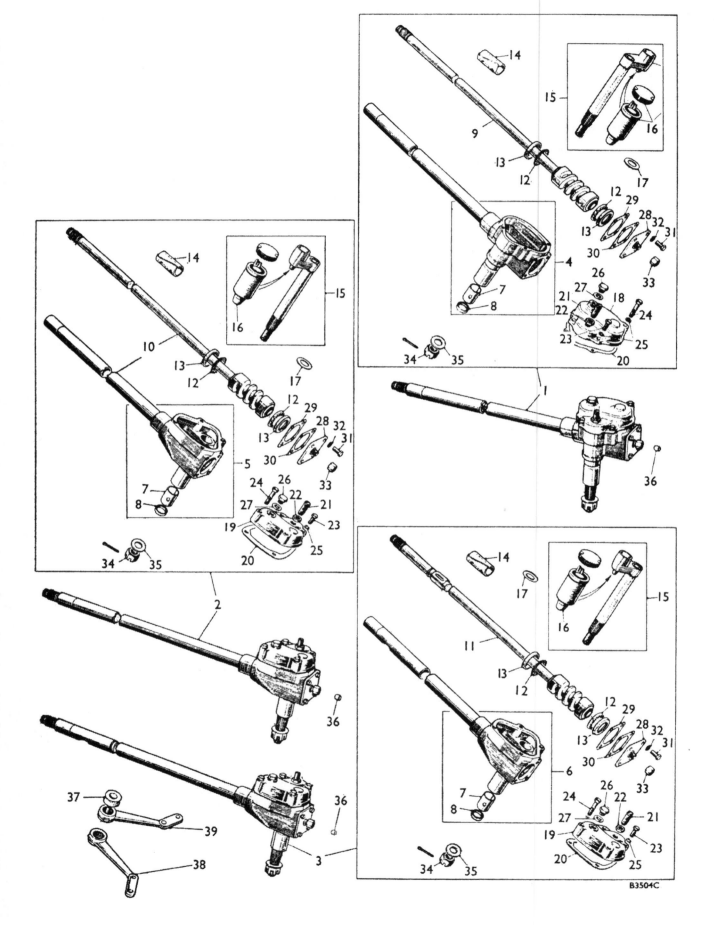

B3504C

	DESCRIPTION	Part No.	Illus. No.	Quantity	Change Point	REMARKS

STEERING

		Page	Plate
†COLUMN—ADJUSTABLE STEERING		MJ 2	J 2
COLUMN—FIXED STEERING		MJ 1·1	J 1
†GEAR—ADJUSTABLE STEERING		MJ 2	J 2
GEAR—FIXED STEERING		MJ 1·1	J 1
†GEAR—IDLER		MJ 3	J 3·1
†LEVER—IDLER GEAR		MJ 3	J 3·1
LEVER—STEERING		MJ 1·1	J 1
†LOCK—STEERING COLUMN		MJ 2·1	J 3
†ROD—STEERING		MJ 3	J 3·1
†WHEEL—STEERING		MJ 2·1	J 3

STEERING

Description		Part No.	Illus. No.	Quantity	Remarks
Gear assembly—steering—adjustable					See page MJ 2
Gear assembly—steering	RHD	AHB 8388	1	1	
	LHD	AHB 8389	2	1	
	LHD	AHB 9162	3	1	Required when steering lock is fitted
Box and outer column	RHD	17H 6109	4	1	
	LHD	17H 6107	5	1	
	LHD	17H 6542	6	1	Required when steering lock is fitted
Bush		1B 6257	7	1	
Seal—oil		7H 6589	8	1	
Column with cam	RHD	17H 6110	9	1	
	LHD	17H 6108	10	1	
	LHD	17H 5648	11	1	Required when steering lock is fitted
Cage—ball		7H 6079	12	2	
Cup—ball—cage		7H 6116	13	2	
Bush (felt)		ACA 5297	14	1	
Shaft assembly—rocker		17H 6106	15	1	
Cam—roller		7H 6507	16	1	
Washer—belleville		7H 6620	17	6	
Cover—side	RHD	7H 6599	18	1	
Cover—side	LHD	7H 6598	19	1	
Washer—joint—side cover		17H 8153	20	1	
Screw—thrust		17H 6108	21	1	
Locknut—screw		7H 6155	22	1	
Bolt		HNS 0506	23	2	
Bolt		HBZ 0512	24	2	
Washer—spring		LWZ 205	25	4	
Plug—oil		7H 6391	26	1	
Washer—joint—plug		7H 6392	27	1	
Cover—end		7H 6267	28	1	
Washer—joint—end-cover		17H 2660	29	1	
Shim					
·0024″ (·060 mm)		7H 6118	30	A/R	
·005″ (·127 mm)		7H 6128	30	A/R	
·010″ (·254 mm)		7H 6129	30	A/R	
Bolt		HNS 0506	31	4	
Washer—spring		LWZ 205	32	4	
Nut—stator tube		7H 6167	33	1	
Nut—steering lever to rocker shaft		7H 6486	34	1	
Washer—plain		PWN 112	35	1	
Olive		3H 660	36	1	
Cover—dust—oil seal		1G 6236	37	1	
Lever—steering	RHD	1B 6277	38	1	
Lever—steering	LHD	1B 6278	39	1	

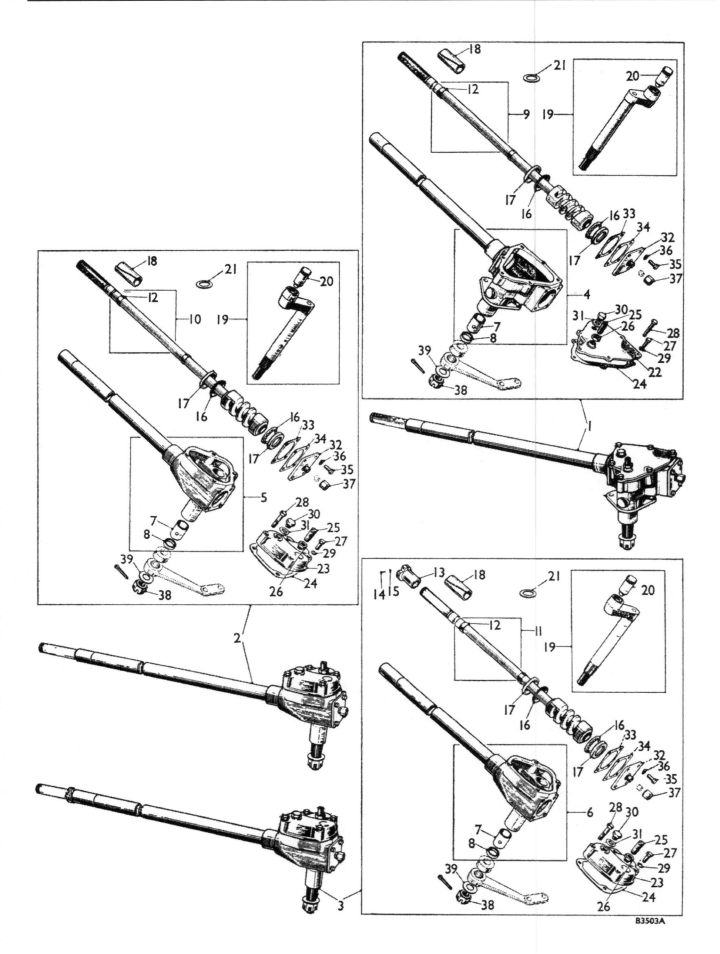

B3503A

	DESCRIPTION	Part No.	Illus. No.	Quantity	Change Point	REMARKS

Steering—*continued*

ADJUSTABLE STEERING (Optional Extra)
Gear assembly—steering

	DESCRIPTION	Part No.	Illus. No.	Quantity	Change Point	REMARKS
	RHD	AHB 8314	1	1		
	LHD	AHB 8312	2	1		
BJ7 ⎡	**RHD**	AHB 9163	1	1		For use when
⎣	**LHD**	AHB 9164	3	1		steering lock is
BJ8 ⎡	**RHD**	AHB 6026	1	1		fitted
⎣	**LHD**	AHB 6027	3	1		
Box and outer column						
	RHD	17H 6161	4	1		
	LHD	†17H 6163	5	1		Correction; was 17H 6131
BJ7 ⎡	**RHD**	27H 8068	4	1		For use when
⎣	**LHD**	17H 6545	6	1		steering lock is
BJ8 ⎡	**RHD**	27H 2349	4	1		fitted
⎣	**LHD**	27H 2350	6	1		
Bush		1B 6257	7	1		
Seal—oil		7H 6589	8	1		
Column (with cam)						
	RHD	17H 6162	9	1		
	LHD	17H 6164	10	1		
BJ7 ⎡	**RHD**	27H 8067	9	1		For use when
⎣	**LHD**	17H 6544	11	1		steering lock is
BJ8 ⎡	**RHD**	27H 2348	9	1		fitted
⎣	**LHD**	27H 2347	11	1		
Ring (rubber)		7H 6460	12	2		
Ring—locking		17H 6536	13	1		For use with
Screw—ring		PMZ 0316	14	1		AHB 9136 or
Washer—shakeproof		LWZ 403	15	1		AHB 9164
Cage—ball		7H 6079	16	2		
Cup—ball cage		7H 6116	17	2		
Bush (felt)		ACA 5297	18	1		
Shaft—rocker		17H 6106	19	1		
Roller—cam		7H 6507	20	1		
Washer—belleville		7H 6620	21	6		
Cover—side	**RHD**	7H 6599	22	1		
Cover—side	**LHD**	7H 6598	23	1		
Washer—joint—side cover		†7H 6515	24	1		W.S.E.; use **17H 8153**
Washer—joint—side cover		17H 8153	24	1		
Screw—thrust		17H 6103	25	1		
Locknut		7H 6155	26	1		
Bolt—side cover—short		HNS 0506	27	2		
Bolt—side cover—long		HBZ 0512	28	2		
Washer—spring		LWZ 205	29	4		
Plug—oil filler		7H 6391	30	1		
Washer—joint		7H 6392	31	1		
Cover—end		7H 6267	32	1		
Washer—joint—end cover		7H 6130	33	1		
Shim						
·0024″ (·060 mm.)		7H 6118	34	A/R		
·005″ (·127 mm.)		7H 6128	34	A/R		
·010″ (·254 mm.)		7H 6129	34	A/R		
Bolt—end cover		HNS 0506	35	4		
Washer—spring		LWZ 205	36	4		
Nut—stator tube		7H 6167	37	1		
Nut—steering lever to rocker shaft		7H 6436	38	1		
Washer—plain		PWN 112	39	1		

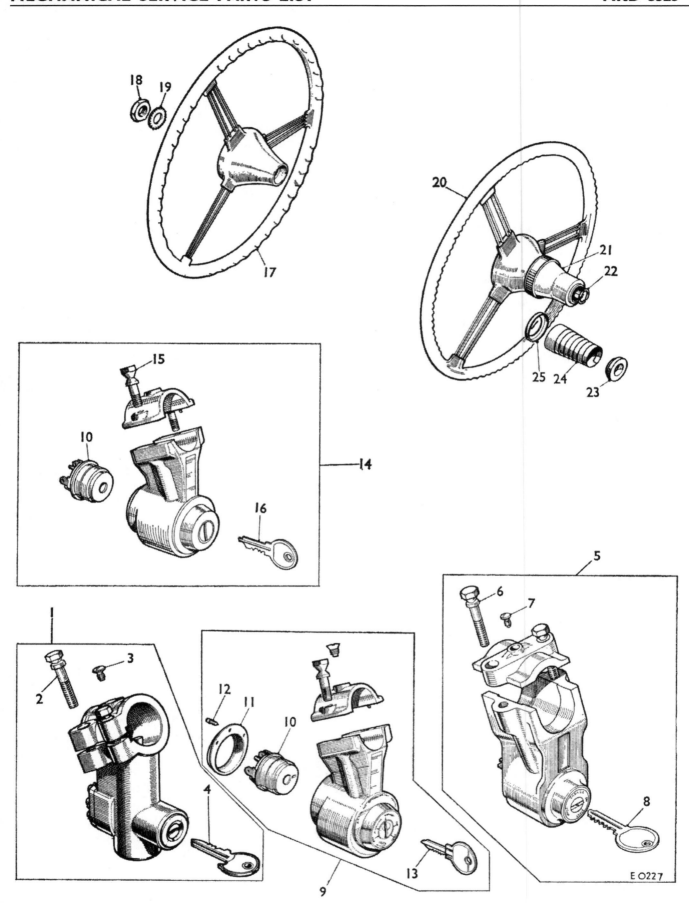

E O227

	DESCRIPTION	Part No.	Illus. No.	Quantity	Change Point	REMARKS
	Steering—*continued*					
	Lock assembly—steering column	†ACB 9425	1	1		W.S.E. use 13H 4180
	Bolt—shear	ACB 9427	2	2		
	Screw—locating	ACB 9428	3	1		
	Key—cut	27H 2797	4	2		Always quote key or car no. when ordering
	Lock assembly—steering column	†13H 709	5	1		W.S.E. use 13H 4180
	Bolt—shear	17H 2805	6	2		
	Screw—locating	17H 8659	7	1		
	Key—cut	17H 2807	8	2		Always quote key or car no. when ordering
	Lock assembly—steering column	†13H 2972	9	1		W.S.E. use 13H 4180
	Switch	27H 6237	10	1		
	Cap—switch	27H 6236	11	1		
	Screw	27H 6238	12	2		
	Key—cut	27H 6245	13	2		Always quote key or car no. when ordering
	Lock assembly—steering column	13H 4180	14	1		
	Switch	27H 6237	11	1		
	Bolt—shear	27H 9394	15	2		
	Key—cut	27H 9391	16	2		Always quote key or car no. when ordering
	Wheel—steering—17″ (43·18 cm)	8G 624	17	1	} Alternatives	} For use with standard steering
	Wheel—steering—16½″ (41·91 cm)	AHB 6000	17	1		
	Nut—steering wheel to column	2K 5057	18	1		
	Washer—shakeproof	2K 8929	19	1		
	Wheel—steering	1B 6299	20	1		} For use with adjustable steering
	Nut—clamping	1B 6300	21	1		
	Ring—spring	1F 6158	22	1		
	Support—dust cover	1B 6214	23	1		
	Cover—dust (telescopic spring)	1D 6132	24	1		
	Cup—dust cover	1B 6301	25	1		

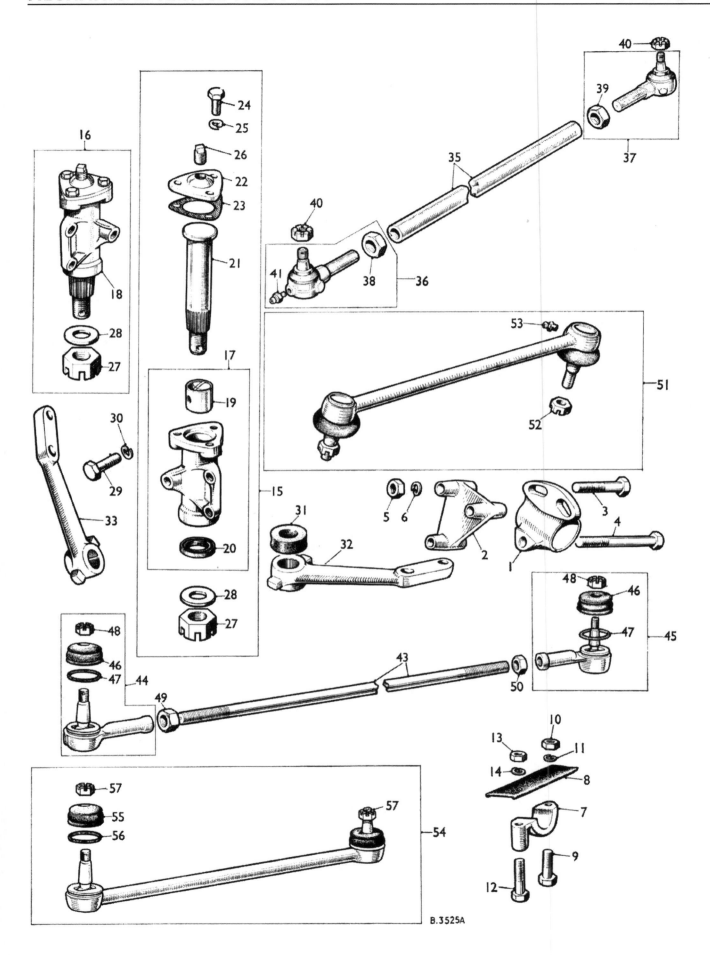

B.3525A

	DESCRIPTION	Part No.	Illus. No.	Quantity	Change Point	REMARKS
	Steering—*continued*					
	Bracket—steering box	1B 6127	1	1		
	Spacer—bracket	1B 6195	2	1		
	Bolt	HBZ 0626	3	2		
	Bolt	HBZ 0638	4	1		
	Nut	FNZ 106	5	3		
	Washer—spring	LWZ 306	6	3		
	Clamp—half—steering column support	1B 6199	7	2		
	Piece—packing (rubber)	4B 2502	8	1		
	Bolt	†53K 1551	9	1		W.S.E. use HBZ 0418
	Bolt	†HBZ 0418	9	1		
	Nut	FNZ 104	10	1		
	Washer—spring	LWZ 304	11	1		
	Bolt	HBZ 0524	12	1		
	Nut	FNZ 105	13	1		
	Washer—spring	LWZ 305	14	1		
	Gear assembly—idler **RHD**	1B 6281	15	1		
	Gear assembly—idler **LHD**	1B 6286	16	1		
	Body assembly—idler **RHD**	1B 6282	17	1		
	Body assembly—idler **LHD**	1B 6287	18	1		
	Bush	1B 6257	19	2		
	Seal—oil	1B 6256	20	1		
	Shaft—idler	1B 6258	21	1		
	Cover—idler body	1B 6137	22	1		
	Washer—joint	1B 6138	23	A/R		
	Screw	HZS 0506	24	3		
	Washer—spring	LWZ 305	25	3		
	Plug—filler	2K 8209	26	1		
	Nut	51K 370	27	1		
	Washer—plain	PWZ 112	28	1		
	Bolt	HBZ 0624	29	3		
	Washer—spring	LWZ 306	30	3		
	Cover—dust—oil seal	†1G 6236	21	1		W.S.E. use 27H 6995
	Cover—dust—oil	†27H 6995	31	1		
	Lever—steering—idler gear **RHD**	1B 6278	32	1		
	Lever—steering—idler gear **LHD**	1B 6277	33	1		
	Rod assembly—cross	NSP		1		Was AHB 8883
	Rod—cross	1B 6340	35	1		W.S.E. use 17H 2144 with 1 off 17H 2142 and 1 off 17H 2143
	End assembly—RHT	1G 6353	36	1		
	End assembly—LHT	1G 6354	37	1	(C) H–BJ7–17551 to 19190	
	Locknut—RHT	53K 320	38	1		
	Locknut—LHT	53K 365	39	1		
	Lubricator	UHN 400	41	1		
	Nut	FNZ 307	40	1		
	Rod assembly—cross	NSP		1		Was AHB 9608
	Rod—cross	17H 2144	43	1		
	End assembly—RHT	17H 2142	44	1		
	End assembly—LHT	17H 2143	45	1		
	Cover—dust	7H 6892	46	2	(C) H–BJ7–19191 to 25314	
	Ring—spring	7H 6893	47	2	(C) H–BJ8–25315 on	W.S.E. use 17H 9170
	Ring—spring	17H 9170	47	2		
	Nut	FNZ 407	48	2		
	Locknut—RHT	FNZ 210	49	1		
	Locknut—LHT	FNZ 2210	50	1		
	Rod assembly—side	7H 3777	51	2		W.S.E. use AHB 9609
	Nut	FNZ 307	52	4	(C) H–BJ7–17551 to 19190	
	Lubricator	UHN 400	53	4		
	Rod assembly—side	AHB 9609	54	2		
	Cover—dust	7H 6892	55	4	(C) H–BJ7–19191 to 25314	
	Ring—spring	7H 6893	56	4	(C) H–BJ8–25315 on	W.S.E. use 17H 9170
	Ring—spring	17H 9170	56	4		
	Nut	FNZ 407	57	4		

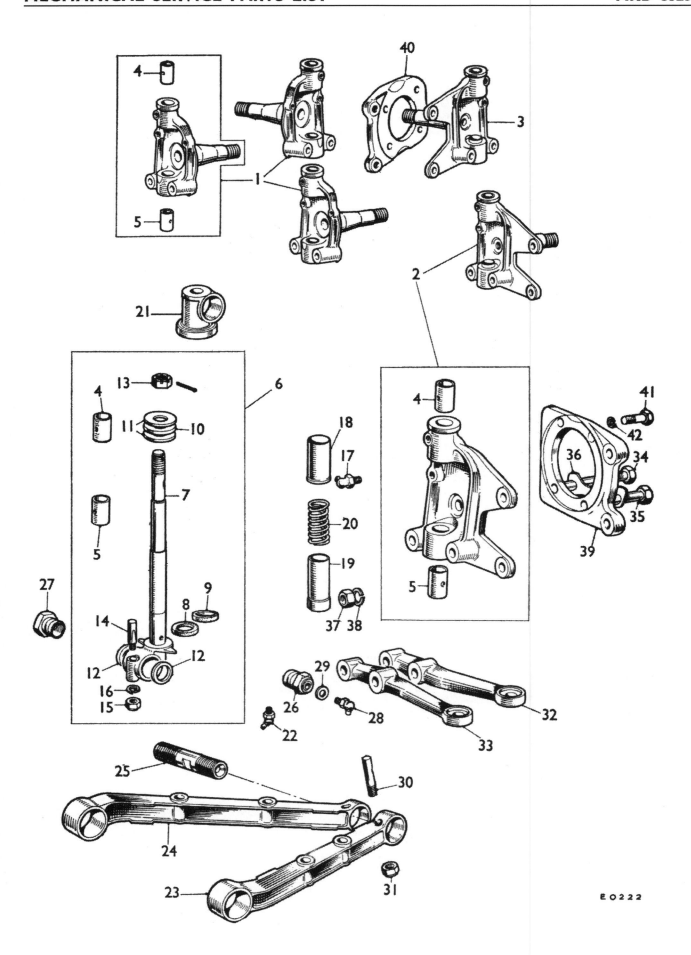

E O 2 2 2

	DESCRIPTION	Part No.	Illus. No.	Quantity	Change Point	REMARKS

FRONT SUSPENSION

		Page	*Plate*
ABSORBER—SHOCK—FRONT	... ...	MK 2	K 2
AXLE—SWIVEL		MK 1·1	K 1
BAR—ANTI-ROLL		MK 5	K 5
BRAKES—FRONT (BJ7)		MK 3	K 3
BRAKES—FRONT (BJ8)		MK 4	K 4
HUB—FRONT		MK 2	K 2
†KIT REPAIR—SWIVEL PIN AND BUSH		MK 1·1	K 1
LEVER—STEERING		MK 1·1	K 1
LINK—LOWER		MK 1·1	K 1
PIN—SWIVEL		MK 1·1	K 1
SPRING—ROAD—COIL		MK 5	K 5

FRONT SUSPENSION

DESCRIPTION	Part No.	Illus. No.	Quantity	Change Point	REMARKS
Suspension assembly—RH	NSP		1		
Suspension assembly—LH	NSP		1		
Axle assembly—swivel	1B 4517	1	2	(C) H–BJ7–17551 to 21766	
	BTC 324	1	2	(C) H–BJ7–21767 to 25314	
				(C) H–BJ8–25315 to 26704	
Right-hand	BTC 372	2	1	] (C) H–BJ8–26705 on	
Left-hand	†BTC 373	3	1	]	
Bush Top	1A 4744	4	2		
Bottom	1A 4745	5	2	(C) H–BJ7–17551 to 21766	
Bottom	11H 924	5	2	(C) H–BJ7–21767 to 25314	
				(C) H–BJ8–25315 on	
Kit—repair—swivel pin	†8G 4191		1 set]	(C) H–BJ7–17551 to 21766	W.S.E. use 2 off 8G 4217
	8G 4217	6	2 sets]		
	†8G 4194		1 set]	(C) H–BJ7–21767 to 25314	W.S.E. use 2 off 8G 4219
	8G 4219	6	2 sets]	(C) H–BJ8–25315 on	
Pin—swivel	†NSP		1		Was 11H 1018
Bush Top	1A 4744	4	2		
Bottom	1A 4745	5	2	(C) H–BJ7–17551 to 21766	
Bottom	11H 924	5	2	(C) H–BJ7–21767 to 25314	
				(C) H–BJ8–25315 on	
Ring (cork)	1A 4746	8	2		
Ring—sealing—bottom excluder tube	TRS 1519	9	2	(C) H–BJ7–21767 to 25314	
				(C) H–BJ8–25315 on	
Washer—thrust	1A 4751	10	2		
Washer—floating thrust					
·052 to ·057″ (1·32 to 1·44 mm)	1A 4752	11	A/R		]
·058 to ·063″ (1·47 to 1·60 mm)	1A 4753	11	A/R		] 2 off of each included in swivel pin repair kits
·064 to ·069″ (1·62 to 1·75 mm)	1A 4754	11	A/R		]
Ring—fulcrum pin (cork)	1G 4505	12	2		
Nut	53K 329	13	2		
Pin—cotter	53K 1764	14	2		] Alternatives
Pin—cotter	53K 1770	14	2		]
Nut	FNZ 104	15	2		
Washer—spring	LWZ 204	16	2		
Lubricator—top bush	UHN 490	17	2		
Tube—dust excluder Top	1G 4271	18	2		
Bottom	1A 4756	19	2	(C) H–BJ7–17551 to 21766	
Bottom	11H 921	19	2	(C) H–BJ7–21767 to 25314	
				(C) H–BJ8–25315 on	
Spring—dust excluder	2K 8951	20	2		
Trunnion—suspension link	1A 4760	21	2		
Lubricator—swivel pin—lower	3H 3028	22	2		
Link—lower—LH front—RH rear	1B 4365	23	2		
Link—lower—RH front—LH rear	1B 4366	24	2		
Pin—fulcrum—lower link	1A 4788	25	2		
Bush—lower link front end	1G 4346	26	2		
Bush—lower link rear end	1G 4348	27	2		
Lubricator—lower link front bush	3H 3028	28	2		
Washer—lubricator	2K 4974	29	2		
Pin—cotter—lower to swivel pin fulcrum	1G 4350	30	4		
Nut	53K 1662	31	4		
Lever—steering—RH	1B 4475	32	1		
Lever—steering—LH	1B 4476	33	1		
Bolt—steering lever Short	HBZ 0728	34	2	] (C) H–BJ7–17551 to 25314	
Long	HBZ 0730	35	2	] (C) H–BJ8–25315 to 26704	
Short	BTC 876	34	2	] (C) H–BJ8–26705 on	
Long	BTC 877	35	2	]	
Washer—lock	1B 4457	36	2	]	
Nut	FNZ 507	37	4	]	
Washer—spring	LWZ 207	38	4	] (C) H–BJ7–17551 to 25314	
Plate—adaptor—RH	BTC 134	39	1	] (C) H–BJ8–25315 to 26704	
Plate—adaptor—LH	BTC 135	40	1	]	
Screw	ATB 7258	41	4	]	
Washer—spring	LWZ 206	42	4	]	

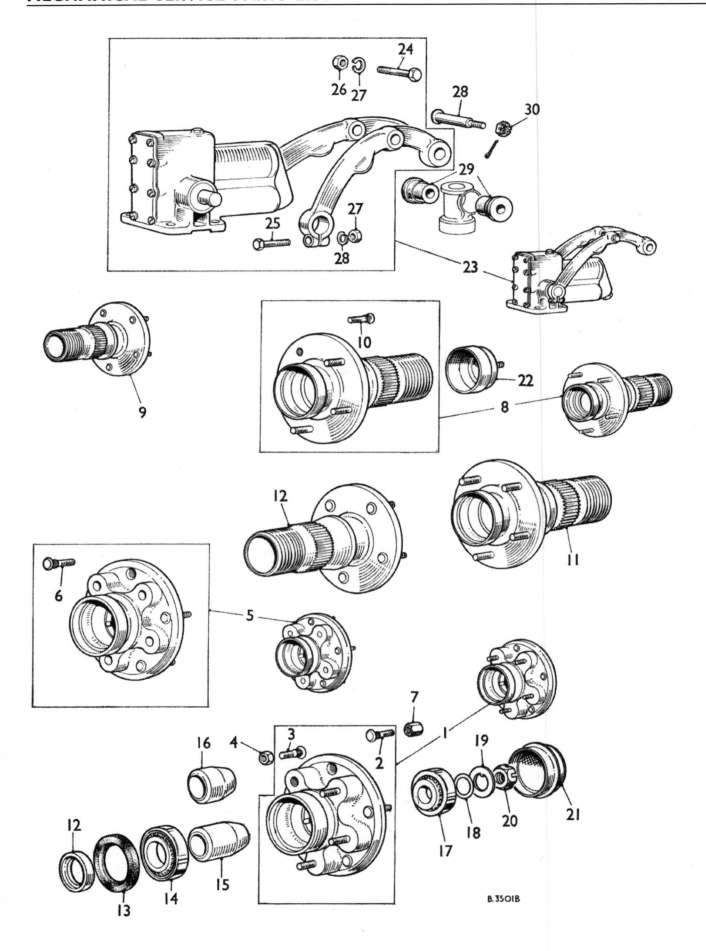

B.3501B

DESCRIPTION	Part No.	Illus. No.	Quantity	Change Point	REMARKS
Front suspension—*continued*					
Hub assembly	BTC 101	1	2	(C) H–BJ7–17551 to 25314	
Stud—wheel	ATC 4257	2	10		
Stud—disc	BTC 103	3	10	(C) H–BJ8–25315 to 26704	
Nut—disc brake stud	ATB 7265	4	10		
Hub assembly	BTC 395	5	2	(C) BJ8–26705 on	Disc wheels only
Stud—wheel	ATC 4257	6	10		
Nut—wheel stud	†88G 275	7	10		Part No. change; was ATB 7285 and 1G 8075
Hub assembly—RH	BTC 108	8	1	(C) H–BJ7–17551 to 25314	
Hub assembly—LH	BTC 109	9	1		
Stud—brake disc	BTC 103	10	10	(C) H–BJ8–25315 to 26704	Wire wheels only
Hub assembly—RH	BTC 390	11	1	(C) H–BJ8–26705 on	
Hub assembly—LH	BTC 391	12	1		
Spacer—swivel axle	BTC 431	12	2	(C) H–BJ8–26705 on	
Seal—oil	8G 554	13	2		
Bearing—hub—inner	BTC 280	14	2		
Piece—distance—bearing	1B 4527	15	2	(C) H–BJ7–17551 to 25314 (C) H–BJ8–25315 to 26704	
Piece—distance—bearing	†88G 484	16	2	(C) H–BJ8–26705 on	Part No. change; was ATB 4289 and BTB 515
Bearing—hub—outer	1B 4400	17	2	(C) H–BJ7–17551 to 25314 (C) H–BJ8–25315 to 26704	
Bearing—hub—outer	ATB 4238	17	2	(C) H–BJ8–26705 on	
Shim					
·003″ (·076 mm)	1B 4528	18	A/R		
·005″ (·127 mm)	1B 4529	18	A/R	(C) H–BJ7–17551 to 25314	
·010″ (·254 mm)	1B 4530	18	A/R	(C) H–BJ8–25315 to 26704	
·030″ (·762 mm)	BTC 370	18	A/R		
·003″ (·076 mm)	ATB 4240	18	A/R		
·005″ (·127 mm)	ATB 4241	18	A/R	(C) H–BJ8–26705 on	
·010″ (·254 mm)	ATB 4242	18	A/R		
·030″ (·762 mm)	BTB 656	18	A/R		
Washer	1B 4392	19	2		
Nut—bearing retaining	53K 330	20	2		
Cup—grease retaining	ATB 4098	21	2		Disc wheels
	1B 4316	22	2	(C) H–BJ7–17551 to 25314 (C) H–BJ8–25315 to 26704	Wire wheels
	BTC 392	22	2	(C) H–BJ8–26705	
Absorber—shock	AYH 4040	23	2		
Bolt—shock absorber arm	HBZ 0620	24	2		
Bolt—clamping—arm to shaft	HBZ 0616	25	2		
Nut	FNZ 106	26	4		
Washer—spring	LWZ 306	27	4		
Pin—fulcrum	1G 4349	28	2		
Bearing—top link	2A 4144	29	4		
Nut—fulcrum pin	FNZ 407	30	2		

PLATE K 3

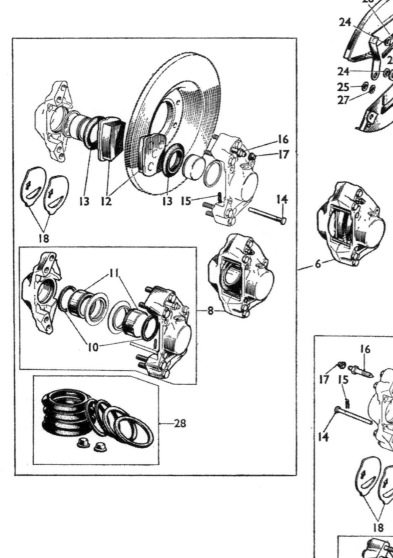

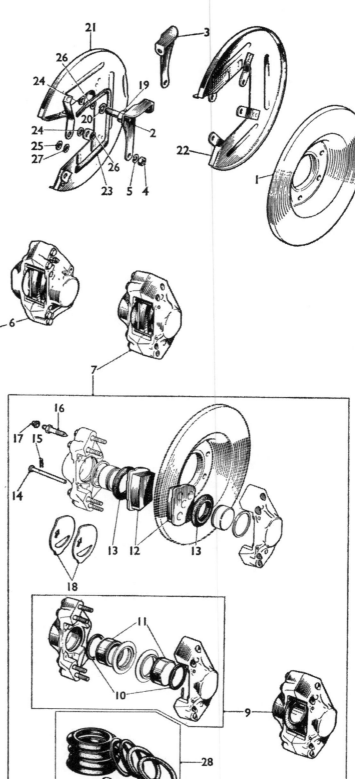

E O174

DESCRIPTION	Part No.	Illus. No.	Quantity	Change Point	REMARKS
Front Suspension—*continued*					
Disc—brake	BTC 104	1	2		
Bracket—brake hose—RH	BTC 126	2	1		
Bracket—brake hose—LH	BTC 127	3	1	(C) H–BJ7–17551 to 25314	
Nut	FNZ 105	4	4	(C) H–BJ8–25315 to 26704	
Washer—spring	LWZ 305	5	4		
Calliper unit assembly (with pads)—RH	BTC 172	6	1		W.S.E. use 27H 7993 with 18G 8178
Calliper unit assembly (with pads)—LH	BTC 173	7	1		
Calliper unit assembly (with pads)—RH	27H 7993	6	1		
Calliper unit assembly (with pads)—LH	27H 7994	7	1		
Body assembly—RH	NSP	8	1		Was 17H 4815
Body assembly—LH	NSP	9	1		Was 17H 4814
Ring—cylinder sealing	17H 4642	10	4		
Piston	17H 4679	11	4	(C) H–BJ7–17551 to 25314	W.S.E. use 17H 4960
Kit—repair—calliper unit	8G 8279	28	1 set		Standard brakes BJ7
Ring—cylinder sealing	17H 4642	10	4		
Boot (rubber)	NSP		4		Was 17H 4643
Cap—bleed screw	7H 4419	17	2		
Pad—friction	8G 8476	12	1 set		W.S.E. use 18G 8178
	18G 8163	12	1 set		
	18G 8178	12	1 set		
Pin—pad retaining	17H 4640	14	4		
Clip—pin	17H 4639	15	4		
Screw—bleed	17H 4637	16	2		
Calliper unit assembly—RH	BTC 260	6	1		
Calliper unit assembly—LH	BTC 261	7	1		
Body assembly—RH	17H 4959	8	1		
Body assembly—LH	17H 4958	9	1		
Ring—cylinder sealing	17H 4642	10	4		
Piston	17H 4960	11	4		
Kit—repair—calliper unit	8G 8279	28	1 set		Servo-assisted brakes—optional extra BJ7, standard fitting BJ8
Ring—cylinder sealing	17H 4642	10	4		
Boot (rubber)	NSP	8	4		Was 17H 4643
Cap—bleed screw	7H 4419	17	2	(C) H–BJ8–25315 to 26704	
Pad—friction	8G 8660	12	1 set		
Shim—anti-squeal	BHA 4195	18	4		
Boot (rubber)	NSP	13	4		Was 17H 4643
Pin—pad retaining	17H 4640	14	4		
Clip—pin	17H 4639	15	4		
Screw—bleed	17H 4637	16	2		
Cap—bleed screw	7H 4419	17	2		
Bolt	BTC 125	19	4		
Washer—spring	LWZ 207	20	4		
Cover—dust—brake disc—RH	BTC 204	21	1		
Cover—dust—brake disc—LH	BTC 205	22	1		
Seal—dust cover (rubber)	BTC 171	23	2	(C) H–BJ7–17551 to 25314	
Washer				(C) H–BJ8–25315 to 26704	
Plain	PWZ 106	24	2		
Plain	BTC 211	25	2		
Shakeproof	LWZ 506	26	2		
Shakeproof	LWZ 507	27	6		

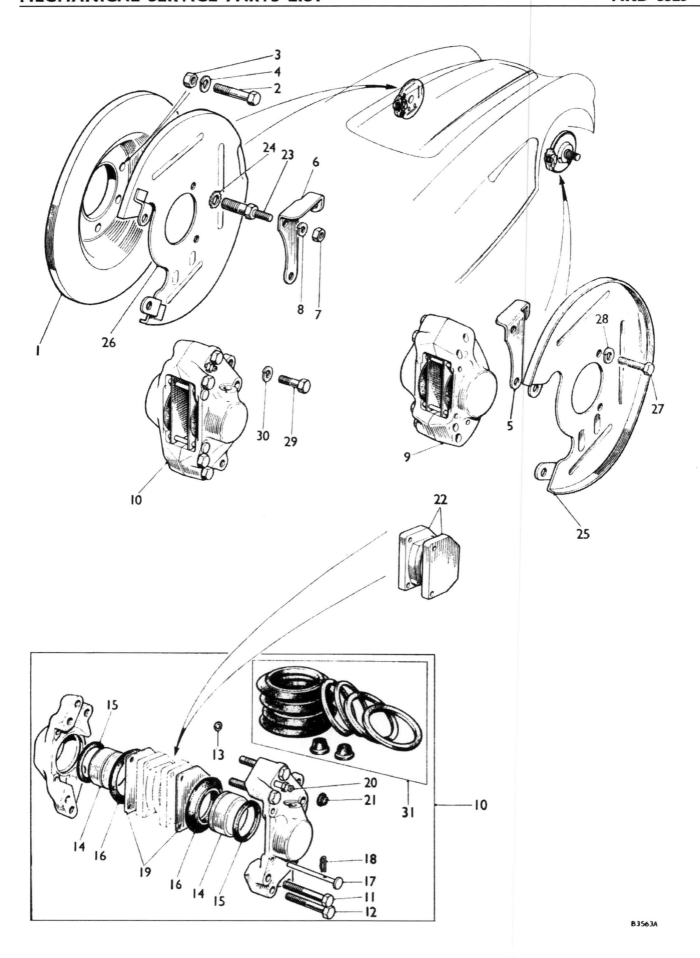

B3563A

DESCRIPTION	Part No.	Illus. No.	Quantity	Change Point	REMARKS
Front Suspension—*continued*					
Disc—brake	BTC 371	1	2		
Bolt—brake disc to hub	BTC 378	2	10		
Nut	FNZ 106	3	10		
Washer—spring	LWZ 206	4	10		
Bracket—brake hose—RH	BTC 380	5	1		
Bracket—brake hose—LH	BTC 381	6	1		
Nut	FNZ 105	7	4		
Washer—spring	LWZ 305	8	4		
Calliper unit assembly (less pads and shims) **—RH**	27H 2988	9	1		
Calliper unit assembly (less pads and shims) **—LH**	27H 2989	10	1		
Calliper—RH	NSP		1		
Calliper—LH	NSP		1		
Bolt—bridge—inner	NSP		4		Was 27H 2945
Bolt—bridge—outer	NSP		4		Was 27H 2946
Seal—fluid channel	NSP		2		Was 27H 2947
Piston	27H 2949	14	4		
Kit—repair calliper unit	8G 8943	31	1 set	†(C) H–BJ8–26705 on	
Ring—cylinder sealing	27H 2948	15	4		
Boot (rubber)	27H 2950	16	4		
Cap—bleed screw	7H 4419	21	2		
Pin—pad retaining	17H 4640	17	4		
Clip—pin	17H 4689	18	4		
Screw—bleed	27H 2951	20	2		W.S.E. use 17H 4637
Screw—bleed	17H 4637	20	2		
Cap—bleed screw	†7H 4419	21	2		Also included in repair kit 8G 8943
Pad—friction	8G 8940	22	1 set		
Pad—friction **USA**	†18G 8400	22	1 set		
Shim—anti-squeal	27H 2953	19	4		
Bolt—mounting	BTC 379	23	4		
Washer—shakeproof	LWZ 507	24	4		
Cover—dust—brake disc—RH	BTC 382	25	1		
Cover—dust—brake disc—LH	BTC 383	26	1		
Bolt	HZS 0504	27	4		
Washer—spring	LWZ 205	28	4		
Bolt	HZS 0403	29	4		
Washer—spring	LWZ 204	30	4		

MECHANICAL SERVICE PARTS LIST

AKD 3523

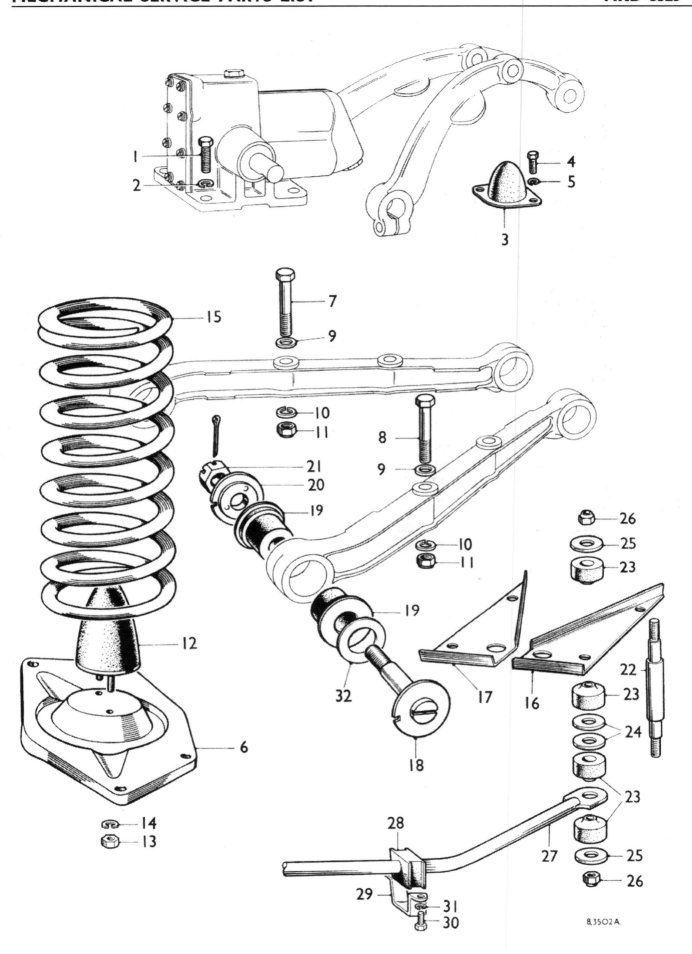

B.3502A.

PLATE K 5   Issue 2   142

DESCRIPTION	Part No.	Illus. No.	Quantity	Change Point	REMARKS
Front Suspension—*continued*					
Setscrew—shock absorber to frame	HZS 0608	1	8		
Washer—spring—screw	LWZ 306	2	8		
Buffer—rebound	1G 4276	3	2		
Screw—rebound buffer to frame	HZS 0405	4	4		
Washer—spring—screw	LWZ 304	5	4		
Seat—spring	1G 4279	6	2		
Bolt—spring seat to lower link	HBZ 0618	7	4		
Bolt—spring seat and anti-roll plate to lower link	HBZ 0620	8	4		
Washer—bolt	PWZ 106	9	8		
Washer—spring—bolt	LWZ 306	10	8		
Nut—bolt	LNZ 206	11	8		
Bumper—front suspension	1B 4501	12	2		
Nut—suspension bumper to spring seat	FNZ 105	13	4		
Washer—spring—nut	LWZ 205	14	4		
Spring—road coil	1H 4092	15	2		
Plate—anti-roll bar—RH	1B 7354	16	1		
Plate—anti-roll bar—LH	1B 7355	17	1		
Pin—fulcrum—lower links	1B 4518	18	4		
Washer—plain—fulcrum pin	†AHB 7130	32	4		
Bearing—lower link	ACB 9274	19	8		
Washer—fulcrum pin	1A 4785	20	4		
Nut—fulcrum pin	FNZ 408	21	4		
Link—anti-roll bar	1B 4486	22	2		
Bush—link	3H 3079	23	8		
Washer—special—link bush—top	PWZ 207	24	4		
Washer—special—link bush—bottom	6K 9582	25	4		
Nut—link	LNZ 105	26	4		
Bar—anti-roll	1B 4525	27	1		
Bearing—anti-roll bar (rubber)	1B 4526	28	2		
Strap—bearing	1B 7356	29	2		
Setscrew—bearing strap	HZS 0506	30	4		
Washer—spring—screw	LWZ 205	31	4		

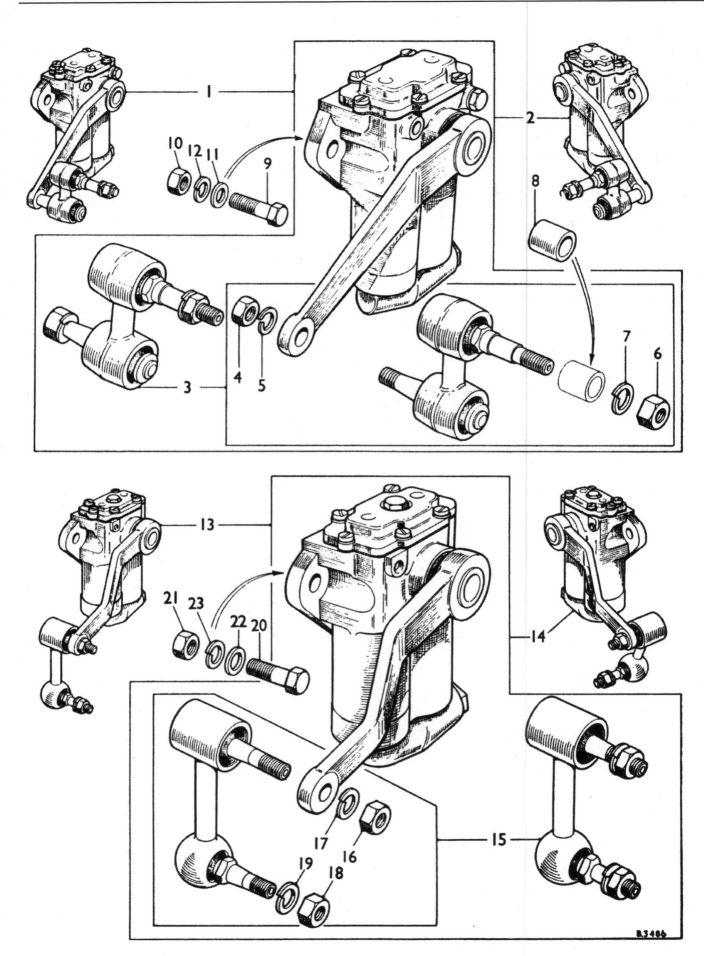

PLATE L 2   Issue 1   144

DESCRIPTION	Part No.	Illus. No.	Quantity	Change Point	REMARKS

SHOCK ABSORBERS

SHOCK ABSORBERS

DESCRIPTION	Part No.	Illus. No.	Quantity	Change Point	REMARKS
Absorber—assembly—shock					
Front					See section K
Rear—RH	1B 7472	1	1		
Rear—LH	1B 7473	2	1		
Link assembly	1B 7463	3	2		
Nut	FNZ 106	4	2		
Washer—spring	LWZ 306	5	2		
Nut	FNZ 107	6	2	(C) 17551 to 26704	
Washer—spring	LWZ 307	7	2		
Tube—distance—link to axle bracket	1B 7464	8	2		
Bolt	53K 1048	9	4		
Nut	FNZ 506	10	4		
Washer—plain	PWZ 106	11	4		
Washer—spring	LWZ 306	12	4		
Absorber—shock—rear—RH	AHB 9974	13	1		W.S.E. use 37H 3054 together with 1 off link 17H 9276
Absorber—shock—rear—LH	AHB 9975	14	1		W.S.E. use 37H 3055 together with 1 off link 17H 9276
Absorber—shock (less link)—rear—RH	†37H 3054		1		
Absorber—shock (less link)—rear—LH	†37H 3055		1		
Link assembly	17H 9276	15	2	(C) 26705 on	
Nut	FNZ 507	16	2		
Washer—spring	LWZ 307	17	2		
Nut	FNZ 508	18	2		
Washer—spring	LWZ 308	19	2		
Bolt	AHB 9996	20	4		
Nut	FNZ 107	21	4		
Washer—plain	PWZ 107	22	4		
Washer—spring	LWZ 207	23	4		

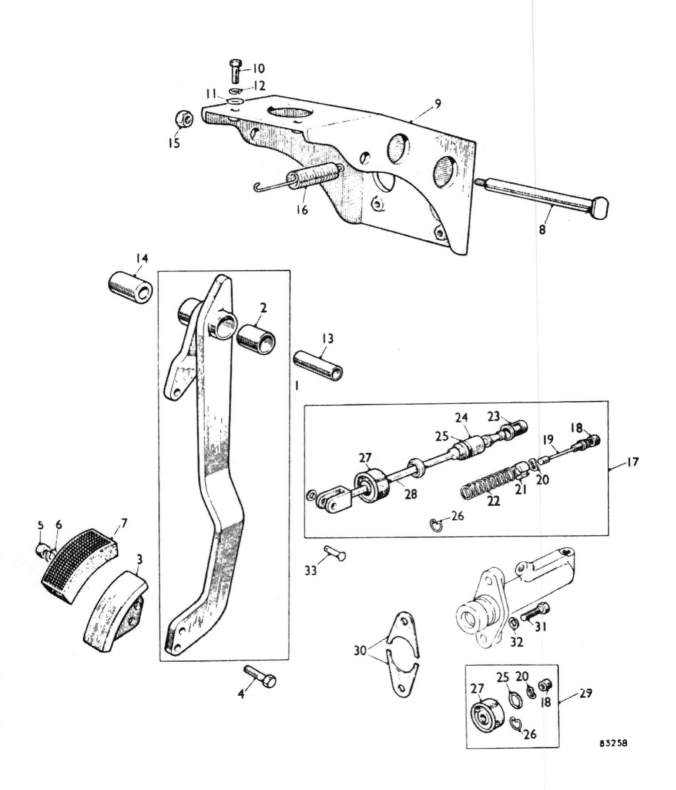

83258

	DESCRIPTION	Part No.	Illus. No.	Quantity	Change Point	REMARKS

BRAKE CONTROLS

BRAKE CONTROLS

Description	Part No.	Illus. No.	Qty	Change Point
Lever assembly—pedal	AHB 9182	1	1	
Bush	1G 9310	2	2	
Pad—pedal	AHB 9185	3	1	
Bolt—pad to lever	HBZ 0409	4	2	
Nut	FNZ 104	5	2	
Washer—spring	LWZ 304	6	2	
Rubber—pedal pad	1B 8751	7	1	
Shaft—brake and clutch pedal	11B 5277	8	1	
Bracket—pedal levers	11B 5273	9	1	
Screw—bracket to pedal box	HZS 0505	10	2	
Washer—plain	PWZ 205	11	2	
Washer—spring	LWZ 205	12	2	
Sleeve—pedal shaft	1G 9314	13	2	
Piece distance—pedal levers	11B 5279	14	1	
Nut—shaft	LNZ 205	15	1	
Spring—pedal return	11B 5283	16	1	
Cylinder assembly—master	11B 5510	17	1	
Body	NSP		1	
Stem—valve	7H 4751	19	1	
Spacer—valve	17H 4182	21	1	
Spring	7H 4944	22	1	
Retainer—spring	17H 4827	23	1	
Plunger	17H 8113	24	1	
Push-rod	17H 4513	28	1	(C) H–BJ7–17551 to 25314
Kit—master cylinder repair	8G 8807	29	1	
Seal—valve	†17H 4561	18	1	
Washer—valve	†7H 4752	20	1	
Seal—plunger	†17H 8112	25	1	
Circlip	†7H 4451	26	1	
Cover—dust	†17H 4831	27	1	
Tube of grease	†NSP		1	
Piece packing—master cylinder	11B 5138	30	2	
Screw—master cylinder to pedal bracket	HZS 0508	31	2	
Washer—spring	LWZ 205	32	2	
Pin—push-rod to pedal lever	CLZ 0513	33	1	(C) H–BJ7–17551 to 25314
Pin—push-rod to pedal lever	CLZ 0515	33	1	(C) H–BJ8–25315 on

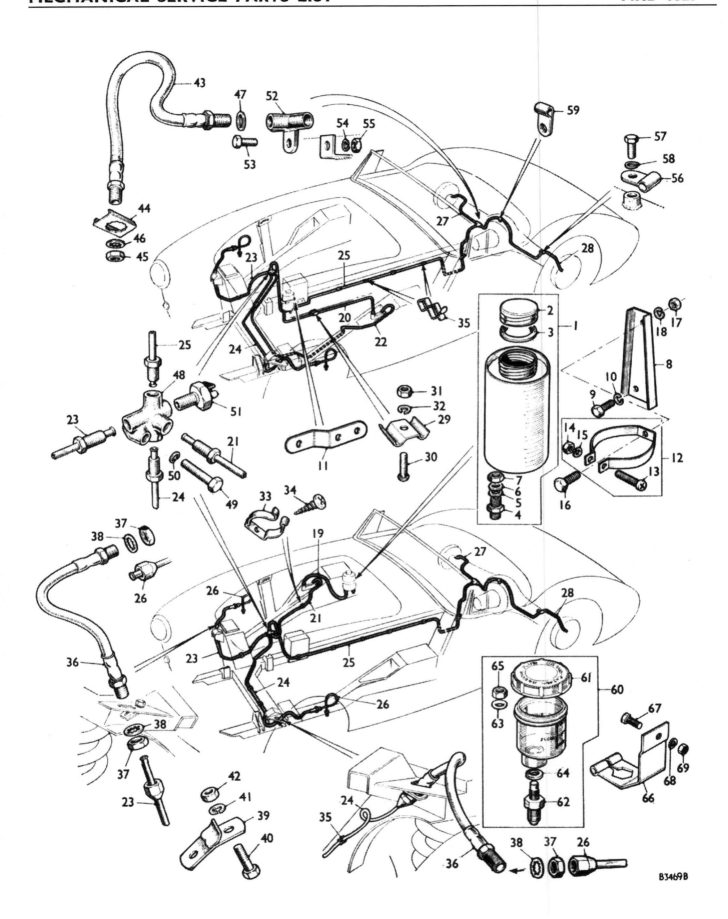

B3469B

DESCRIPTION	Part No.	Illus. No.	Quantity	Change Point	REMARKS
Brake Controls—*continued*					
SUPPLY TANK, PIPES, AND FITTINGS					
Tank assembly—dual supply	ACB 5856	1	1		
Cap—filler	17H 4508	2	1		
Washer—cap	7H 4726	3	1		
Adaptor	17H 4238	4	2		
Gasket—adaptor	41K 5011	5	2		
Washer—sealing (inside body)	17H 4528	6	1		
Nut—adaptor	7H 4867	7	2		
Bracket—tank to pedal bar	11B 5522	8	1		
Screw **RHD**	HZS 0403	9	2		
Washer—spring	LWZ 204	10	2		
Bracket—tank to support channel **LHD**	AHB 9067	11	1		W.S.E. use 11B 5521
Bracket—tank to support channel	11B 5521	11	1		
Clip assembly—tank to bracket	13H 297	12	1		
Screw	PMZ 0314	13	1		
Nut	FNZ 103	14	1		
Washer—spring	LWZ 203	15	1		
Screw	HZS 0404	16	1		
Nut	FNZ 104	17	1		
Washer—spring	LWZ 204	18	1		
Tank assembly—supply—fluid (plastic)	BMK 1555	60	1		
Cap	27H 9196	61	1		
Adaptor—outer	27H 9197	62	1		
Washer—spacing **Benelux**	27H 9198	63	1		
Washer **and**	27H 9199	64	1	(C) H–BJ8–41930 on	
Nut—adaptor securing **France**	FNZ 206	65	1		
Bracket—tank	AHB 7193	66	1		
Screw—bracket	HZS 0415	67	1		
Washer—spring	LWZ 204	68	1		
Nut	FNZ 104	69	1		
Pipe					
Supply tank to master cylinder **RHD**	17H 4519	19	1		Use 11B 5513 for this application
Supply tank to master cylinder **RHD**	11B 5513	19	1		
Supply tank to master cylinder **LHD**	17H 4515	20	1		
Master cylinder to 5-way connection **RHD**	17H 4518	21	1		
Master cylinder to 5-way connection **LHD**	17H 4514	22	1	(C) H–BJ7–17551 to 25314	
5-way connection to RH front hose	17H 4556	23	1		STD brakes
5-way connection to LH front hose	17H 4557	24	1		
5-way connection to rear hose	17H 4666	25	1		
4-way connection to RH front hose	17H 4556	23	1		Servo-assisted brakes
4-way connection to LH front hose	17H 4557	24	1		
4-way connection to rear hose	17H 4666	25	1		
Flexible hose to calliper	BHA 4137	26	2		Use AHB 7128 RH or AHB 7129 LH for this application
Flexible hose to calliper—RH	AHB 7128		1		
Flexible hose to calliper—LH	AHB 7129		1		
3-way connection to RH rear brake	17H 4559	27	1	(C) H–BJ7–17551 to 25314 (C) H–BJ8–25315 to 26704	
3-way connection to RH rear brake	†AHB 6926	27	1	(C) H–BJ8–26705 on	
3-way connection to LH rear brake	17H 4665	28	1	(C) H–BJ7–17551 to 25314 (C) H–BJ8–25315 to 26704	
3-way connection to LH rear brake	1H 2112	28	1	(C) H–BJ8–26705 on	

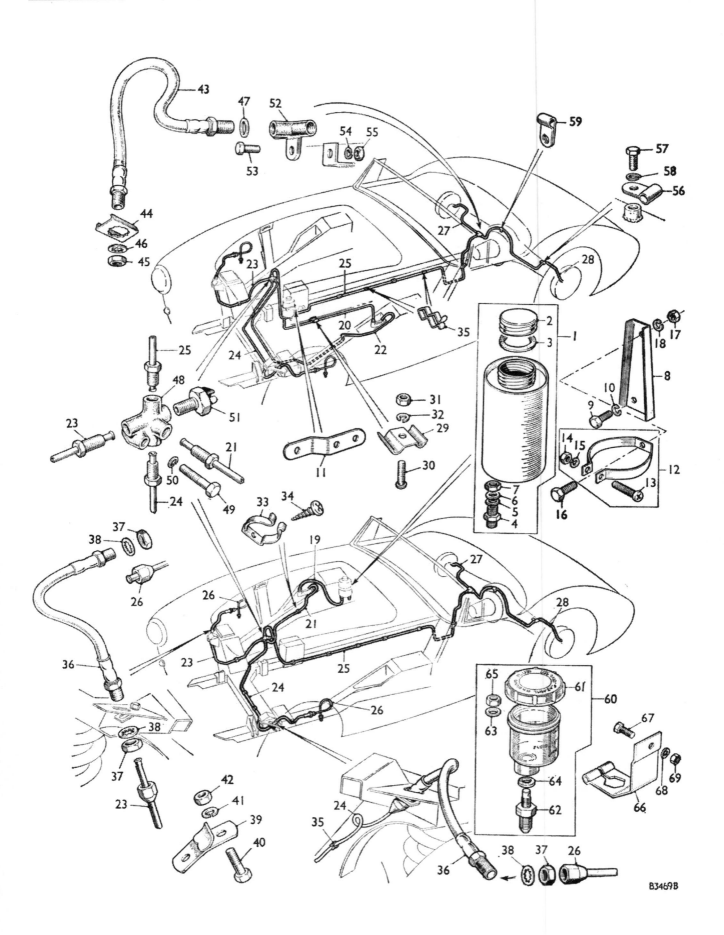

B3469B

	DESCRIPTION	Part No.	Illus. No.	Quantity	Change Point	REMARKS
	Brake Controls—*continued*					
	Supply Tank, Pipes, and Fittings—*continued*					
	Clip—supply tank pipe to front wheel arch	2H 400	29	1		
	Bolt **LHD**	PMZ 0307	30	1		
	Nut	FNZ 108	31	1		
	Washer—spring	LWZ 203	32	1		
	Clip—pipe to frame—master cylinder to 5-way connection **RHD**	2H 174	33	1	(C) H–BJ7–17551 to 25314	STD brakes
	Screw	PTZ 1004	34	1		
	Clip—pipe to frame	6K 85	35	10		
	Hose—flexible—front	10K 5451	36	2		W.S.E. use 18G 8441
	†18G 8441		36	2		
	USA 18G 8441		36	2		
	Nut	FNZ 206	37	4		
	Washer—shakeproof	LWN 406	38	4		
	Bracket—brake hose	11B 5149	39	2		
	Screw	HZS 0406	40	2		
	Washer—spring	LWZ 204	41	2		
	Nut	FNZ 104	42	2		
	Hose—flexible—rear	2A 7227	43	1		W.S.E. use 18G 8430
	†18G 8430		43	1		
	USA 18G 8430		43	1		
	Plate—locking	1G 9622	44	1		
	Nut	FNZ 206	45	1		
	Washer—shakeproof	LWN 406	46	1		
	Gasket—hose to 3-way connection	3H 2287	47	1		
	Connection—5-way	1B 8926	48	1	(C) H–BJ7–17551 to 25314	
	Bolt	HBZ 0410	49	1		
	Washer—spring	LWZ 304	50	1		
	Switch—stop light	3H 1894	51	1		W.S.E. use 13H 2303
	Switch—stop light	13H 2303	51	1		
	Connection—3-way	2A 5346	52	1		
	Screw	HZS 0506	53	1		
	Washer—spring	LWZ 205	54	1		
	Nut	FNZ 105	55	1		
	Clip—LH rear brake pipe to axle	2K 5217	56	1		
	Screw	HZS 0404	57	1		
	Washer—spring	LWZ 304	58	1		
	Clip—LH rear brake pipe to gear carrier stud	2K 5218	59	1		

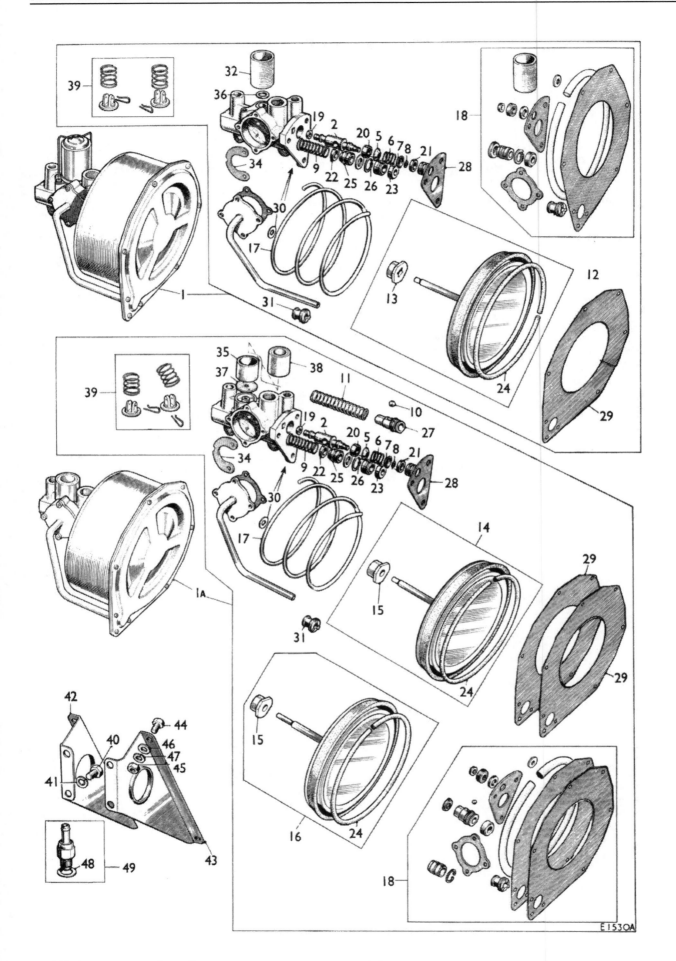

	DESCRIPTION	Part No.	Illus. No.	Quantity	Change Point	REMARKS

Brake Controls—*continued*

SERVO SYSTEM
(Optional Extra—BJ7;
Standard Equipment—BJ8)

DESCRIPTION	Part No.	Illus. No.	Qty	Change Point	REMARKS
Servo assembly—vacuum	AHB 9109	1	1	(C) H–BJ7–17551 to 25314 (C) H–BJ8–25315 to 25399 approx.	W.S.E. use 13H 1573
	13H 1573	1A	1	(C) H–BJ8–25400 approx. on	W.S.E. use 13H 3360
	13H 3360	1A	1		
Piston—valve operating	7H 6966	2	1		
Abutment—piston spring	7H 6961	5	1		
Spring—piston return	7H 6967	6	1		
Retainer—spring	7H 6962	7	1		
Circlip—retainer	7H 6959	8	1		
Spring—piston return	17H 4930	9	1		
Spring—piston return	27H 7562	10	1		
Ball—piston	BLS 105	11	1		Also included in kit 8G 8126] For use with 13H 3360
Spring—piston	27H 6874	11	1		For use with 13H 3360
Piston and rod assembly	27H 8199	12	1	[(C) H–BJ7–17551 to 25314	
Piston and rod	NSP		1	(C) H–BJ8–25315 to 25399	
Bush—piston rod guide	7H 6960	13	1	approx.	
Piston and rod assembly	27H 8056	14	1	]	
Piston and rod	NSP		1	(C) H–BJ8–25400 approx. on	
Bush—piston rod guide	27H 2418	15	1		
Piston and rod assembly	27H 8198	16	1		
Piston and rod	NSP		1		] For use with 13H 3360
Bush—piston rod guide	27H 2418	15	1		
Spring—cylinder piston return	17H 4929	17	1		
Kit—repair—servo unit	8G 8703	18	1	(C) H–BJ7–17551 to 25314 (C) H–BJ8–25315 to 25399 approx.	W.S.E. use 8G 8911] For use with AHB 9109 or 13H 1573
	8G 8911	18	1	(C) H–BJ8–25400 approx. on	
	†18G 8126	18	1		Correction; was 8G 8126. For use with 13H 3360
Seal					
Operating piston—small	7H 6964	19	1		
Operating piston—large	17H 6965	20	1		
Piston—cylinder plug	17H 4914	21	1		
Taper—hydraulic piston	17H 4509	22	1		
Gland—vacuum cylinder piston	17H 4908	23	1		
Locking plate	7H 6958	24	1		
Piston—hydraulic	17H 4837	25	1		] Included in kits 8G 8703 and 8G 8911 only
Circlip—seating spacer retaining	17H 4952	26	1		
Piston—hydraulic	27H 6873	27	1		Included in kit 8G 8126 only
Gasket					
Cylinder to body	17H 4913	28	1		
Cylinder end cover	7H 6963	29	1/2		Quantity increased in kit 8G 8126
Vacuum pipe to body	NSP		1		Was 17H 4951
Washer—cylinder to body bolt (copper)	17H 4910	30	1		
Sleeve—vacuum pipe to cylinder (rubber)	17H 4917	31	1		
Element—air filter	17H 4950	32	1		Included in kit 8G 8703 only
Ball	BLS 105	33	1		Included in kit 8G 8126 only

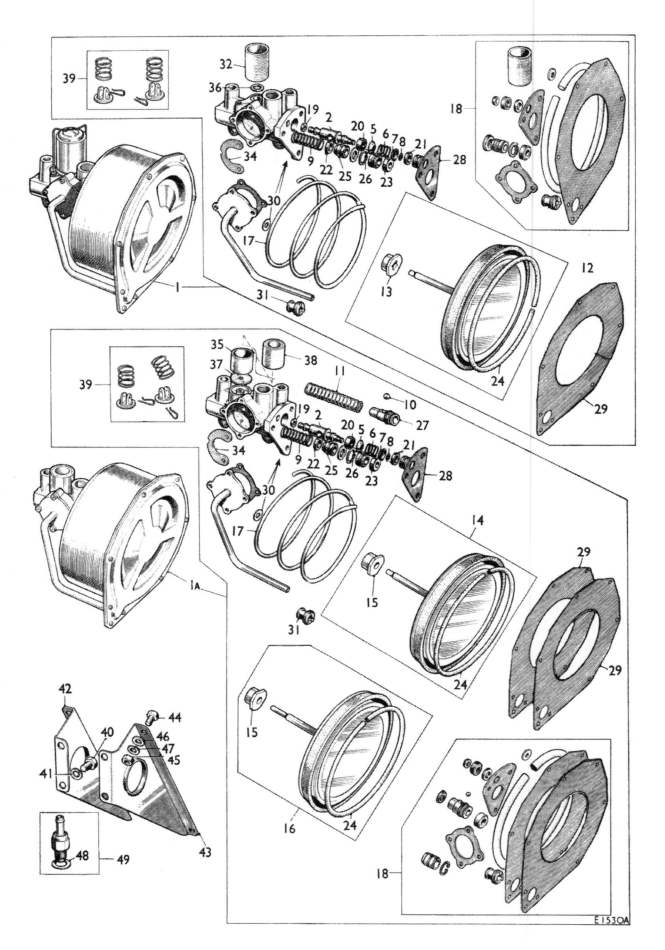

E153OA

	DESCRIPTION	Part No.	Illus. No.	Quantity	Change Point	REMARKS
	Brake Controls—*continued*					
	Servo System—*continued*					
	Spring—control valve return	17H 4931	34	1		
	Element—air filter	17H 4950	32	1	(C) H–BJ7–17551 to 25314	Also included in repair kit
					(C) H–BJ8–25315 to 25399 approx.	8G 8703
	Element—air filter	27H 2419	35	1	(C) H–BJ8–25400 approx. on	
	Seal—air filter to body	17H 4915	36	1	(C) H–BJ7–17551 to 25314	
					(C) H–BJ8–25315 to 25399 approx.	
	Seal—air filter to body	27H 2420	37	1	(C) H–BJ8–25400 approx. on	
	Cover—air filter	27H 5941	38	1		For use with 13H 3360
	Kit—repair—air valve	18G 8341	39	1 set		
	Valve	NSP		2		
	Spring	NSP		2		
	Clip—spring	NSP		2		
	Screw	HZS 0606	40	3		
	Washer—spring	LWZ 206	41	3		
	Bracket—mounting—RH	AHB 9118	42	1		
	Bracket—mounting—LH	AHB 9117	43	1		
	Screw	HZS 0506	44	4		
	Nut	FNZ 105	45	4		
	Washer—plain	PWZ 205	46	4		
	Washer—spring	LWZ 205	47	4		
	Valve—non-return	NSP		1		Was AHB 9119 and BHA 4560 W.S.E. use 27H 6960
	Kit—non-return valve	†27H 6960	49	1		
	Valve—non-return	†NSP		1		
	Gasket—valve	†11K 8309	48	1		

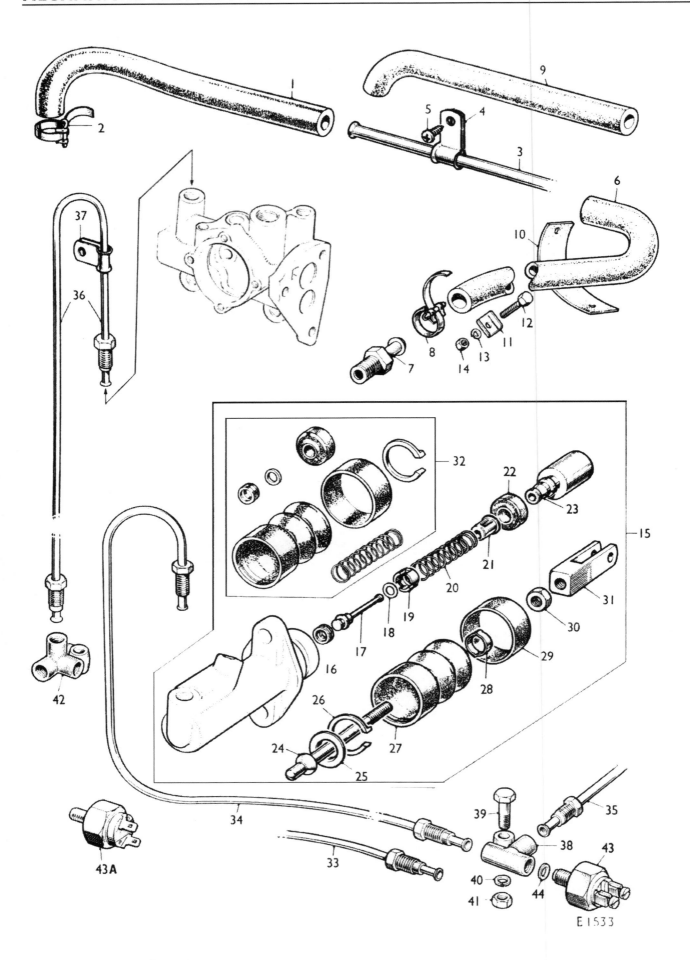

E1533

DESCRIPTION	Part No.	Illus. No.	Quantity	Change Point	REMARKS
Brake Controls—*continued*					
Servo System—*continued*					
Hose—valve to vacuum pipe	AHB 9120	1	1		
Clip—hose	21K 8341	2	2		Part No. change; was ACB 5521
Pipe—vacuum	AHB 9112	3	1	(C) H–BJ7–17551 to 25314	
Clip	PCR 0607	4	2		
Screw	PTZ 1004	5	1		
Hose—vacuum pipe to union on inlet manifold	AHB 9887	6	1		
Union—hose to manifold	21K 8342	7	1		
Clip—hose	21K 8341	8	2		Part No. change; was ACB 5521
Hose—vacuum—non-return valve to manifold union	AHB 6713	9	1		
Strap—hose	AHB 6712	10	1		
Plate—strap	AHH 6866	11	2	(C) H–BJ8–25315 on	
Screw	PMZ 0314	12	1		
Washer—spring	LWZ 203	13	1		
Nut	FNZ 103	14	1		
Cylinder assembly—master	†AHB 9110	15	1		W.S.E. use 27H 4717
Cylinder assembly—master	27H 4717	15	1		
Body	NSP		1		
Stem—valve	7H 4751	17	1		
Washer—valve	†7H 4752	18	1		Also included in repair kits 8G 8648 and 18G 8011
Spacer—valve	17H 4182	19	1		
Spring	†17H 4898	20	1		Also included in repair kits 8G 8648 and 18G 8011
Retainer—spring	17H 4827	21	1		
Plunger	17H 4899	23	1		
Push-rod	17H 4897	24	1		
Washer—retaining	17H 4601	25	1		
Circlip	17H 4602	26	1		
Clip—dust cover	17H 4597	28	1		
Nut—lock	FNZ 205	30	1		
Fork end	17H 4896	31	1		
Kit—repair—master cylinder	†8G 8648	32	1		W.S.E. use 18G 8011
Kit—repair—master cylinder	†18G 8011		1		
Seal—valve	†17H 4561	16	1		
Spring	†17H 4898	20	1		
Washer—valve	†7H 4752	18	1		
Seal—plunger	†17H 4900	22	1		
Circlip	†17H 4602	26	1		
Cover—dust	†17H 4596	27	1		
Band—retaining	†17H 4603	29	1		
Pipe					
Master cylinder to 3-way connection **RHD**	13H 1596	33	1		Use AHB 9127 for this application
Master cylinder to 3-way connection **RHD**	AHB 9127	33	1		
Master cylinder to 3-way connection **LHD**	AHB 9111	34	1		
3-way connection to servo unit	11B 5760	35	1		Use AHB 9126 for this application
3-way connection to servo unit	AHB 9126	36	1		
Servo unit to 4-way connection	AHB 9113	36	1		
Clip	PCR 0307	37	1		
Connection—3-way	†ATB 7289	38	1		W.S.E. use BTB 657
Connection—3-way	BTB 657	38	1		
Bolt	HBZ 0410	39	1		
Washer—spring	LWZ 304	40	1		
Nut	FNZ 104	41	1		
Connection—4-way	17H 4141	42	1		
Switch—stop light	†2A 5304	43	1	(C) H–BJ7–17551 to 25314	
	†1H 5719	43A	1	(C) H–BJ8–25315 on	W.S.E. use 27H 4754
	†27H 4754	43A	1		
Gasket—switch to 3-way connection	3H 2429	44	1		

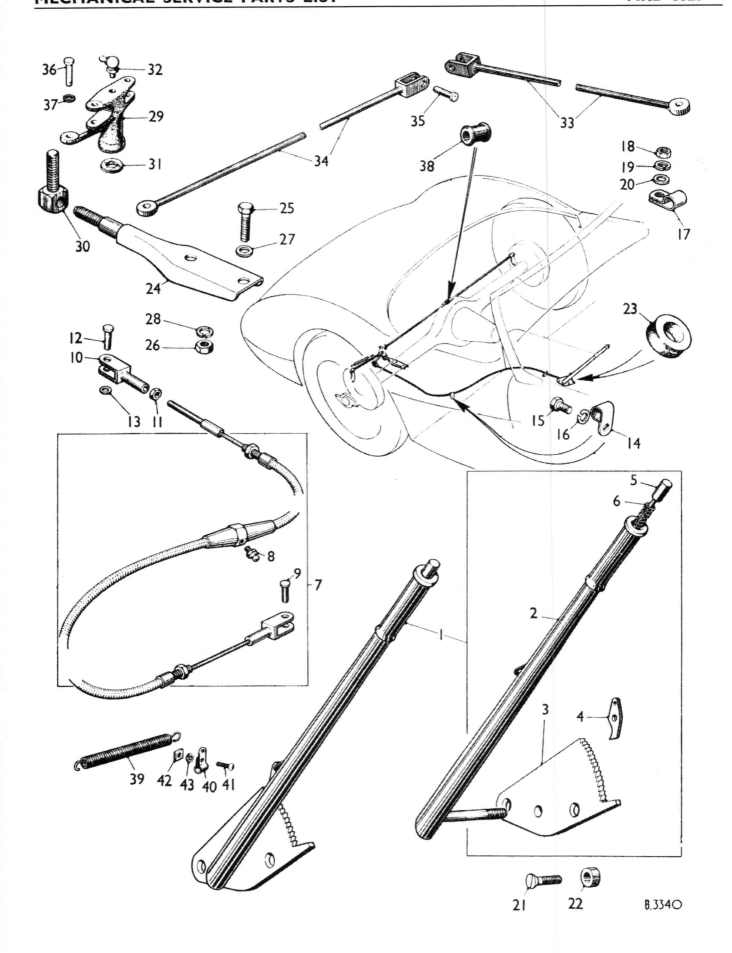

B.334○

	DESCRIPTION	Part No.	Illus. No.	Quantity	Change Point	REMARKS
	Brake Controls—*continued*					
	HAND BRAKE MECHANISM					
	Hand brake assembly	11B 5282	1	1		
	Lever—hand brake	17H 786	2	1		
	Plate—ratchet	17H 787	3	1		
	Pawl—ratchet	17H 788	4	1		
	Button	17H 789	5	1		
	Spring	17H 790	6	1		
	Cable assembly—hand brake	11B 5338	7	1		
	Lubricator	UHN 305	8	1		
	Pin—joint—cable to hand brake lever	2K 5616	9	1		
	Fork end	1B 7862	10	1		
	Nut	FNZ 204	11	1		
	Pin—joint—cable to balance lever	2K 5221	12	1		
	Washer—plain	PWZ 104	13	1		
	Clip—cable to heelboard	1B 9074	14	1		⎤
	Clip—cable to heelboard	PCR 0609	14	1		⎦ Alternatives
	Screw	HZS 0403	15	1		
	Washer—spring	LWZ 204	16	1		
	Clip—cable to floor	PCR 0609	17	1		
	Nut	FNZ 104	18	1		
	Washer—spring	LWZ 204	19	1		
	Washer—plain	PWZ 204	20	1		
	Screw—hand brake lever to frame	88G 293	21	2		Part No. change; was 1B 8895
	Piece—distance—screw	1B 8896	22	2		
	Seal—hand brake lever to frame	†1G 6236	23	1		W.S.E. use 27H 6959
	Seal—hand brake lever to frame	†27H 6995	23	1		
	Support—balance lever	1B 7424	24	1		
	Screw	HZS 0506	25	2		
	Nut	FNZ 105	26	2		
	Washer—plain	PWZ 105	27	2		
	Washer—spring	LWZ 305	28	2		
	Lever—balance	1G 7485	29	1		
	Carrier—balance lever	1G 7484	30	1		
	Ring (felt)	2K 5213	31	1		
	Lubricator	UHN 490	32	1		
	Cross-rod—RH	ATC 7251	33	1		
	Cross-rod—LH	1G 7549	34	1		
	Pin—cross-rod to brake lever	2K 6930	35	2		
	Pin—cross-rod to balance lever	2K 5243	36	2		
	Ring—pin (felt)	2K 5291	37	8		
	Ferrule—cross-rod steady	1B 5329	38	1		
	Spring—pull-off	47H 5524	39	2		
	Clip—spring	1G 7574	40	2		
	Screw	PMZ 0306	41	2		
	Nut	NZS 103	42	2		
	Washer—spring	LWZ 203	43	2		

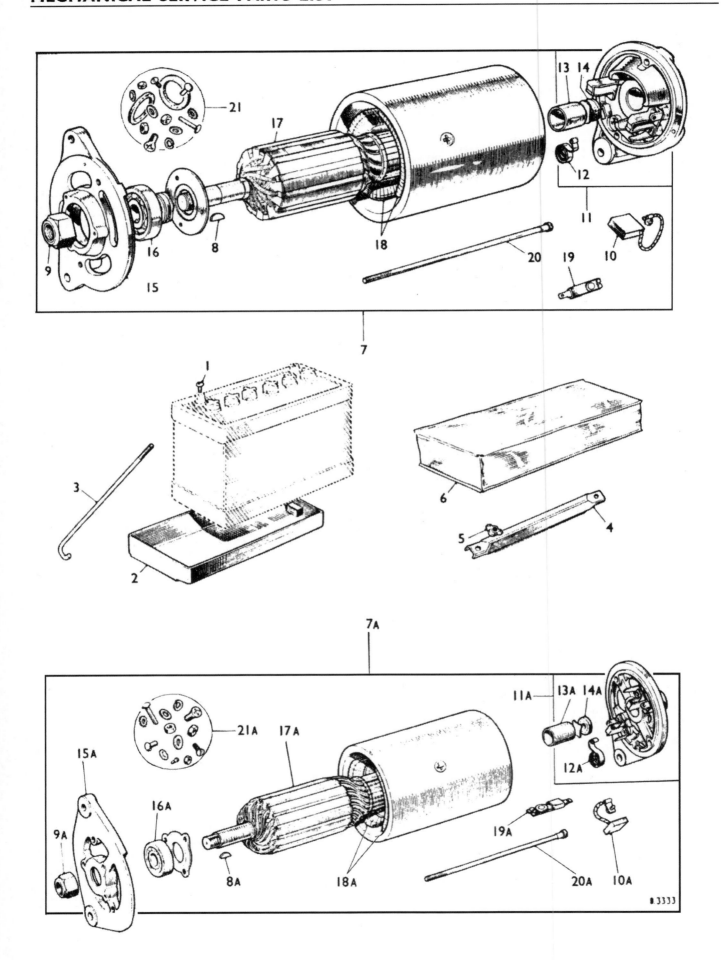

	DESCRIPTION	Part No.	Illus. No.	Quantity	Change Point	REMARKS

ELECTRICAL EQUIPMENT

ELECTRICAL EQUIPMENT

BATTERY

DESCRIPTION	Part No.	Illus. No.	Quantity	Change Point	REMARKS
Battery	NSP		1		
Screw—battery lug	2K 8645	1	4		
Tray—battery	14G 1702	2	1		
Rod—battery fixing	AHB 8385	3	2		
Bar—battery fixing	14G 5509	4	1		
Nut	WNZ 104	5	2		
Cover—battery	14B 8816	6	1		

DYNAMO

DESCRIPTION	Part No.	Illus. No.	Quantity	Change Point	REMARKS
Dynamo	AEJ 22	7	1		
Key	WKN 405	8	1		
Nut	LNZ 206	9	1		
Brush	47H 5413	10	1 set		W.S.E. use **17H 2472**
Brush	17H 2472	10	1 set		
Bracket—commutator end	47H 5414	11	1		
Spring—brush tension	47H 5415	12	1 set		
Bush—commutator end	17H 5434	13	1		
Oiler	37H 5487	14	1	(C) 17551 to 25314	
Bracket—drive end	7H 5525	15	1		
Bearing—drive end	7H 5021	16	1		
Armature	47H 5416	17	1		
Coil—field	7H 5025	18	1 set		
Terminal	47H 5392	19	1		
Bolt—bracket	27H 5534	20	2		
Sundry parts	7H 5528	21	1 set		
Dynamo	17D 121	7A	1		
Key	WKN 405	8A	1		
Nut	FNN 207	9A	1		
Brush	57H 5427	10A	1 set		
Bracket—commutator end	57H 5428	11A	1		
Spring—brush tension	47H 5389	12A	1 set		
Bush—commutator end	57H 5429	13A	1		
Oiler	47H 5394	14A	1		
Bracket—drive end B*	57H 5485	15A	1		W.S.E. use **27H 4829** together with bearing **17H 5043**
Bearing—drive end B*	97H 626	16A	1	(C) 25315 on	
Bracket—drive end D and E*	†27H 4829	15A	1		W.S.E. use **27H 3817** with bearing **97H 626**
Bracket—drive end D and E*	†27H 3817	15A	1		
Bearing—drive end D and E*	17H 5043	16A	1		
Armature A to F*	†57H 5431	17A	1		W.S.E. use **27H 813,**
Armature H and J*	27H 8136	17A	1		
Coil—field	57H 5432	18A	1 set		
Terminal	47H 5392	19A	1		
Bolt—bracket	57H 5433	20A	2		
Sundry parts	57H 5085	21A	1 set		

* Reference must always be made to the suffix letter of the manufacturers Part No. stamped on the dynamo casing to ensure ordering of correct component parts. Example: Bracket—drive end 27H 4829 is for dynamo, suffix letters D and E.

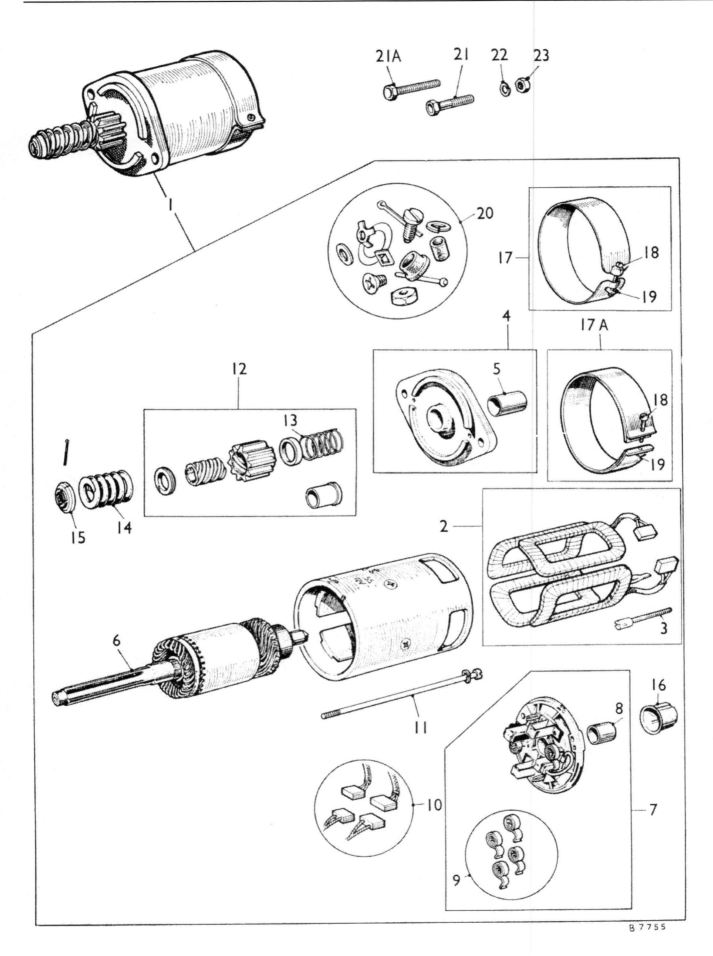

B 7755

MECHANICAL SERVICE PARTS LIST

DESCRIPTION	Part No.	Illus. No.	Quantity	Change Point	REMARKS
Electrical Equipment—*continued*					
STARTER					
Starter assembly	†13H 837	1	1		
Coil—field—set	†7H 5013	2	1		
Terminal	†27H 7816	3	1		
Bracket assembly—drive end	†7H 5010	4	1		
Bush—bearing	†7H 5011	5	1		
Armature	†7H 5012	6	1		
Bracket assembly—commutator end	†7H 5498	7	1		
Bush—bearing	†7H 5004	8	1		
Spring—brush tension—set A*	†7H 5005	9	1		
Spring—brush tension—set B*	†27H 2291	9	1		
Brush—set	†7H 5002	10	1		
Bolt—through-fixing	†7H 5339	11	2		
Pinion and sleeve assembly	†7H 5008	12	1		
Spring—pinion return	†7H 5009	13	1		
Spring—main	†7H 5007	14	1		
Nut—shaft	†7H 5006	15	1		
Cap—shaft	†7H 5001	16	1		
Band—cover	†7H 5000	17	1		Use 57H 5369 for this application
Band—cover	†57H 5369	17A	1		
Screw	†AJD 1252 Z	18	1		
Nut	†AJD 8612	19	1		
Sundry parts—set	†7H 5156	20	1		
Bolt	†HBZ 0615	21	2		Use HBZ 0620 for this application
Bolt	†HBZ 0620	21A	2		
Washer—spring	†LWZ 206	22	2		
Nut	†FNZ 106	23	2		

* Reference must always be made to the suffix letter of the manufacturer's Part No. stamped on the starter casing to ensure ordering of correct component parts. Example: Spring 7H 5005 is for starter, suffix letter 'A'.

† Revised Information.   163   Issue 4   MN 2

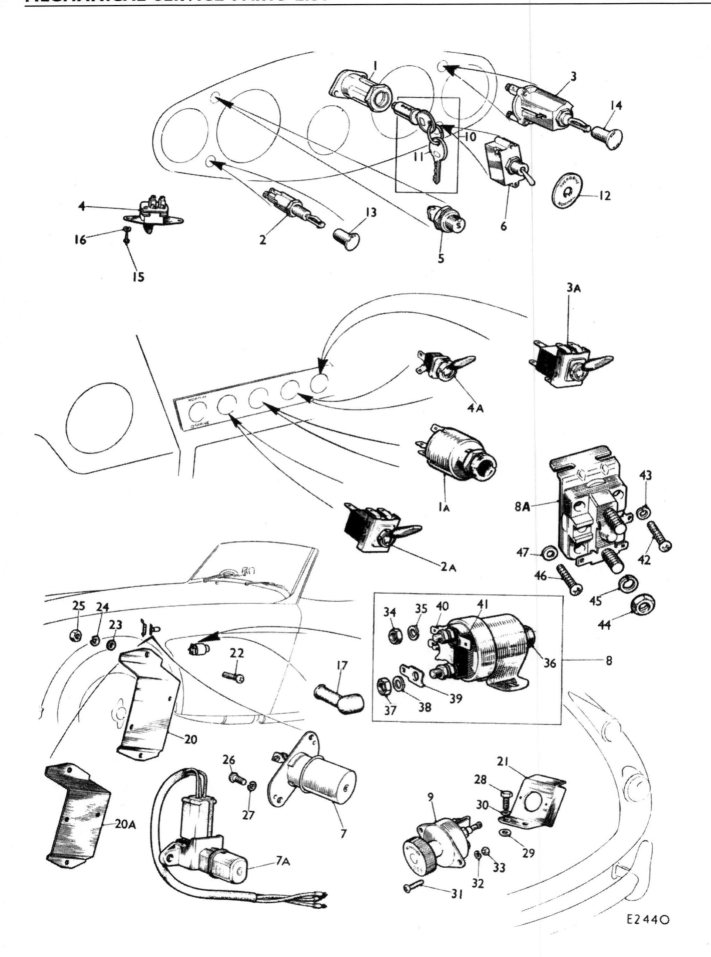

E2440

	DESCRIPTION	Part No.	Illus. No.	Quantity	Change Point	REMARKS

Electrical Equipment—*continued*

SWITCHES

Switch

	DESCRIPTION	Part No.	Illus. No.	Quantity	Change Point	REMARKS
	Ignition	3H 2825	1	1		Required when steering lock is not fitted
	Windscreen wiper	27H 5278	2	1		
	Head and sidelamp	3H 3098	3	1	(C) H–BJ7–17551 to 25314	
	Panel light	3H 3100	4	1		
	Starter solenoid push	3H 3058	5	1		
	Overdrive	1B 9030	6	1		
	Headlamp dipper	11G 2007	7	1		
	Windscreen wiper	BHA 4237	2A	1		
	Head and sidelamp	BCA 4294	3A	1		
	Panel light	BCA 4312	4A	1		
	Auxiliary or overdrive	BCA 4312	4A	1	(C) H–BJ8–25315 on	
	Headlamp dipper	†88G 440	7A	1		Correction; was 88G 6440
	Headlamp dipper	†37H 1366	7A	1		Part No. change; was BHA 4438 — W.S.E. use 37H 2099
	Headlamp dipper	†37H 2099	7A	1		
	Battery master	†1B 2804	9	1		
Switch assembly—starter solenoid		†BCA 4501	8	1		W.S.E. use BMK 1727
Nut		†AJD 8019 Z	34	2		
Washer spring		†LWZ 203	35	2		
Cap (rubber)		†27H 5576	36	1		
Nut—contact screw		†47H 5204	37	4		W.S.E. use 13H 4485
Washer—spring		†LWZ 205	38	4		
Connector—Lucar						
	Starter-push	†47H 5160	39	1		
	Fusebox	†47H 5158	40	1		
	Control box	†21K 9068	41	1		
Screw		†PMZ 0306	42	2		
Washer—spring		†LWZ 203	43	2		
Switch—starter solenoid		†BMK 1727	8A	1		
Nut		†13H 4485	44	2		
Washer—spring		†13H 4486	45	2		
Screw		†PMZ 0308	46	2		
Washer—plain		†PWZ 103	47	2		
Switch assembly—ignition and starter		13H 337	1A	1		Required when steering lock is not fitted
Nut—locking		47H 5481		1		
Lock assembly—ignition switch		27H 4185	10	1		W.S.E. use 24G 1345
Lock assembly—ignition switch		24G 1345	10	1		
Key		ANK 4646	11	2		
Escutcheon—overdrive switch		1B 9031	12	1		
Knob—windscreen wiper switch		3H 3096	13	1		
Knob—head and sidelamp switch		3H 3099	14	1	(C) H–BJ7–17551 to 25314	
Screw		AJD 1708 N	15	2		
Washer—spring		LWZ 302	16	2		
Bootee—insulating—starter solenoid terminal		8G 548	17	1		
Screw		PMZ 0306	18	2		
Washer—spring		LWZ 203	19	2		
Bracket						
	Dipper switch	1A 1880	20	1	(C) H–BJ7–17551 to 25314	
	Dipper switch	AHB 6504	20A	1	(C) H–BJ8–25315 on	
	Battery master switch	14B 6895	21	1		
Screw		PMZ 0410	22	2		
Washer—plain		PWZ 104	23	2		
Washer—spring		PWZ 204	24	2		
Nut		FNZ 104	25	2		
Screw		PMZ 0308	26	2		
Washer—spring		LWZ 203	27	2		
Screw		HZS 0404	28	2		
Washer—plain		PWZ 104	29	2		
Washer—spring		LWZ 204	30	2		
Screw		PMZ 0207	31	2		
Washer—spring		LWZ 302	32	2		
Nut		CNZ 102	33	2		

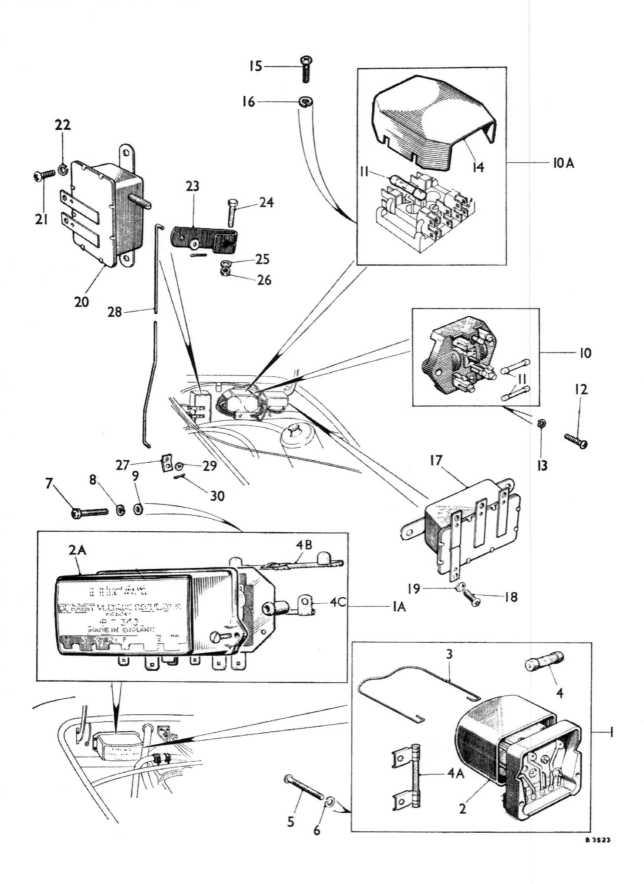

B 3523

	DESCRIPTION	Part No.	Illus. No.	Quantity	Exp.	UK	D	Change Point	REMARKS
					Stock recoms. DIST.				

Electrical Equipment—*continued*
Switches—*continued*

DESCRIPTION	Part No.	Illus. No.	Quantity	Exp.	UK	D	Change Point	REMARKS
Box—control	3H 1836	1	1	★	★			
Cover	7H 5522	2	1					
Clip—cover	7H 5128	3	1					
Resistance—63 ohms (carbon type)	7H 6066	4	1				†(C) H–BJ7–17551 to 25814	See Austin Service Journal A/326
Resistance—60 ohms (wire wound)	47H 5589	4A	1					
Screw	PMZ 0820	5	2					
Washer—spring	LWZ 203	6	2					
Box—control	†BCA 4663	1A	1	★	★			
Cover	57H 5398	2A	1					W.S.E.; use 27H 5873
Cover	†27H 5873	2A	1					
Resistance—55 ohms	57H 5396	4B	1					
Resistance—40 ohms	57H 5397	4C	1				†(C) H–BJ8–25315 on	
Screw	PMZ 0318	7	3					
Washer—spring	LWZ 203	8	3					
Washer—plain	PWZ 103	9	3					
Box—fuse	3H 1910	10	1	★	★			
Fuse—35 amp	7H 5067	11	2	★	★	★		
Fuse—50 amp	7H 5540	11	2	★	★	★	(C) H–BJ7–17551 to 25814	
Screw	PMZ 0307	12	2					
Washer—spring	LWZ 203	13	2					
Box—fuse	13H 252	10A	1	★	★			
Cover	47H 5212	14	1					
Fuse—35 amp	7H 5067	11	4	★	★	★	†(C) H–BJ8–25315 on	
Screw	PMZ 0310	15	2					
Washer—spring	LWZ 203	16	2					
Relay—overdrive	1B 2836	17	1				(C) H–BJ7–17551 to 25814	
Relay—overdrive	BMK 685		1				(C) H–BJ8–25315 on	
Screw	PMZ 0808	18	2					
Washer—spring	LWZ 203	19	2					
Switch—throttle	1B 2837	20	1					
Screw	PMZ 0308	21	2					
Washer—spring	LWZ 203	22	2					Required when overdrive is fitted
Lever—throttle switch	11B 2163	23	1					
Bolt	53K 129	24	1					
Washer—plain	PWZ 103	25	2					
Nut	FNZ 103	26	1					
Eye—throttle switch link	1B 2721	27	1					
Link—throttle switch	AHB 9053	28	1					
Washer—plain	PWZ 102	29	2					
Pin—split	2K 1881	30	2					

† Revised Information.

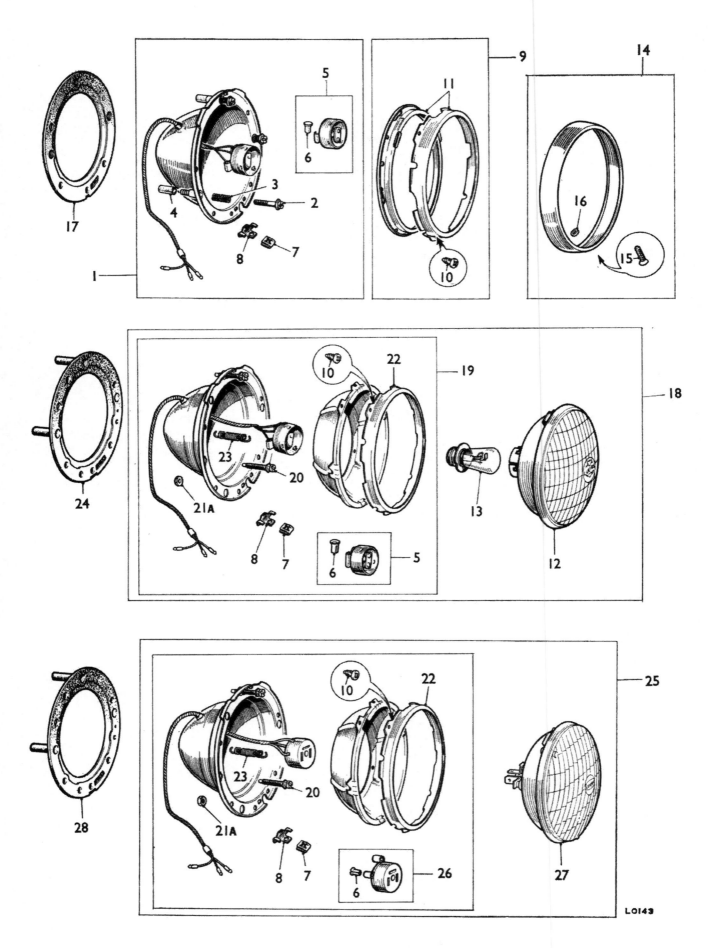

DESCRIPTION	Part No.	Illus. No.	Quantity	Change Point	REMARKS
Electrical Equipment—*continued*					
LAMPS (ROAD)					
Headlamp complete—left dip—Mk. VI	NSP		2		
Body assembly	7H 6838	1	2		W.S.E. use 27H 8209 together with 1 off rim 37H 5530 and 1 off gasket 57H 5456
Screw—trimmer	17H 5394	2	6		
Spring—trimmer screw	17H 5231	3	6		
Sleeve—sealing	27H 5253	4	6		
Adaptor (with cable)	27H 2333		2		
Adaptor assembly	17H 5306	5	2		
Sleeve—terminal	27H 6713	6	6		Part No. change; was 37H 5271 and 7H 5582
Nut—rim fixing screw	27H 5354	7	2	(C) H–BJ7–17551 to 25314	
Bracket—rim fixing screw	37H 5190	8	2	(C) H–BJ8–25315 to	
Plate assembly—light unit retaining	17H 5205	9	2	(B) H–BJ8–78042	
Screw—rim	PJZ 602	10	6		
Rim—unit seating	17H 5895	11	2		
Unit—light	7H 5483	12	2		
Bulb	†BFS 354	13	2		W.S.E. use BFS 414
Bulb	†BFS 414		2		
Rim assembly	37H 5580	14	2		
Screw	AJA 5081	15	2		
Washer	21G 9057	16	2		
Gasket (rubber)	57H 5457	17	2		
Headlamp assembly—left dip—Mk. X	†27H 8209	18	2		W.S.E. use 27H 8495
Body assembly	27H 5979	19	2		W.S.E. use 27H 8209
Screw—trimmer	67H 5025	20	4		
Nut—trimmer screw	27H 6482	21A	4		
Adaptor (with cable)	27H 2333		2		
Adaptor assembly	17H 5306	5	2		
Sleeve—terminal	27H 6713	6	6		
Nut—rim fixing screw	27H 5354	7	2		
Bracket—rim fixing screw	37H 5190	8	2		
Plate—light unit retaining	27H 3338	22	2		
Screw	PJZ 602	10	6		
Spring—unit seating rim **RHD**	67H 5026	23	2		
Unit—light	7H 5483	12	2	(B) H–BJ8–78043 to	
Bulb	BFS 414	13	2	(C) H–BJ8–81365	
Headlamp assembly—left dip—Mk. X	†27H 8495		2		
Screw—trimmer	†67H 5025		4		
Nut—trimmer screw	†27H 6482		4		
Adaptor assembly	†17H 5306		2		
Sleeve—terminal	†27H 6713		6		
Nut—rim fixing screw	†27H 5354		2		
Bracket—rim fixing screw	†37H 5190		2		
Plate—light unit retaining	†27H 3338		2		
Screw	†PJZ 602		6		
Spring—unit seating rim	†67H 5026		2		
Unit—light	†7H 5483		2		
Bulb	†BFS 414		2		
Rim assembly	37H 5580	14	2		
Screw	AJA 5081	15	2		
Washer	21G 9057	16	2		
Gasket (rubber)	57H 5456	24	2		
Headlamp assembly—left dip—Mk. X	27H 8203	25	2		
Screw—trimmer	67H 5025	20	4		
Nut—trimmer screw	27H 6482	21A	4		
Adaptor assembly	47H 5126	26	2		
Sleeve terminal	27H 6713	6	6		
Nut—rim fixing screw	27H 5354	7	2		
Bracket—rim fixing screw	37H 5190	8	2		
Plate—light unit retaining	27H 3338	22	2	(C) H–BJ8–81366 on	
Screw	PJZ 602	10	6		
Spring—unit seating rim	67H 5026	23	2		
Unit—light	13H 496	27	2		
Rim—assembly	37H 5580	14	2		
Screw	AJA 5081	15	2		
Washer	21G 9057	16	2		
Gasket (rubber)	27H 6967	28	2		

See T.I.B. IB 45 F18 for identification of Mk. VI and Mk. X headlamps

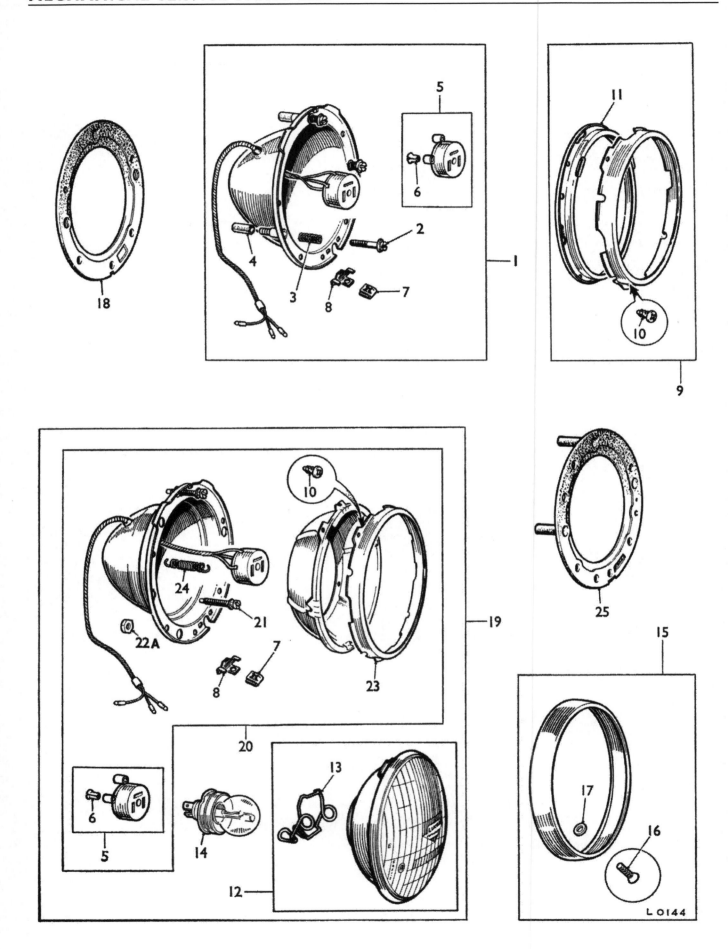

L 0144

DESCRIPTION	Part No.	Illus. No.	Quantity	Change Point	REMARKS
Electrical Equipment—*continued*					
Lamps (Road)—*continued*					
Headlamp complete—vertical dip —Mk VI	†NSP		2		
Body assembly	†67H 5028	1	2		W.S.E.; use 27H 8204 together with 1 off rim 37H 5530 and 1 off gasket 57H 5456
Screw—trimmer	†17H 5394	2	6		
Spring—trimmer screw	†17H 5231	3	6		
Sleeve—sealing	†27H 5253	4	6		
Adaptor (with cable)	†BHA 4235		2		W.S.E.; use 47H 5126
Adaptor assembly	†47H 5126	5	2		
Sleeve—terminal	†27H 6713	6	6		Part No. change; was 37H 5172 and 7H 5582
Nut—rim fixing screw	†27H 5354	7	2	(C) H–BJ7–17551 to 25314	
Bracket—rim fixing screw	†37H 5190	8	2	(C) H–BJ8–25315 to ▼	
Plate assembly—light unit retaining	†17H 5205	9	2		
Screw—rim	†PJZ 602	10	6		
Rim—unit seating	†17H 5395	11	2		
Unit assembly—light	†47H 5124	12	2		
Unit assembly—light Europe except France	†27H 4146	12	2		W.S.E.; use 27H 4146
Spring—bulb retaining	†47H 5125	13	2		
Bulb	†BFS 410	14	2		
Rim assembly	†37H 5530	15	2		
Screw	†AJA 5081	16	2		
Washer	†21G 9057	17	2		
Gasket (rubber)	†57H 5457	18	2		
Headlamp assembly—vertical dip —Mk X	†27H 8204	19	2		
Body assembly	†67H 5024	20	2		W.S.E.; use 27H 8204
Screw—trimmer	†67H 5025	21	4		
Nut—trimmer screw	†27H 6482	22A	4		
Adaptor (with cable)	†27H 2817		2		W.S.E.; use 47H 5126
Adaptor assembly	†47H 5126	5	2		
Sleeve—terminal	†27H 6713	6	6		
Nut—rim fixing screw	†27H 5354	7	2	(C) H–BJ8–▼ on	
Bracket—rim fixing screw	†37H 5190	8	2		
Plate—light unit retaining	†27H 3338	23	2		
Screw	†PJZ 602	10	6		
Spring—unit seating rim	†67H 5026	24	2		
Unit assembly—light	†27H 4146	12	2		
Spring—bulb retaining	†47H 5125	13	2		
Bulb	†BFS 410	14	2		
Rim assembly	†37H 5530	15	2		
Screw	†AJA 5081	16	2		
Washer	†21G 9057	17	2		
Gasket (rubber)	†57H 5456	25	2		

See T.I.B. 1B 45 for identification of Mk VI and Mk X headlamps.

▼ Change point not available

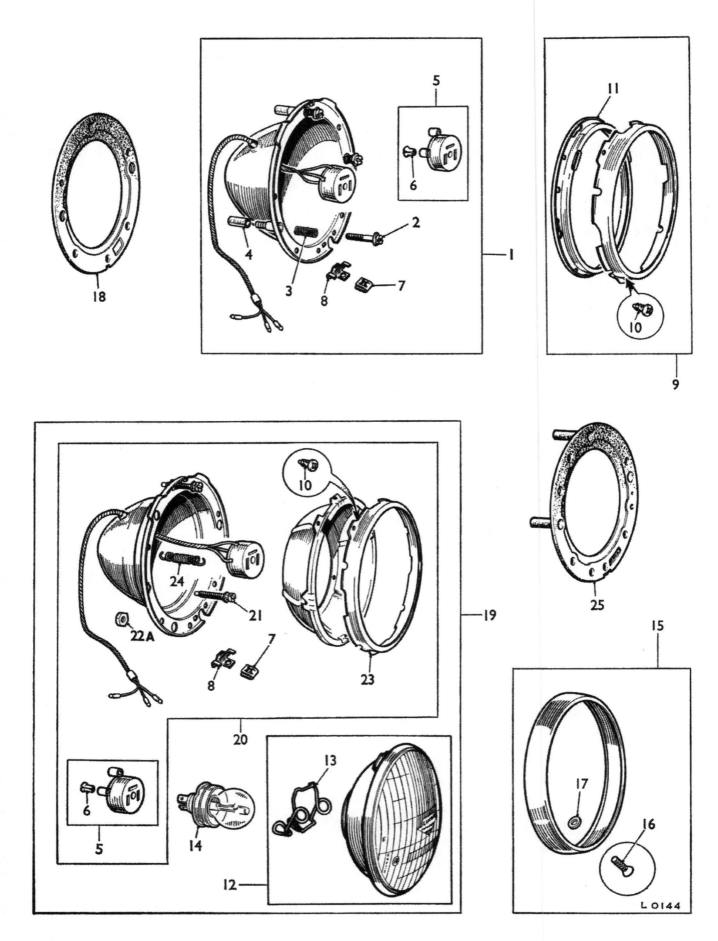

DESCRIPTION	Part No.	Illus. No.	Quantity	Change Point	REMARKS
Electrical Equipment—*continued*					
Lamps (Road)—*continued*					
Headlamp complete—vertical dip —Mk VI	†NSP		2		
Body assembly	†67H 5028	1	2		W.S.E.; use 27H 8205 together with 1 off rim 37H 5530 and 1 off gasket 57H 5456
Screw—trimmer	†17H 5394	2	6		
Spring—trimmer screw	†17H 5331	3	6		
Sleeve—sealing	†27H 5353	4	6		
Adaptor (with cable)	†BHA 4235		2		W.S.E.; use 47H 5126
Adaptor assembly	†47H 5126	5	2		
Sleeve—terminal	†27H 6713	6	6		Part No. change; was 37H 5271 and 7H 5582
Nut—rim fixing screw	†27H 5354	7	2	(C) H–BJ7–17551 to 25314	
Bracket—rim fixing screw	†37H 5190	8	2	(C) H–BJ8–25315 to ▼	
Plate assembly—light unit retaining	†17H 5205	9	2		
Screw—rim	†PJZ 602	10	6		
Rim—seating unit	†17H 5395	11	2		
Unit assembly—light	†47H 5124	12	2		W.S.E.; use 27H 4146
Unit assembly—light	†27H 4146	12	2		
Spring—bulb retaining	France †47H 5125	13	2		
Bulb	†BFS 411	14	2		
Rim assembly	†37H 5530	15	2		
Screw	†AJA 5081	16	2		
Washer	†21G 9057	17	2		
Gasket (rubber)	†57H 5457	18	2		
Headlamp assembly—vertical dip —Mk X	†27H 8205	19	2		W.S.E.; use 37H 1368
Headlamp assembly—vertical dip —Mk X	†37H 1368	19	2		
Body assembly	†67H 5024	20	2		W.S.E.; use 27H 8205
Screw—trimmer	†67H 5025	21	4		
Nut—trimmer screw	†27H 6482	22A	4		
Adaptor (with cable)	†27H 2817		2		W.S.E.; use 47H 5126
Adaptor assembly	†47H 5126	5	2	(C) H–BJ8–▼ on	
Sleeve—terminal	†27H 6713	6	6		
Nut—rim fixing screw	†27H 5254	7	2		
Bracket—rim fixing screw	†37H 5190	8	2		
Plate—light unit retaining	†27H 3338	23	2		
Screw	†PJZ 602	10	6		
Spring—unit seating rim	†67H 5026	24	2		
Unit assembly—light	†27H 4146	12	2		
Spring—bulb retaining	†47H 5125	13	2		
Bulb	†BFS 411	14	2		
Rim assembly	†37H 5530	15	2		
Screw	†AJA 5081	16	2		
Washer	†21G 9057	17	2		
Gasket (rubber)	†57H 5456	25	2		

See T.I.B. IB 45 F18 for identification of Mk VI and Mk X headlamps   ▼ Change point not available

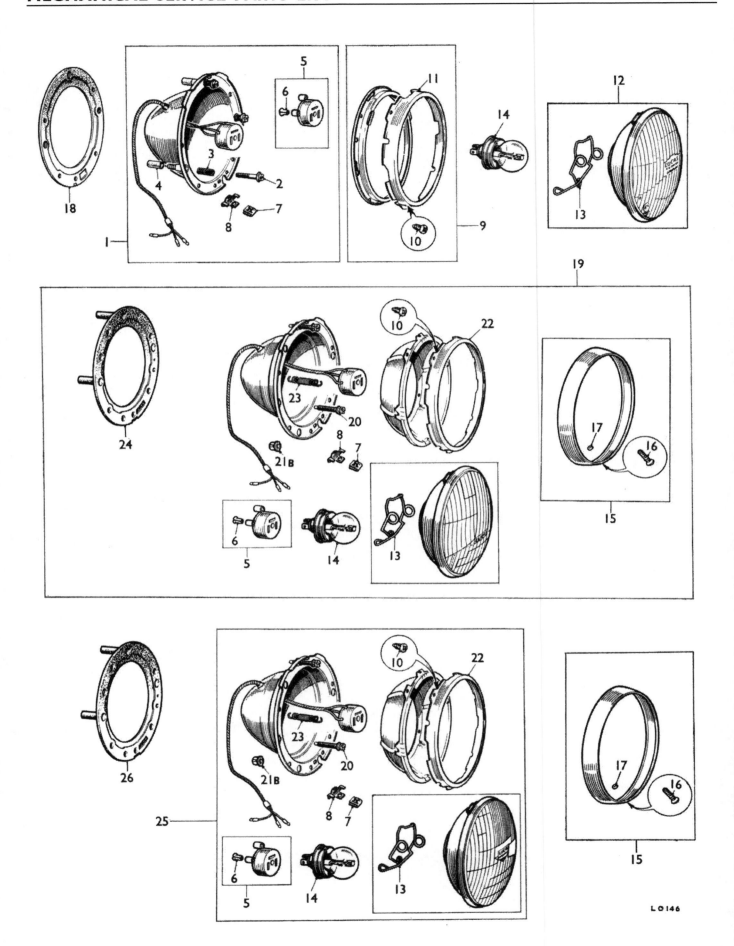

L 0 146

DESCRIPTION	Part No.	Illus. No.	Quantity	Change Point	REMARKS
Electrical Equipment—*continued*					
Lamps (Road)—*continued*					
Headlamp complete—vertical dip —Mk VI	†NSP		2		
Body assembly	†67H 5028	1	2		W.S.E.; use 27H 8284
Screw—trimmer	†17H 5394	2	6		
Spring—trimmer screw	†17H 5231	3	6		
Sleeve—sealing	†27H 5253	4	6		
Adaptor (with cable)	†BHA 4235	5	2		W.S.E.; use 47H 5126
Adaptor assembly	†47H 5126	4	2		
Sleeve—terminal	†27H 6713	6	6		
Nut—rim fixing screw	†27H 5354	7	2		
Bracket—rim fixing screw	†37H 5190	8	2		
Plate assembly—light unit retaining	†17H 5205	9	2		
Screw—rim	†PJZ 602	10	6		
Rim—unit seating	†17H 5395	11	2		
Unit assembly—light	†47H 5528	12	2		
Spring—bulb retaining	†47H 5125	13	2		
Bulb	†BFS 410	14	2		
Rim assembly	†37H 5530	15	2	(C) H–BJ8–25315 to ▼	
Screw	†AJA 5081	16	2		
Washer	†21G 9057	17	2		
Gasket (rubber) **Sweden**	†57H 5457	18	2		
Headlamp complete—vertical dip —Mk X	†27H 8284	19	2		
Screw—trimmer	†67H 5025	20	4		
Retainer—trimmer screw	†27H 7824	21B	4		
Adaptor assembly	†47H 5126	5	2		
Sleeve—terminal	†27H 6713	6	6		
Nut—rim fixing screw	†27H 5354	7	2		
Bracket—rim fixing screw	†37H 5190	8	2		
Plate—light unit retaining	†27H 3338	22	2		
Screw	†PJZ 602	10	6		
Spring—unit seating rim	†67H 5026	23	2		
Unit assembly—light	†NSP		2		Serviced by Agebe, Sweden
Spring—bulb retaining	†47H 5125	13	2		
Bulb	†BFS 410	14	2		
Rim assembly	†37H 5530	15	2		
Screw	†AJA 5081	16	2		
Washer	†21G 9057	17	2		
Gasket (rubber)	†27H 6967	24	2		
Headlamp assembly—vertical dip —Mk X	†27H 8287	25	2		
Screw—trimmer	†67H 5025	20	4		
Retainer—trimmer screw	†27H 7824	21B	4		
Adaptor assembly	†47H 5126	5	2		
Sleeve—terminal	†27H 6713	6	6		
Nut—rim fixing screw	†27H 5354	7	2	(C) H–BJ8–▼ to ▼	
Bracket—rim fixing screw	†37H 5190	8	2		
Plate—light unit retaining	†27H 3338	22	2		
Screw	†PJZ 602	10	6		
Spring—unit seating rim	†67H 5026	23	2		
Unit assembly—light	†NSP		2		Serviced by Agebe, Sweden
Spring—bulb retaining	†47H 5125	13	2		
Bulb	†BFS 410	14	2		
Rim assembly	†37H 5530	15	2		
Screw	†AJA 5081	16	2		
Washer	†21G 9057	17	2		
Gasket (rubber)	†57H 5456	26	2		

See T.I.B. IB 45 F18 for identification of Mk VI and Mk X headlamps

▼ Change point not available

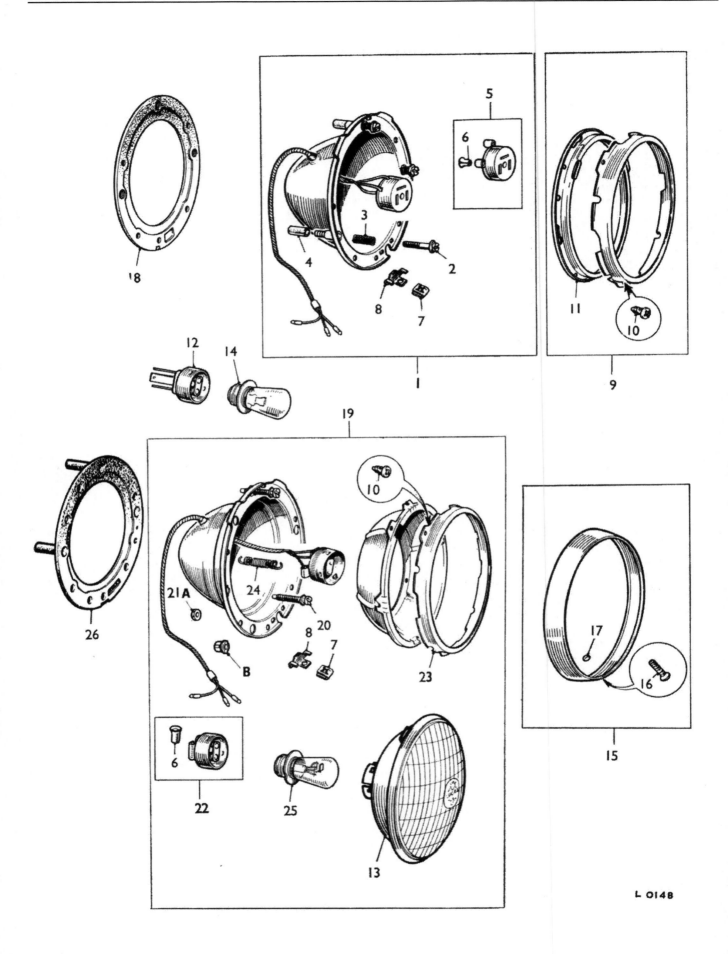

L 0148

DESCRIPTION		Part No.	Illus. No.	Quantity	Change Point	REMARKS
Electrical Equipment—*continued*						
Lamps (Road)—*continued*						
Headlamp complete—right dip —Mk VI		†NSP		2		
Body assembly		†67H 5028	1	2		W.S.E.; use 27H 8206 together with 1 off rim 37H 5530 and 1 off gasket 27H 6967
Screw—trimmer		†17H 5394	2	6		
Spring—trimmer screw		†17H 5231	3	6		
Sleeve—sealing		†27H 5253	4	6		
Adaptor (with cable)		†BHA 4235		2		W.S.E.; use 47H 5126
Adaptor assembly		†47H 5126	5	2		
Sleeve—terminal		†27H 6713	6	6		Part No. change; was 37H 5271 and 7H 5582
Nut—rim fixing screw		†27H 5354	7	2		
Bracket—rim fixing screw		†37H 5190	8	2		
Plate assembly—light unit retaining	**LHD**	†17H 5205	9	2		
Screw—rim	**except**	†PJZ 602	10	6		
Rim—unit seating	**Europe**	†17H 5395	11	2		
Adaptor—conversion	**and**	†17H 5546	12	2		
Unit—light	**N. America**	†17H 5375	13	2		
Bulb		†BFS 355	14	2		
Rim assembly		†37H 5530	15	2		
Screw		†AJA 5081	16	2		
Washer		†21G 9057	17	2		
Gasket (rubber)		†57H 5457	18	2		
Headlamp assembly—right dip —Mk X		†27H 8206	19	2		
Screw—trimmer		†67H 5025	20	4		
Nut—trimmer screw		†27H 6482	21A	4		
Adaptor assembly		†17H 5306	22	2		
Sleeve—terminal		†27H 6713	6	6		
Nut—rim fixing screw		†27H 5354	7	2		
Bracket—rim fixing screw		†37H 5190	8	2		
Plate—light unit retaining		†27H 3338	23	2		
Screw		†PJZ 602	10	6		
Spring—unit seating rim		†67H 5026	24	2		
Unit—light		†17H 5375	13	2		
Bulb		†BFS 415	25	2		
Rim assembly		†37H 5530	15	2		
Screw		†AJA 5081	16	2		
Washer		†21G 9057	17	2		
Gasket (rubber)		†27H 6967	26	2		

See T.I.B. IB 45 F18 for identification of Mk VI and Mk X headlamps

† Revised Information.

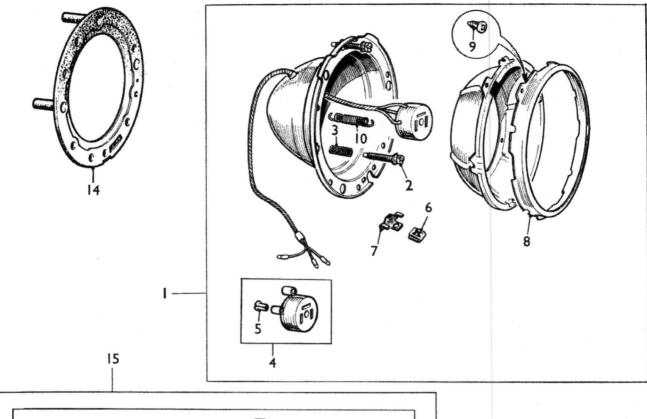

14

15

1

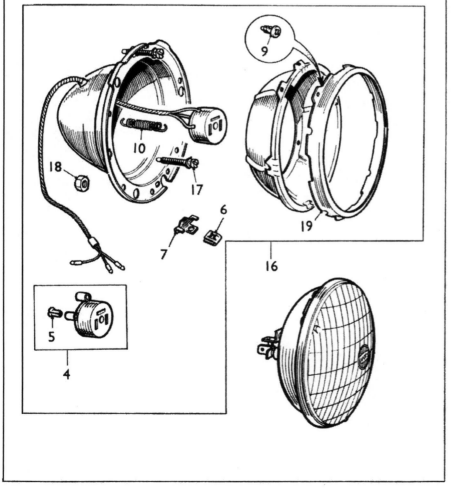

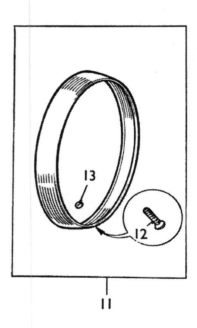

11

L 0147

DESCRIPTION		Part No.	Illus. No.	Quantity	Change Point	REMARKS
Electrical Equipment—*continued*						
Lamps (Road)—*continued*						
Headlamp—less light unit—						
Mk VIII		†NSP		2		
Body assembly		†67H 5029	1	2		W.S.E.; use 27H 8207 together with 1 off rim 57H 5018 and 1 off gasket 57H 5456
Screw—trimmer		†17H 5230	2	4		
Spring—trimmer screw		†17H 5231	3	4		
Adaptor (with cable)		†BHA 4235		2		W.S.E.; use 47H 5126
Adaptor assembly		†47H 5126	4	2	(C) H–BJ7–17551 to 18763	
Sleeve—terminal		†27H 6713	5	6		Part No. change; was 37H 5271 and 7H 5582
Nut—rim fixing screw		†27H 5354	6	2		
Bracket—rim fixing screw		†37H 5190	7	2		
Plate—light unit retaining		†17H 5273	8	2		
Screw		†PJZ 602	9	6		
Spring—unit seating rim		†17H 5277	10	2		
Rim assembly		†57H 5018	11	2		
Screw		†AJA 5081	12	2		
Washer	**North**	†21G 9057	13	2		
Gasket (rubber)	**America**	†57H 5456	14	2		
Headlamp assembly—Mk X		†27H 8207	15	2		
Body assembly		†67H 5024	16	2		W.S.E.; use 27H 8207
Screw—trimmer		†67H 5025	17	4		
Nut—trimmer		†27H 6482	18	4		
Adaptor (with cable)		†BHA 4235		2		W.S.E.; use 47H 5126
Adaptor assembly		†47H 5126	4	2		
Sleeve—terminal		†27H 6713	5	6		Part No. change; was 37H 5271 and 7H 5582
Nut—rim fixing screw		†27H 5354	6	2	(C) H–BJ7–18764 to 25314	
Bracket—rim fixing screw		†37H 5190	7	2	(C) H–BJ8–26135 on	
Plate—light unit retaining		†57H 5292	19	2		
Plate—light unit retaining		†27H 3338	19	2		W.S.E.; use 27H 3338
Screw		†PJZ 602	9	6		
Spring—unit seating rim		†67H 5026	10	2		
Unit—light		†NSP		2		
Rim assembly		†57H 5018	11	2		
Screw		†AJA 5081	12	2		
Washer		†21G 9057	13	2		
Gasket (rubber)		†57H 5456	14	2		
Screw		†RMZ 0310		8		
Washer—spring		†LWZ 203		8		
Nut		†1B 2805		8		

See T.I.B. 1B 45 F18 for identification of Mk VI and Mk X headlamps

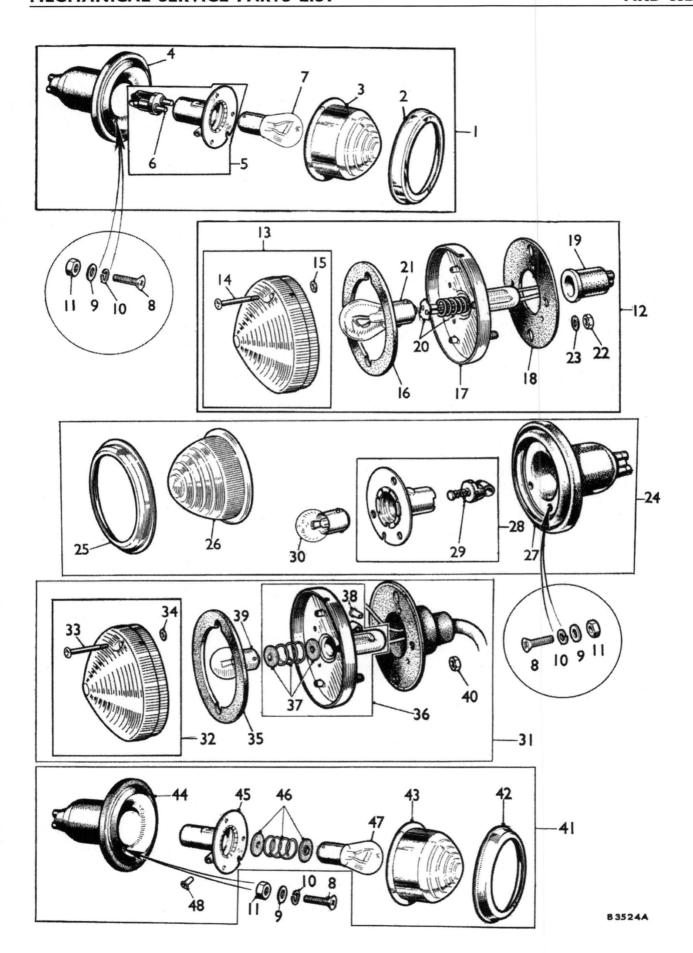

B 3524A

	DESCRIPTION		Part No.	Illus. No.	Quantity	Change Point	REMARKS

Electrical Equipment—*continued*
Lamps (Road)—*continued*

DESCRIPTION		Part No.	Illus. No.	Quantity	Change Point	REMARKS
Lamp assembly—side and flasher		1B 9100	1	2		
Rim		7H 5182	2	4		
Lens		37H 5519	3	2		
Body		37H 5527	4	4		
Holder assembly—bulb		27H 5545	5	4	(C) H–BJ7–17551 to 25314	
Interior—bulbholder		7H 5111	6	4	(C) H–BJ8–25315 to 26704	
Bulb		BFS 380	7	4		
Screw		PMZ 0207	8	12		
Washer—plain	**Except**	PWZ 102	9	12		
Washer—spring	**West**	LWZ 302	10	12		
Nut	**Germany**	CNZ 102	11	12		
Lamp assembly—side and flasher	**and**	BHA 4465	12	2		
Lens assembly	**Sweden**	17H 6763	13	2		
Screw		17H 6764	14	8		
Washer		21G 9057	15	8		
Gasket—lens seating		17H 6765	16	4		
Body		27H 2725	17	4	(C) H–BJ8–26705 to	
Gasket—lamp seating		27H 2724	18	4	(B) H–BJ8–76137	
Grommet—cable entry		57H 5496	19	4		
Interior—bulbholder		37H 5459	20	4		
Bulb		BFS 380	21	4		
Nut		FNZ 103	22	4		
Washer—shakeproof		LWZ 403	23	4		
Lamp assembly—side		47H 5033	24	2		
Rim		7H 5182	25	2	(C) H–BJ7–17551 to 25314	
Lens		37H 5519	26	2	(C) H–BJ8–25315 to	
Body	**West**	37H 5527	27	2	(B) H–BJ8–75201	
Holder assembly—bulb	**Germany**	37H 5528	28	2	West Germany	
Interior—bulb holder	**and**	7H 5202	29	2	(C) H–BJ8–25315 to	
Bulb	**Sweden**	BFS 207	30	2	(B) H–BJ8–76137	
Screw		PMZ 0207	8	6	Sweden	
Washer—plain		PWZ 102	9	6		
Washer—spring		LWZ 302	10	6		
Nut		CNZ 102	11	6		
Lamp assembly—side		BHA 4476	31	2		
Lens assembly		17H 6763	32	2		
Screw		†27H 4678	33	4		W.S.E. use PMP 0218
Screw		†PMP 0218	33	4		
Washer		21G 9057	34	4		
Gasket—lens seating	**Except**	17H 6765	35	2		
Body assembly	**West**	27H 4886	36	2		
Interior—bulbholder	**Germany**	37H 5452	37	2	(B) H–BJ8–76138 on	
Sleeve—terminal		27H 6713	38	2		Part No. change; was 37H 5271
Bulb		BFS 207	39	2		
Nut—lamp to body		†27H 6202	40	2		W.S.E. use FNZ 103 together with 4 off washer LWZ 403
Nut		†FNZ 103		4		Correction; was FNZ 6202
Washer—shakeproof		LWZ 403		4		
Lamp assembly—side		BHA 4495	41	2		
Rim		7H 5182	42	2		
Lens		27H 6241	43	2		
Body		37H 5527	44	4		
Bulbholder		27H 6242	45	2		
Interior—bulbholder	**West**	37H 5452	46	2		
Bulb	**Germany**	†NSP	47	2	(B) H–BJ8–75208 on	Was BMK 1273
Sleeve—terminal		27H 6713	48	2		Part No. change; was 37H 5271
Screw—lamp to body		PMZ 0207	8	6		
Washer—plain		PWZ 102	9	6		
Washer—spring		LWZ 302	10	6		
Nut		CNZ 102	11	6		

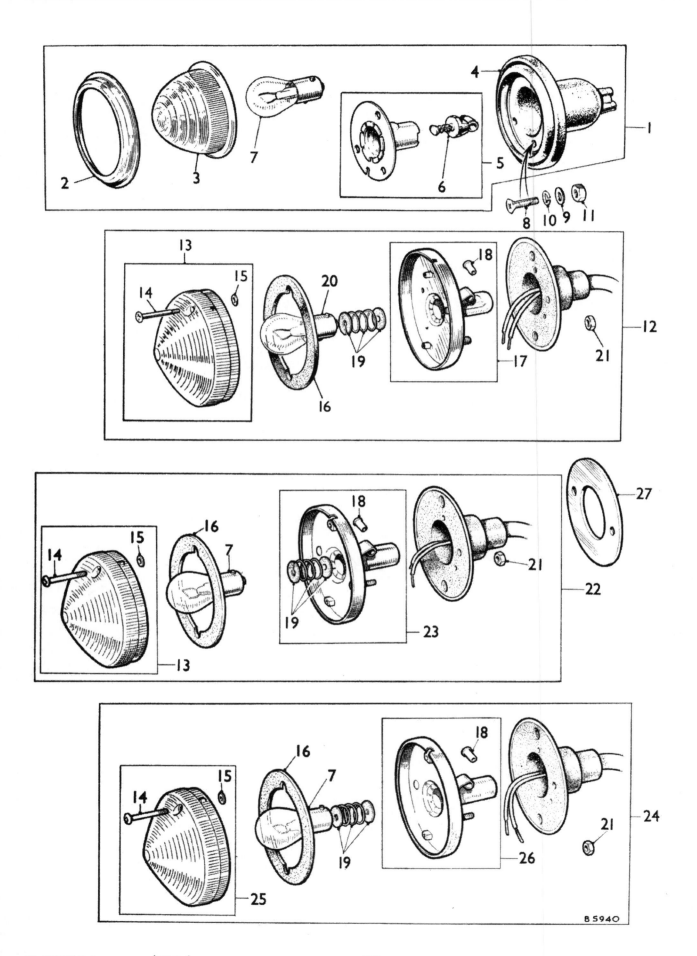

B 5940

	DESCRIPTION	Part No.	Illus. No.	Quantity	Change Point	REMARKS
	Electrical Equipment—*continued*					
	Lamps (Road)—*continued*					
	Lamp assembly—flasher—front	2A 9013	1	2		
	Rim	7H 5182	2	2		
	Lens	37H 5520	3	2	(C) H–BJ7–17551 to 25314	
	Body	West 37H 5527	4	2	(C) H–BJ8–25313 to	
	Holder assembly—bulb	Germany 37H 5528	5	2	(B) H–BJ8–75207	
	Interior—bulb holder	and 7H 5202	6	2	West Germany	
	Bulb	Sweden BFS 382	7	2	(C) H–BJ8–25815 to	
	Screw	PMZ 0207	8	6	(B) H–BJ8–76137	
	Washer—plain	PWZ 102	9	6	Sweden	
	Washer—spring	LWZ 302	10	6		
	Nut	CNZ 102	11	6		
	Lamp assembly—flasher—front	BHZ 4492	12	2		
	Lens assembly—amber	27H 3800	13	2		
	Screw	†27H 4678	14	4		
	Screw	†PMP 0218	14	4		W.S.E. use PMP 0218
	Washer	21G 9057	15	4		
	Gasket—lens seating	West 17H 6765	16	2		
	Body assembly	West 27H 4929	17	2		
	Sleeve—terminal	Germany 27H 6713	18	2	(B) H–BJ8–75208 on	Part No. change; was 37H 5271
	Interior—bulbholder	37H 5452	19	2		
	Bulb	NSP	20	2		Was 13H 2754
	Nut—lamp to body	†27H 6202	21	4		W.S.E. use FWZ 103 together with 4 off washer LWZ 403
	Nut	FNZ 103		4		
	Washer	LWZ 403		4		
	Lamp assembly—flasher—front	BHA 4477	22	2		
	Lens assembly—amber	27H 3800	13	2		
	Screw	†27H 4678	14	4		
	Screw	†PMP 0218	14	4		W.S.E. use PMP 0218
	Washer	21G 9057	15	4		
	Gasket—lens seating	Except 17H 6765	16	2		
	Body assembly	West 27H 4886	23	2		
	Interior—bulbholder	Germany 37H 5452	19	2		
	Sleeve—terminal	and 27H 6713	18	2		Part No. change; was 37H 5271
		Italy				
	Bulb	BFS 382	9	2		
	Nut—lamp to body	†27H 6202	21	4		W.S.E. use FWZ 103 together with 4 off washer LWZ 403
	Nut	FNZ 103		4	(B) H–BJ8–76138 on	
	Washer	LWZ 403		4		
	Lamp assembly—flasher—front	BHA 4493	24	2		
	Lens assembly—white	17H 6763	25	2		
	Screw	†27H 4678	14	4		
	Screw	†PMP 0218	14	4		W.S.E. use PMP 0218
	Washer	21G 9057	15	4		
	Gasket—lens seating	17H 6765	16	2		
	Body assembly	27H 4930	26	2		
	Sleeve—terminal	Italy 27H 6713	18	2		Part No. change; was 37H 5271
	Interior—bulbholder	37H 5452	19	2		
	Bulb	BFS 382	7	2		
	Nut—lamp to body	†27H 6202	21	4		W.S.E. use FWZ 103 together with 4 off washer LWZ 403
	Nut	FNZ 103		4		
	Washer	LWZ 403		4		

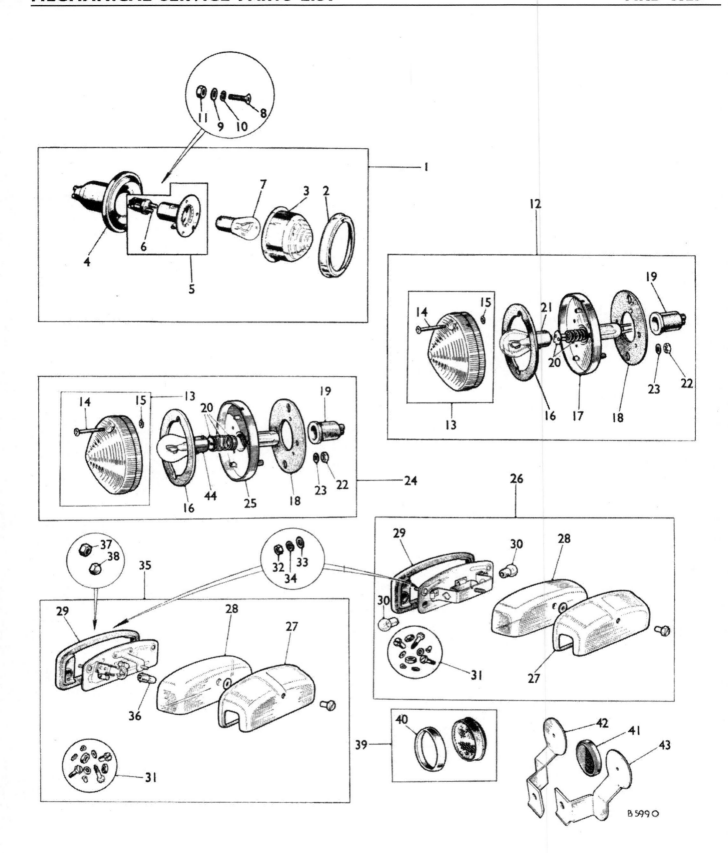

B 5990

DESCRIPTION		Part No.	Illus. No.	Quantity	Change Point	REMARKS

Electrical Equipment—*continued*
Lamps (Road)—*continued*

DESCRIPTION		Part No.	Illus. No.	Quantity	Change Point	REMARKS
Lamp assembly—stop/tail and flasher		1B 9101	1	2		
Rim		7H 5182	2	2		
Lens		37H 5531	3	2		
Body		37H 5527	4	2		
Holder assembly—bulb		27H 5545	5	2	(C) H–BJ7–17551 to 25314	
Interior—bulbholder		7H 5111	6	2	(C) H–BJ8–25315 to 26704	
Bulb		BFS 380	7	2		
Screw		PMZ 0207	8	6		
Washer—plain		PWZ 102	9	6		
Washer—spring	Except	LWZ 302	10	6		
Nut	West	CNZ 102	11	6		
Lamp assembly—stop/tail and flasher	Germany and	BHA 4462	12	2		
Lens assembly	Sweden	17H 6766	13	2		
Screw		17H 6764	14	4		
Washer		21G 9057	15	4		
Gasket—lens seating		17H 6765	16	2		
Body		27H 2725	17	2	(C) H–BJ8–26705 to	
Gasket—lamp seating		27H 2724	18	2	(B) H–BJ8–76137	
Grommet—cable entry		57H 5496	19	2		
Interior—bulbholder		37H 5459	20	2		
Bulb		BFS 380	21	2		
Nut		FNZ 103	22	2		
Washer—shakeproof		LWZ 403	23	2		
Lamp assembly—stop/tail		1B 9101	1	2		
Rim		7H 5182	2	2		
Lens		37H 5531	3	2		
Body	West	37H 5527	4	2	(C) H–BJ7–17551 to 25314	
Holder assembly—bulb	Germany	27H 5545	5	2	(C) H–BJ8–25315 to	
Interior—bulb holder	and	7H 5111	6	2	(B) H–BJ8–75207	
Bulb	Sweden	BFS 380	7	2	West Germany	
Screw		PMZ 0207	8	6	(C) H–BJ8–25315 to	
Washer—plain		PWZ 102	9	6	(B) H–BJ8–76317	
Washer—spring		LWZ 302	10	6	Sweden	
Nut		CNZ 102	11	6		
Lamp assembly—stop/tail		BHA 4462	12	2		
Lens assembly		†17H 6766	13	2		Correction; was 71H 6766
Screw		17H 6764	14	4		
Washer		21G 9057	15	4		
Gasket—lens seating	Except	17H 6765	16	2		
Body	West	27H 2725	17	2	(B) H–BJ8–76138 on	
Gasket—lamp seating	Germany	27H 2724	18	2		
Grommet—cable entry		57H 5496	19	2		
Interior—bulbholder		37H 5459	20	2		
Bulb		BFS 380	21	2		
Nut		FNZ 103	22	2		
Washer—shakeproof		LWZ 403	23	2		
Lamp assembly—stop/tail		BHA 4491	24	2		
Lens assembly		17H 6766	13	2		
Screw		†27H 4678	14	4		
Screw		†PMP 0218	14	4		W.S.E. use PMP 0218
Washer		21G 9057	15	4		
Gasket—lens seating	West	17H 6765	16	2		
Body	Germany	27H 4927	25	2	(B) H–BJ8–75208 on	
Gasket—lamp seating		27H 2724	18	2		
Grommet—cable entry		57H 5496	19	2		
Interior—bulbholder		37H 5459	20	2		
Bulb		NSP	44	2		Was 13H 2755
Nut		AJD 8012 Z	22	2		
Washer—shakeproof		LWZ 403	23	4		

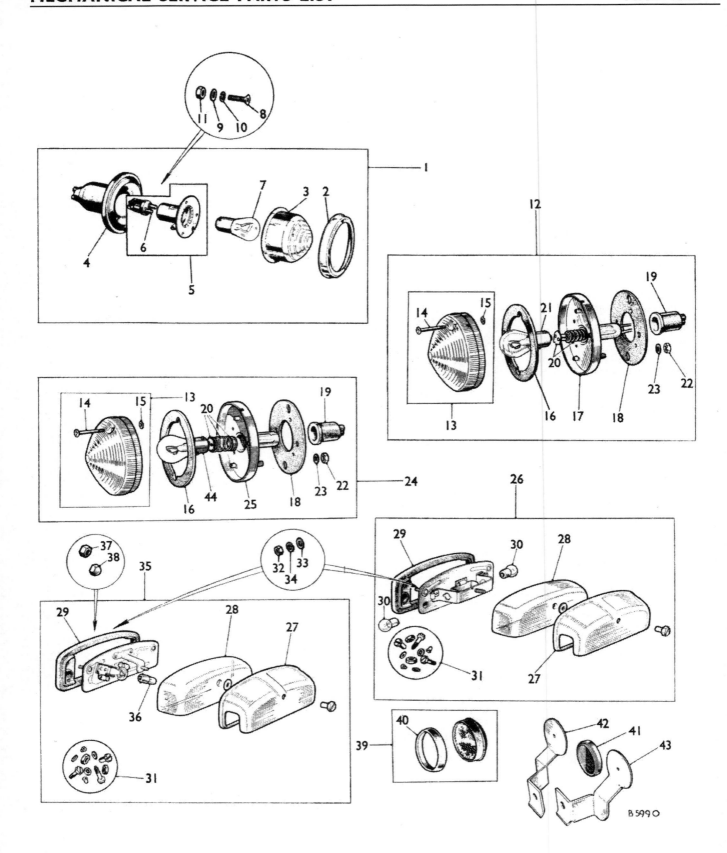

B 5990

DESCRIPTION	Part No.	Illus. No.	Quantity	Exp.	UK	D	Change Point	REMARKS
Electrical Equipment—*continued*								
Lamps (Road)—*continued*								
Lamp assembly—number plate	BHA 4158	26	1	★	★		(C) H–BJ7–17551 to 25814	
Cover	7H 5185	27	1					
Lens	57H 5128	28	1	★	★		(C) H–BJ8–25815 to	
Gasket—lens seating	57H 5868	29	1	★	★		(B) H–BJ8–75207	
Bulb	BFS 989	80	2	★	★	★	West Germany	
Sundry parts	7H 5128	81	1 set				(C) H–BJ8–25815 to	
Nut	AJD 8102 Z	32	2				(B) H–BJ8–76187	
Washer—plain	PWZ 108	88	2				Europe except West	
Washer—spring	LWZ 208	84	2				Germany	
Nut ⎤ N. America	†AJD 8052C	87	2				(C) H–BJ8–25815 on	
Nut—dome ⎦	†6K 9777	88	2				Except Europe	
Lamp assembly—number plate ⎤	BHA 4494	85	2	★			(B) H–BJ8–75208 on	
Cover	7H 5185	27	2				West Germany	
Lens	7H 5121	28	2	★			(B) H–BJ8–76818 on	
Gasket—lens seating **Europe**	57H 5868	29	2	★			Europe except	
Bulb	NSP	86	2	★			West Germany	was 18H 2756
Sundry parts	7H 5128	81	2 sets					
Nut	AJD 8052 C	87	4					
Nut—dome ⎦	6K 9777	88	4					
Reflector assembly ⎤ **Except West Germany**	BHA 4149	89	2				(C) H–BJ7–17551 to 25814	
Rim ⎦ **and Sweden**	AJC 5116	40	2				(C) H–BJ8–25815 to	
							(B) H–BJ8–76187	
Reflector	BHA 4148	41	2				(C) H–BJ7–17551 to 25814	
Bracket—reflector mounting—RH	AHB 8984	42	1				(C) H–BJ8–25815 on	
Bracket—reflector mounting—LH	†AHB 8985	48	1				West Germany and Sweden	Correction; was AHB 8995
							(B) H–BJ8–76188 on Except West Germany and Sweden	

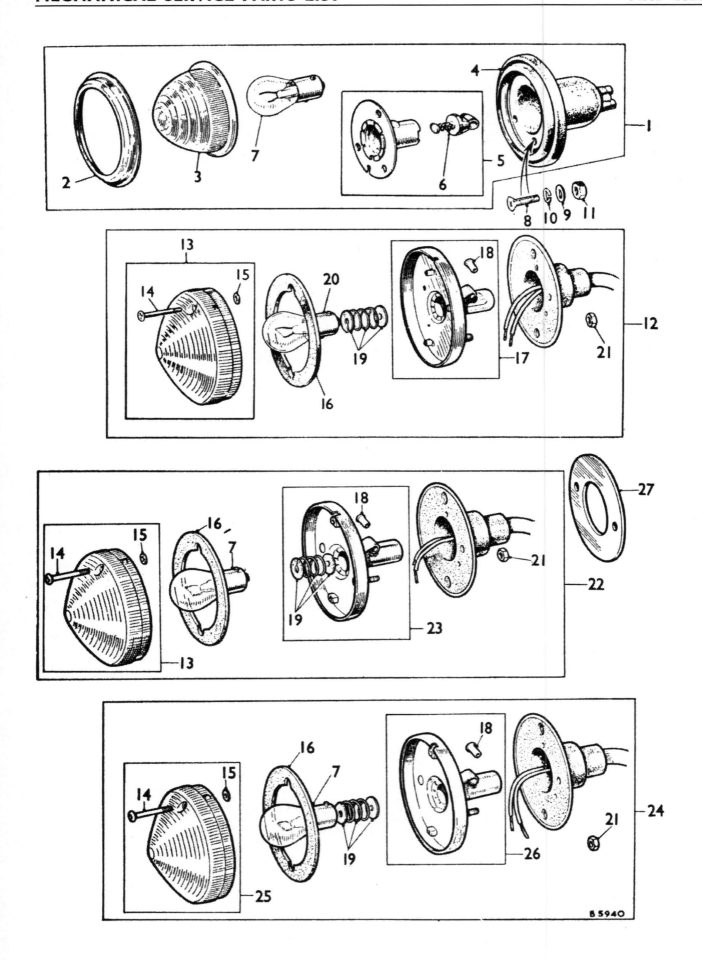

B 5940

	DESCRIPTION		Part No.	Illus. No.	Quantity	Change Point	REMARKS

Electrical Equipment—*continued*
Lamps (Road)—*continued*

DESCRIPTION		Part No.	Illus. No.	Quantity	Change Point	REMARKS
Lamp assembly—flasher—rear		2A 9013	1	2		
Rim		7H 5182	2	2	(C) H—BJ7–17551 to 25314	
Lens		37H 5520	3	2	(C) H–BJ8–25315 to	
Body	**West**	37H 5527	4	2	(B) H–BJ8–75207	
Holder assembly—bulb	**Germany**	37H 5528	5	2	West Germany	
Interior—bulbholder	**and**	7H 5202	6	2		
Bulb	**Sweden**	BFS 382	7	2	(C) H–BJ8–25315 to	
Screw		PMZ 0207	8	6	(B) H–BJ8–76137	
Washer—plain		PWZ 102	9	6	Sweden	
Washer—spring		LWZ 302	10	6		
Nut		CNZ 102	11	6		
Lamp assembly—flasher—rear		BHA 4492	12	2		
Lens assembly		27H 3800	13	2		
Screw		†27H 4678	14	4		W.S.E. use PMP 0218
Screw		†PMP 0218	14	4		
Washer	**West**	21G 9057	15	4		
Gasket—lens seating	**Germany**	17H 6765	16	2		
Body assembly		27H 4929	17	2		
Sleeve—terminal		27H 6713	18	2	(B) H–BJ8–75208 on	Part No. change; was 37H 5271
Interior—bulbholder		37H 5452	19	2		
Bulb		NSP	20	2		Was 13H 2754
Nut—lamp to body		27H 6202	21	4		W.S.E. use FNZ 103 together with 4 off washer LWZ 403
Nut		FNZ 103		4		
Washer—shakeproof		LWZ 403		4		
Lamp assembly—flasher—rear		BHA 4477	22	2		
Lens assembly		27H 3800	13	2		
Screw		†27H 4678	14	4		W.S.E. use PMP 0218
Screw		†PMP 0218	14	4		
Washer		21G 9057	15	4		
Gasket—lens seating		17H 6765	16	2		
Body assembly	**Except**	27H 4886	23	2		
Interior—bulbholder	**West**	37H 5452	19	2	(B) H–BJ8–76138 on	
Sleeve—terminal	**Germany**	27H 6713	18	2		Part No. change; was 37H 5271
Bulb		BFS 382	7	2		
Nut—lamp to body		27H 6202	21	4		W.S.E. use FNZ 103 together with 4 off washer LWZ 403
Nut		FNZ 103		4		
Washer—shakeproof		LWZ 403		4		
Plate—reinforcement—rear flasher lamp aperture		AHB 7136	27	2	(B) H–BJ8–75208 on West Germany (B) H–BJ8–76138 on Except West Germany	

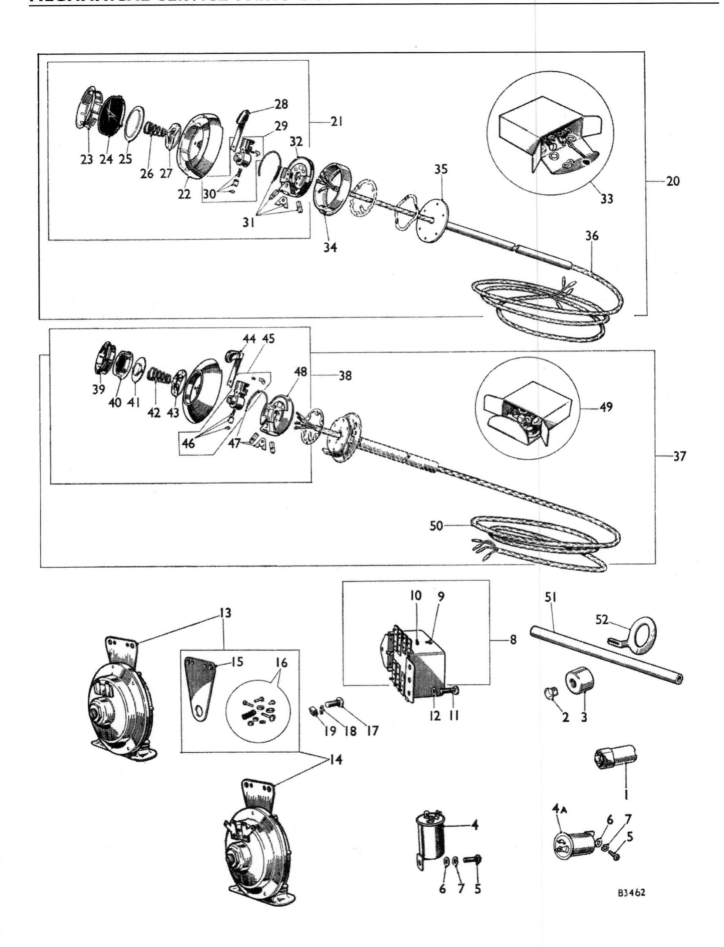

DESCRIPTION	Part No.	Illus. No.	Quantity	Change Point	REMARKS
Electrical Equipment—*continued*					
FLASHER, HORN, AND CONTROLS					
Indicator—flasher warning light	57H 5138	1	1	(C) H–BJ7–17551 to 25314	
Cover and window—flasher warning light	27H 2821	2	2	(C) H–BJ8–25315 on	
Shade—flasher warning light	AJG 5047	3	2		
Unit—flasher	11G 9093	4	1	(C) H–BJ7–17551 to 25314	
	13H 110	4A	1	(C) H–BJ8–25315 on	
				Except West Germany	
				(C) H–BJ8–25315 to	
				(B) H–BJ8–75207	
				West Germany	
West Germany	13H 2639	4A	1	(B) H–BJ8–75208 on	
Screw	PMZ 0408	5	1		
Washer—plain	PWZ 104	6	1	(C) H–BJ7–17551 to 25314	
Washer—spring	LWZ 204	7	1		
Screw	PMZ 0308	5	1		
Washer—plain	PWZ 103	6	1	(C) H–BJ8–25315 on	
Washer—spring	LWZ 203	7	1		
Relay assembly—flasher — Except	3H 1454	8	1		
Screw — West	17H 5594	9	8	(C) H–BJ7–17551 to 25314	
Washer—shakeproof — Germany	27H 1473	10	8	(C) H–BJ8–25315 to	
Screw — and	PMZ 0308	11	3	(B) H–BJ8–76137	
Washer—spring — Sweden	LWZ 203	12	3		
Horn assembly					
High note	BHA 4444	13	1		W.S.E. use BHA 4515
Low note	BHA 4445	14	1	(C) H–BJ7–17551 to 25314	W.S.E. use BHA 4514
High note	BHA 4515	13	1		
Low note	BHA 4514	14	1		
Bracket	57H 5309	14	1		
Sundry parts	57H 5310	16	2 sets		
Horn assembly—high note	13H 2109		1		
Horn assembly—low note	13H 2110		1		
Bracket	57H 5309		2	(C) H–BJ8–25315 on	
Screw	AJD 6257 Z		2		
Washer—shakeproof	LWZ 406		2		
Screw	PMZ 0408	17	4		
Washer—spring	LWZ 204	18	4		
Nut	FNZ 104	19	4	(C) H–BJ7–17551 to 25314	
Horn and direction indicator control assembly	1B 6346	20	1		
Cover assembly—top	47H 5244	21	1		
Moulding	47H 5240	22	1		
Ring—horn-push retaining	47H 5241	23	1		
Horn-push	47H 5245	24	1		
Plate—horn-push contact	47H 5242	25	1		
Spring—horn-push	NSP	26	1		Was 7H 5139
Contact—horn-push	NSP	27	1		Was 7H 5138
Lever—flasher-operating	47H 5243	28	1		Non-adjustable steering
Rotor and plunger assembly—switch	7H 5469	29	1		
Plunger	7H 5142	30	1		
Pawl and spring	7H 5148	31	1 set		
Base—switch	7H 5140	32	1		
Sundry parts	7H 5512	33	1 set		
Ring—striker	7H 5471	34	1		
Tube—stator	7H 5474	35	1		
Cable	47H 5247	36	1		
Horn and direction indicator control assembly	1B 6303	37	1		
Cover assembly—top	47H 5010	38	1		
Ring—horn-push retaining	7H 5468	39	1		
Horn-push	47H 5011	40	1		
Plate—horn-push contact	NSP	41	1		Was AJA 5006
Spring—horn-push	NSP	42	1		Was 7H 5139
Contact—horn-push	NSP	43	1		Was 7H 5138
Lever—flasher-operating	27H 5556	44	1		Adjustable steering Optional extra
Rotor and plunger assembly—switch	7H 5469	45	1		
Plunger	7H 5142	46	1		
Pawl and spring	7H 5143	47	1 set		
Base—switch	27H 5557	48	1		
Sundry parts	7H 5512	49	1 set		
Cable	17H 5259	50	1		
Tune—stator	1B 6226	51	1		
Bracket—indicator strip	2H 2635	52	1		

† Revised Information.

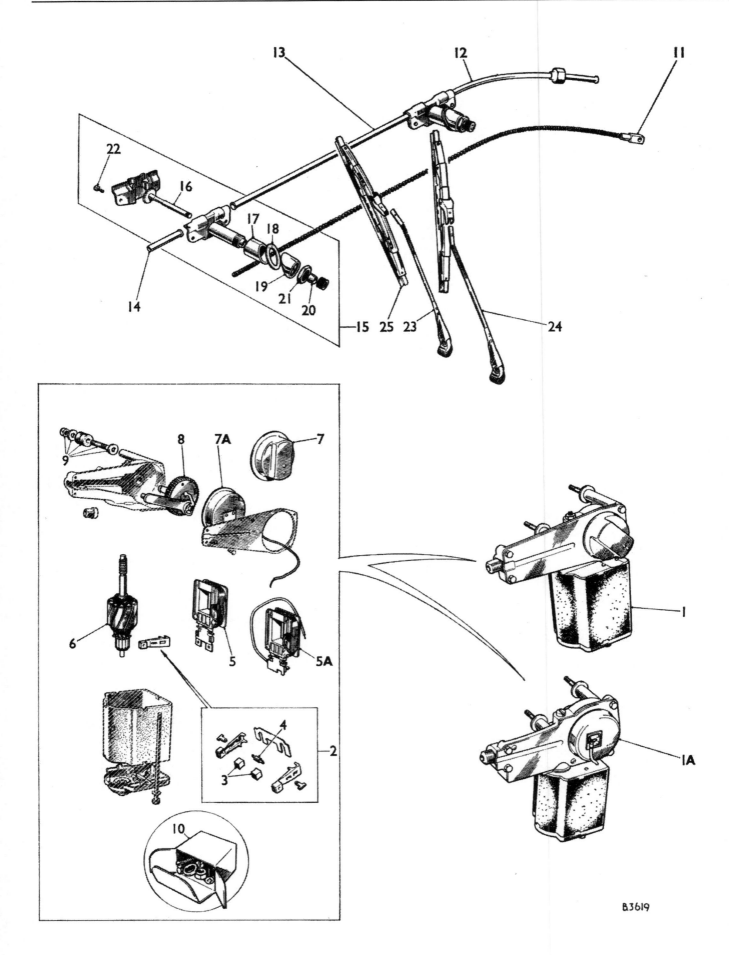

B3619

	DESCRIPTION	Part No.	Illus. No.	Quantity	Change Point	REMARKS

Electrical Equipment—continued

WINDSCREEN WIPERS

DESCRIPTION	Part No.	Illus. No.	Quantity	Change Point	REMARKS
Motor—windscreen wiper A to F*	†37H 5308	1	1		Not available; use 17H 5475
Brush gear	17H 5396	2	1		
Brush	7H 5130	3	1 set		
Spring—brush	27H 5309	4	1 set		
Coil—field A to E*	†37H 5288	5	1		
Coil—field F*	†17H 9391	5A	1		
Armature	17H 5255	6	1		
Switch—parking A to D*	†17H 5442	7	1		
Switch—parking E–F*	†47H 5316	7A	1		
Shaft and gear A to D*	†37H 5437	8	1		
Shaft and gear E–F*	†27H 2568	8	1		
Stud—fixing	17H 5431	9	3 sets		
Sundry parts	17H 5441	10	1 set	(C) H–BJ7–17551 to	
Motor—windscreen wiper A to F, H*	17H 5475	1	1	H–BJ7–60791	
Brush gear	17H 5396	2	1		
Brush	7H 5130	3	1 set		
Spring—brush	27H 5309	4	1 set		
Coil—field A to F*	†37H 5288	5	1		
Coil—field H*	†17H 9391	5A	1		
Armature	17H 5255	6	1		
Switch—parking A to E*	†17H 5442	7	1		
Switch—parking F–H*	†47H 5316	7A	1		
Shaft and gear A to E*	†37H 5437	8	1		
Shaft and gear F–H*	†27H 2568	8	1		
Stud—fixing	17H 5431	9	3 sets		
Sundry parts	17H 5441	10	1 set		
Motor—windscreen wiper	57H 5554	1A	1		Correction; was 37H 5554
Brush gear	17H 5396	2	1		
Brush	7H 5130	3	1 set		
Spring—brush	27H 5309	4	1 set		
Coil—field	57H 5294	5A	1	(B) H–BJ7–60792 to	
Armature	27H 5374	6	1	(C) H–BJ7–25314	
Switch—parking	57H 5559	7A	1	(C) H–BJ8–25315 on	
Shaft and gear	57H 5586	8	1		
Stud—fixing	17H 5431	9	3 sets		
Sundry parts	17H 5441	10	1 set		
Crosshead and rack	37H 5169	11	1		
Casings—outer					
Motor to wheelbox	14B 5589	12	1	(C) H–BJ7–17551 to (B) H–BJ7–60791	
Motor to wheelbox	BHA 4414	12	1	(B) H–BJ7–60792 to (C) H–BJ7–25314 (C) H–BJ8–25315 on	
Wheelbox to wheelbox	14B 5598	13	1		
Wheelbox to extension	14G 3722	14	1		
Wheelbox	BHA 4151	15	2		
Spindle and gear	AJH 5079	16	2		
Bush—rear	AHH 5414	17	2		
Washer (rubber)	ADC 560	18	2		
Bush—front	ADB 826	19	2		
Tube—spindle (rubber)	ANK 3458	20	2		
Nut	ANK 3459	21	2		
Screw—cover	AJD 3202 Z	22	4		
Arm—wiper **RHD**	BHA 4351	23	1		
Arm—wiper **LHD**	BHA 4354	24	1		
Blade—wiper	13H 469	25	2		

* Reference must always be made to the suffix letter of the manufacturers Part No. stamped on the motor casing to ensure ordering of correct component parts. Example: field coil 37H 5288 is for motor suffix letters A to E.

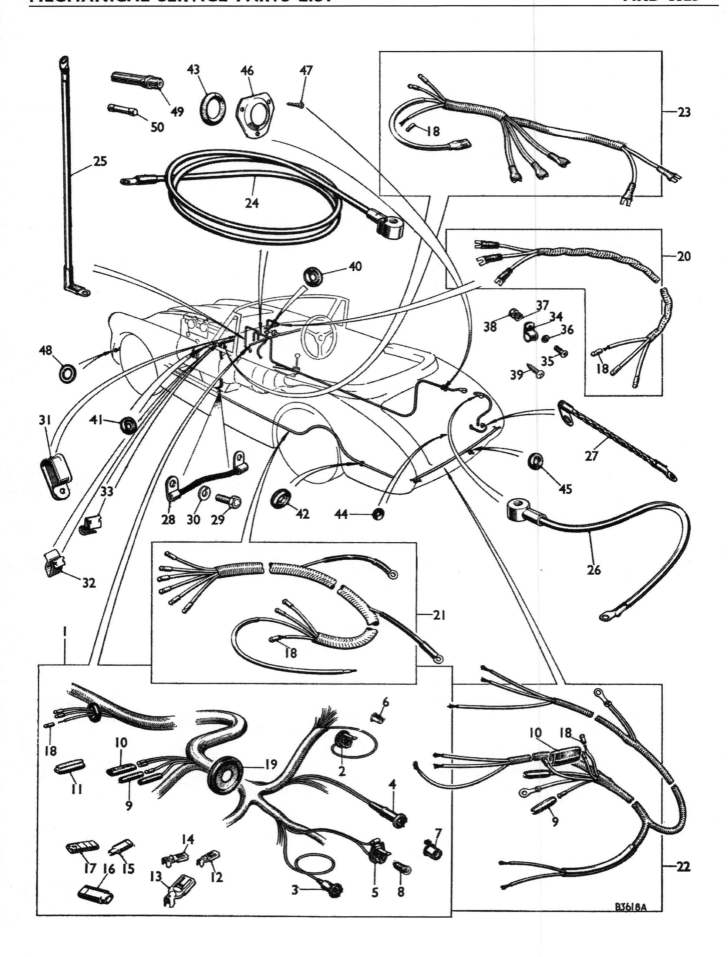

B3618A

	DESCRIPTION	Part No.	Illus. No.	Quantity	Change Point	REMARKS

Electrical Equipment—*continued*

WIRING CABLES—CONNECTIONS— BULB HOLDERS

Description	Part No.	Illus. No.	Quantity	Change Point	Remarks
Cable—main harness—**Except West Germany and Sweden**	†AHB 8707	1	1	(C) H–BJ7–17551 to 25314	
Except West Germany and Sweden	†AHB 6413	1	1	(C) H–BJ8–25315 to (B) H–BJ8–76137	
West Germany and Sweden	†AHB 9142	1	1	(C) H–BJ7–17551 to 25314	
West Germany and Sweden	†AHB 6918	1	1	(C) H–BJ8–23135 to (B) H–BJ8–75207 West Germany (C) H–BJ8–25315 to (B) H–BJ8–76137 Sweden	
	†AHB 7120		1	(B) H–BJ8–75208 on West Germany (B) H–BJ8–76138 on Except West Germany	
Holder—bulb					
Combined instrument and fuel gauge	3H 914	2	2	†(C) H–BJ7–17551 to 25314	
Speedometer, tachometer and main beam warning light	37H 5181	3	3		
Ignition warning light	47H 5166	4	1		
Flasher warning light	2H 4978	5	1		
Combined instrument and fuel gauge	21G 9090	6	2	†(C) H–BJ8–25315 on	
Speedometer and tachometer	37H 5181	3	2		
Main beam and ignition warning	57H 5445	7	2		
Flasher warning light	47H 5166	4	2		
Bulb	BFS 987	8	7/8		†Quantity increased at (C) H–BJ8–25315
Connector					
Snap—single	2H 3406	9	A/R		
Snap—double	2H 2617	10	A/R		
Snap—treble	2H 4992	11	A/R		
Socket—single—17·5 amp	47H 5496	12	A/R	†(C) H–BJ8–25315 on	
Socket—single—35 amp	47H 5419	13	A/R		
Socket—double—17·5 amp	47H 5499	14	A/R		
Insulator—socket connector					
Single—17·5 amp	5L 286	15	A/R	†(C) H–BJ8–25315 on	
Single—35 amp	5L 289	16	A/R		
Double—17·5 amp	5L 287	17	A/R		
Nipple—snap connector	2H 2704	18	A/R		
Grommet	2H 2065	19	1		
Cable—dipper switch harness	†1B 2847	20	1	(C) H–BJ7–17551 to 25314	
Cable—dipper switch harness	†AHB 6414	20	1	(C) H–BJ8–25315 on	
Nipple—snap connector	2H 2704	18	A/R		
Cable—chassis harness **Except West Germany and Sweden**	AHB 9549	21	1		
West Germany and Sweden	†AHB 9551	21	1	(C) H–BJ7–17551 to 25314	
West Germany and Sweden	†AHB 9549	21	1	(C) H–BJ8–25315 to (B) H–BJ8–75207 West Germany (C) H–BJ8–25315 to (B) H–BJ8–76137 Sweden	
	†AHB 7118		1	(B) H–BJ8–75208 on West Germany (B) H–BJ8–76138 on Except West Germany	
Nipple—snap connector	2H 2704	18	A/R		

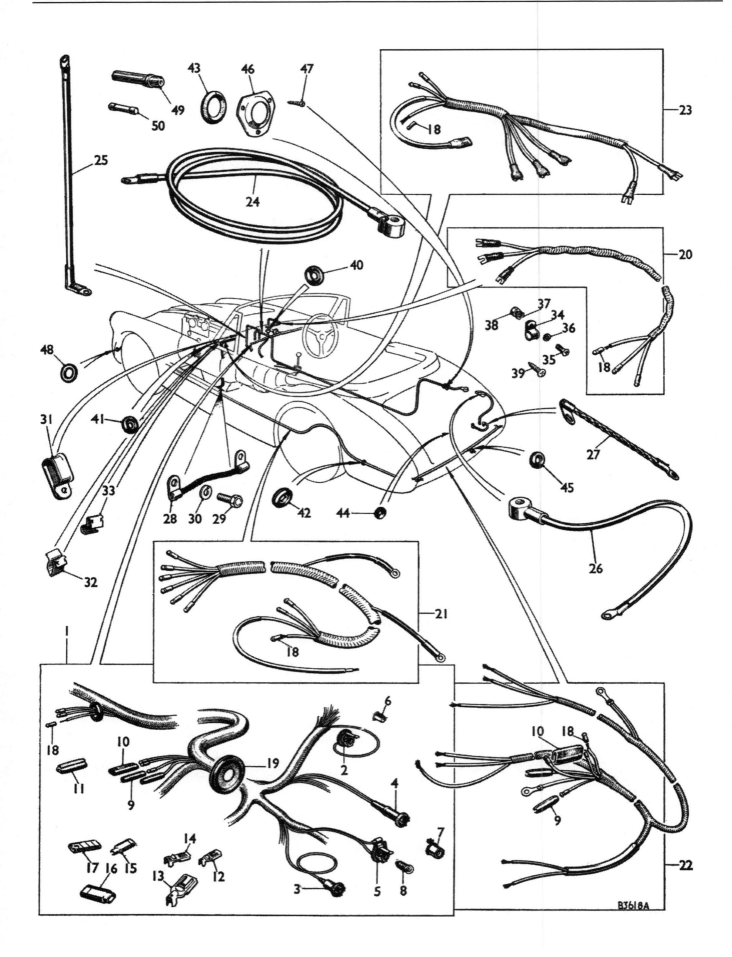

B3618A

DESCRIPTION	Part No.	Illus. No.	Quantity	Change Point	REMARKS
Electrical Equipment—*continued* **Wiring Cables—Connections—Bulb Holders**—*continued*					
Cable—boot harness....**Except West Germany and Sweden**	†1B 2796	22	1	(C) H–BJ7–17551 to 25814 (C) H–BJ8–25815 to 27604	
Except West Germany and Sweden	AHB 7033	22	1	(C) H–BJ8–27605 on	
West Germany and Sweden	†AHB 9145	22	1	(C) H–BJ8–25815 to (B) H–BJ8–75207 West Germany (C) H–BJ8–25815 to (B) H–BJ8–76137 Sweden	
	†AHB 7119		1	(B) H–BJ8–75208 on West Germany (B) H–BJ8–76138 on Except West Germany	
Connector—snap—single	2H 3406	9	A/R		
Connector—snap—double	2H 2617	10	A/R		
Nipple—snap connector	2H 2704	18	A/R		
Cable—number-plate lamp harness	†AHB 7117		1	(B) H–BJ8–75208 on West Germany (B) H–BJ8–76138 on Except West Germany	
Nipple—snap connector	†2H 2704		A/R		
Cable—overdrive harness	AHB 8708	23	1	(C) H–BJ7–17551 to 25814	
Cable—overdrive harness	AHB 6415	23	1	(C) H–BJ8–25815 on	
Cable					
Battery negative to starter solenoid switch	1B 9080	24	1		
Solenoid switch to starter	1B 2801	25	1		
Battery positive to master switch	27H 5578	26	1		
Master switch to earth	1B 9078	27	1		
Engine earth	2H 6167	28	1		
Screw	HZS 0604	29	2		
Washer—spring	LWZ 206	30	2		
Clip					
Main and dipper switch harness to dash	11K 9095	31	1		
Edge—headlamp cable to crossbrace	11K 9181	32	2		
Stator tube cable to crossbrace	ADA 2657	33	1		
Number-plate lamp cable to bracket	†BHA 4225		2	(B) H–BJ8–75208 on West Germany (B) H–BJ8–76138 on Except West Germany	
$\frac{3}{16}$" (4·76 mm) cable dia. × $\frac{11}{32}$" (8·73 mm) fixing hole dia.	PCR 0311	34	1		
$\frac{1}{4}$" (6·35 mm) cable dia. × $\frac{7}{32}$" (5·56 mm) fixing hole dia.	PCR 0407	34	6		
$\frac{5}{16}$" (7·98 mm) cable dia. × $\frac{5}{32}$" (4·00 mm) fixing hole dia.	†PCR 0505	34	4		
$\frac{5}{16}$" (7·98 mm) cable dia. × $\frac{7}{32}$" (5·56 mm) fixing hole dia.	PCR 0507	34	6		
$\frac{5}{16}$" (7·98 mm) cable dia. × $\frac{9}{32}$" (7·14 mm) fixing hole dia.	PCR 0509	34	1		
$\frac{3}{8}$" (9·52 mm) cable dia. × $\frac{7}{32}$" (5·56 mm) fixing hole dia.	PCR 0607	34	9		
$\frac{7}{16}$" (11·11 mm) cable dia. × $\frac{7}{32}$" (5·56 mm) fixing hole dia.	PCR 0707	34	18		
$\frac{7}{16}$" (11·11 mm) cable dia. × $\frac{9}{32}$" (7·14 mm) fixing hole dia.	PCR 0709	34	1		
Screw	PMZ 0308	35	12		
Washer—plain	PWZ 103	36	1		
Washer—spring	LWZ 203	37	12		
Nut	FNZ 103	38	9		
Screw	PTZ 1004	39	A/R		

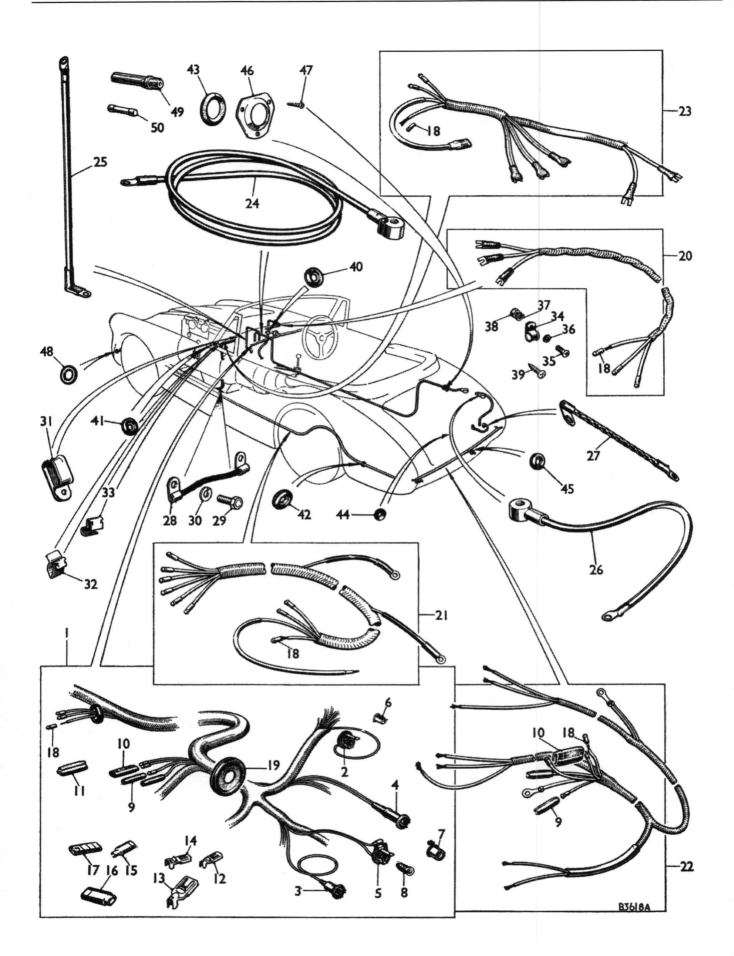

B3618A

DESCRIPTION	Part No.	Illus. No.	Quantity	Change Point	REMARKS
Electrical Equipment—*continued*					
Wiring Cables—Connections—Bulb Holders— *continued*					
Grommet					
Dipper switch harness	RFN 303	40	2		
Chassis harness through wiring plate on dash	RFN 106	41	1		
Chassis harness through boot vertical panel	RFN 405	42	1		
Battery negative cable	BHA 4281	43	2		
Tank unit cable	3F 90	44	1		
Number-plate lamp cable	8H 2144	45	1		
Cap—retaining—battery negative cable grommet	AAA 1891	46	2		
Screw	PTZ 808	47	6		
Ring—sidelamp cables (rubber)	2H 35	48	2	(C) H–BJ7–17551 to 25314	
				(C) H–BJ8–25315 to 26704	
Holder—fuse	**Except** †27H 3588	49	1	(C) H–BJ8–85964 on	
Fuse (10 amp)	**Germany** †27H 5903	50	1		

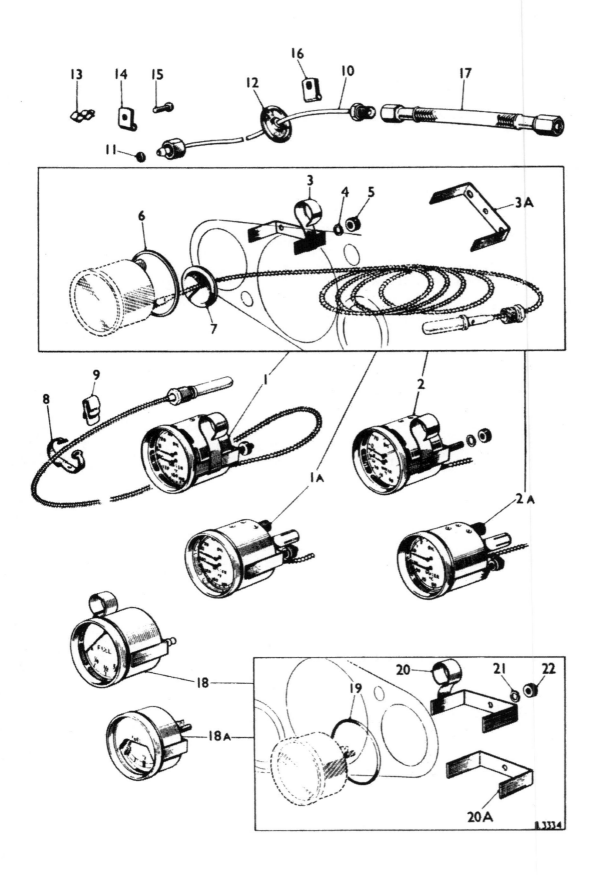

	DESCRIPTION	Part No.	Illus. No.	Quantity	Change Point	REMARKS

INSTRUMENTS

INSTRUMENTS

Gauge—oil pressure and radiator thermometer

Description	Part No.	Illus. No.	Quantity	Change Point	Remarks
Fahrenheit	†BHA 4113	1	1	(C) H–BJ7–17551 to 25314	
Fahrenheit	†BHA 4433	1A	1	(C) H–BJ8–25315 on	
Centigrade	†BHA 4252	2	1	(C) H–BJ7–17551 to 25314	
Centigrade	†BHA 4434	2A	1	(C) H–BJ8–25315 on	
Strap—fixing	†27H 992	3	1	(C) H–BJ7–17551 to 25314	
Strap—fixing	†NSP	3A	1	(C) H–BJ8–25315 on	Was 17H 1676
Washer—spring	LWZ 302	4	2		
Nut—thumb	17H 932	5	2		
Ring (rubber)	†17H 1642	6	1	(C) H–BJ7–17551 to 25314	
Ring (rubber)	†AJH 5184	6	1	(C) H–BJ8–25315 on	
Grommet—capillary tube through dash	3H 2615	7	1		
Strap—tube to breather pipe	ACH 8979	8	1		
Cup—tube	BHA 4081	9	2		
Pipe—oil gauge					
RHD	†11B 2188	10	1	(C) H–BJ7–17551 to 25314	
RHD	†AHB 6895	10	1	(C) H–BJ8–25315 on	
LHD	11B 2186	10	1		
Washer—pipe to gauge	2K 4936	11	1		
Grommet	RFN 403	12	1		
Clip—pipe RHD	6K 35	13	2		
Clip—pipe	2K 5215	14	1		
Screw	PMZ 0307	15	1		
Clip	PCR 0307	16	1		
Hose—flexible	8G 637	17	1		
Gauge—fuel	†1B 9061	18	1	(C) H–BJ7–17551 to 25314	
Gauge—fuel	†BHA 4432	18A	1	(C) H–BJ8–25315 on	
Ring (rubber)	17H 1642	19	1		
Strap—fixing	†17H 1822	20	1	(C) H–BJ7–17551 to 25314	
Strap—fixing	NSP	20A	1	(C) H–BJ8–25315 on	Was 17H 9437
Washer—spring	LWZ 302	21	1		
Nut—thumb	17H 932	22	1		

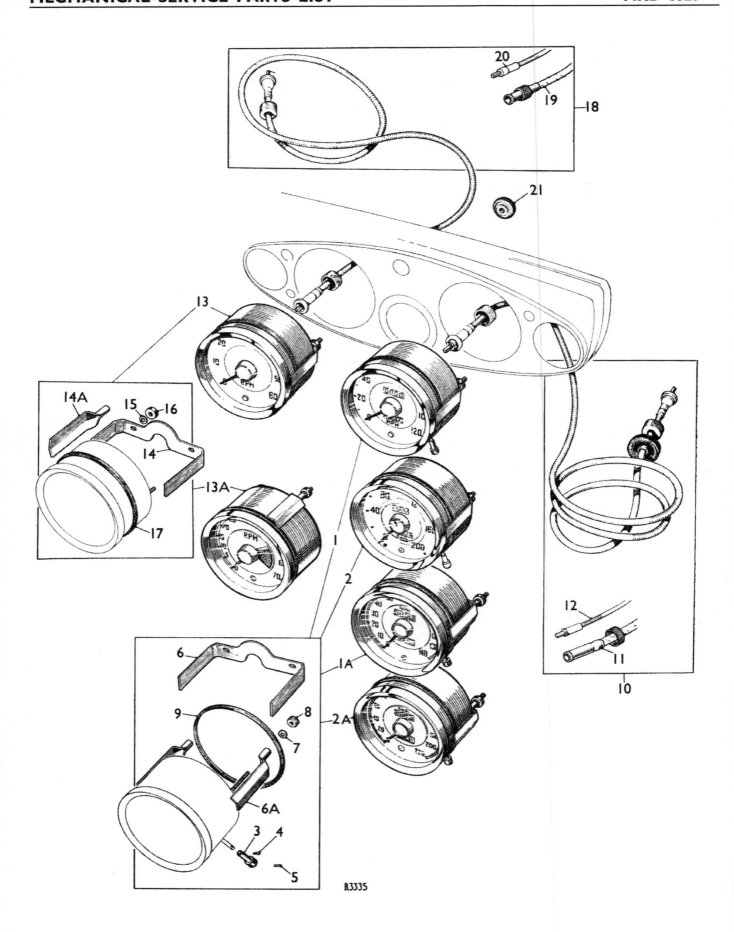

B.3335

	DESCRIPTION	Part No.	Illus. No.	Quantity	Change Point	REMARKS
Instruments—*continued*						
Speedometer						
	MPH (SN6155/19)	BHA 4124	1	1	(C) H–BJ7–17551 to 25314	Final drive ratio 3·545:1
	KPH (SN6155/25)	BHA 4223	2	1		
	MPH (SN6155/21)	BHA 4126	1	1		Required when overdrive is fitted } Final drive ratio 3·909:1
	KPH (SN6155/26)	BHA 4224	2	1		
	MPH (SN6125/20)	BHA 4427	1A	1	(C) H–BJ8–25315 on	Final drive ratio 3·545:1
	KPH (SN6125/21)	BHA 4428	2A	1		
	MPH (SN6125/22)	BHA 4429	1A	1		Required when overdrive is fitted } Final drive ratio 3·909:1
	KPH (SN6125/23)	BHA 4430	3A	1		
Knob—trip return		37H 614	3	1		
Screw—knob		17H 1658	4	1	(C) H–BJ7–17551 to 25314	
Dowel—knob		17H 3745	5	1	(C) H–BJ8–25315 on	
Strap—fixing		AJH 5176	6	1	(C) H–BJ7–17551 to 25314	
Strap—fixing		17H 1662	6A	2	(C) H–BJ8–25315 on	
Washer—shakeproof		2K 1369	7	2		
Nut—thumb		17H 1304	8	2		
Ring (rubber)		AJH 5178	9	1		
Cable—speedometer—3′ 6″ (107 cm)		BHA 4294	10	1		
Cable—outer		†37H 1206	11	1		W.S.E.; use BHA 4294
Cable—inner		37H 1204	12	1		
Cable—speedometer—4′ 3″ (130 cm)		†BHA 4293	10	1		Required when over-drive is fitted
Cable—outer		†37H 1207	11	1		W.S.E.; use BHA 4293
Cable—inner		†17H 1061	12	1		
Tachometer		1B 9188	13	1	(C) H–BJ7–17551 to 25314	
Tachometer—electrical		BHA 4431	13A	1	(C) H–BJ8–25315 on	
Strap—fixing		AJH 5176	14	1	(C) H–BJ7–17551 to 25314	
Strap—fixing		17H 1662	14A	2	(C) H–BJ8–25315 on	
Washer—shakeproof		2K 1369	15	2		
Nut—thumb		17H 1304	16	2		
Ring (rubber)		AJH 5178	17	1		
Cable—tachometer—2′ 9″ (84 cm) RHD		1B 9140	18	1		
Cable—outer		27H 984	19	1		
Cable—inner		27H 985	20	1		
Cable—tachometer—4′ 0″ (122 cm) LHD		1B 9141	18	1	†(C) H–BJ7–17551 to 25314	
Cable—outer		†17H 1343	19	1		W.S.E.; use 1B 9141
Cable—inner		17H 630	20	1		
Grommet		RFN 405	21	1		

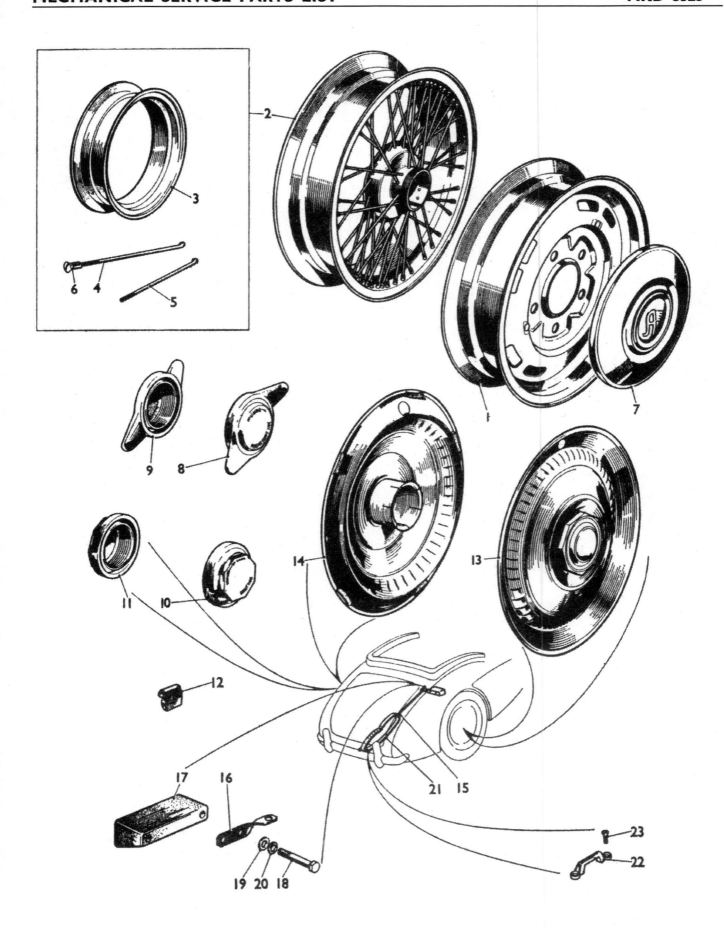

	DESCRIPTION	Part No.	Illus. No.	Quantity	Change Point	REMARKS

WHEELS

			Page	Plate
†CAPS—HUB	... ...		MP 1-1	P 1
†DISCS—LOUVRED	... ...		MP 1-1	P 1
†SPARE WHEEL FIXINGS	... ...		MP 1-1	P 1
†WEIGHTS—WHEEL BALANCE	... ...		MP 1-1	P 1
†WHEELS	... ...		MP 1-1	P 1

ROAD WHEELS

Description	Part No.	Illus. No.	Quantity	Change Point	Remarks
Wheel—disc	1B 8057	1	5		
Wheel—wire	1B 8048	2	5		
Rim	7H 1804	3	5		
Spoke—long	7H 1805	4	80	(C) H–BJ7–17551 to 24366	
Spoke—short	7H 1806	5	160		
Nipple—spoke	7H 1709	6	240		Optional extra
Wheel—wire	AHH 8001	2	5		
Spoke—long	17H 8619	4	100	(C) H–BJ7–24867 to 25314	
Spoke—short	17H 8620	5	200	(C) H–BJ8–25315 on	
Nipple—spoke	7H 1709	6	800		
Cap—hub					
Disc wheel	†1G 8084	7	4		
Wire wheel—RH	†AHH 7317	8	2	(C) H–BJ7–17551 to 25314	
Wire wheel—LH	†AHH 7318	9	2	(C) H–BJ8–25315 to 26704	
Wire wheel—RH	†AHA 7373	8	2	(C) H–BJ8–26705 on	
Wire wheel—LH	†AHA 7374	9	2		
Wire wheel—RH	†AHH 7315	10	2	(C) H–BJ7–17551 to 25314	
Wire wheel—LH	†AHH 7316	11	2	(C) H–BJ8–25315 to 26704	
Wire wheel—RH (Except UK)	†AHA 7375	10	2	(C) H–BJ8–26705 on	
Wire wheel—LH	†AHA 7376	11	2		
Weight—wheel balance					
½ oz (14·17 gm)	†1B 8036	12	A/R		W.S.E.; use AKF 1446
½ oz (14·17 gm)	†AKF 1446	12	A/R		
1 oz (28·35 gm)	†1B 8037	12	A/R		W.S.E.; use AKF 1447
1 oz (28·35 gm)	†AKF 1447	12	A/R		
1½ oz (42·52 gm)	†1B 8038	12	A/R		W.S.E.; use AKF 1448
1½ oz (42·52 gm)	†AKF 1448	12	A/R		
2 oz (56·70 gm)	†1B 8039	12	A/R		W.S.E.; use AKF 1449
2 oz (56·70 gm)	†AKF 1449	12	A/R		
2½ oz (70·87 gm)	†1B 8040	12	A/R		W.S.E.; use AKF 1450
2½ oz (70·37 gm)	†AKF 1450	12	A/R		
3 oz (85·05 gm)	†1B 8041	12	A/R		W.S.E.; use AKF 1451
3 oz (85·05 gm)	†AKF 1451	12	A/R		
Disc—louvred—disc wheel—RH	BHA 4167	13	2		Optional extra
Disc—louvred—disc wheel—LH	BHA 4168	14	2		
Rod—retaining—spare wheel	14B 6756	15	1		
Bracket—rod	14B 6757	16	1		
Block—spare wheel	4B 3257	17	2		
Bolt	HBZ 0422	18	4		
Washer—plain	PWZ 104	19	4		
Washer—spring	LWZ 204	20	4		
Strap—securing—spare wheel	†14B 6771	21	1		W.S.E.; use AHB 7187
Strap—securing—spare wheel	†AHB 7187	21	1		
Staple—breeching	2K 9579	22	1		
Screw	RMP 0310	23	2		

B.6947

	DESCRIPTION	Part No.	Illus. No.	Quantity	Change Point	REMARKS

TOOLS

TOOLS

Description	Part No.	Illus. No.	Quantity	Change Point	Remarks
Bag—tool	AHB 8983	1	1		
Spanner—box—sparking plug	1B 8995	2	1		
Tommy-bar—box spanner	ACA 5216	3	1		
Brace—wheel	1B 8997	4	1		
Lever—hub cap removal	†11H 1051	5	1		W.S.E. use 11H 1686 } Disc wheels
Lever—hub cap removal	†11H 1686	5	1		
Hammer—hub cap	88G 329	6	1		Part No. change; was 11B 5166 } Wire wheels
Spanner—hub cap	**Not UK** AHH 5839	7	1		
Jack	AHH 5986	8	1		
Tommy-bar—jack	AHH 5987	9	1		
Strap—jack securing	AAA 4258	10	1		W.S.E. use AHA 5217
Strap—jack securing	AHA 5217	10	1		

**© Copyright Austin Motor Company Limited 1969
and Brooklands Books Limited 2014**

This book is published by Brooklands Books Limited and based upon text and
illustrations protected by copyright and published in 1969 by
Austin Motor Company Limited and may not be reproduced
transmitted or copied by any means without the prior written permission
of British Motor Corporation Limited and Brooklands Books Limited.

Brooklands Books Ltd., PO Box 904, Amersham, Bucks,
HP6 9JA, England   www.brooklandsbooks.com

Part No. AKD 3523

S.U. CARBURETTER SERVICE PARTS LIST

	Model Application	Specification No.	Type	Section
AUSTIN-HEALEY	3000 Mark II (Series BJ7) ...	AUC 981	HS6	SK
	3000 Mark III (Series BJ8) ...	AUD 124	HD8	SG

CARBURETTER THROTTLE SIZES

Type	Throttle Diameter
HS6	$1\frac{3}{4}''$ (4·44 cm)
HS8	$2''$ (5·08 cm)

CARBURETTER PISTON SPRING IDENTIFICATION

Paint Colour on End Coil	Load at Length		Part No.
Blue	$2\frac{1}{2}$ oz (70·9 gm)	$2\frac{5}{8}''$ (6·67 cm)	AUC 4587
Red	$4\frac{1}{2}$ oz (127·6 gm)	$2\frac{5}{8}''$ (6·67 cm)	AUC 4387
Yellow	8 oz (226·8 gm)	$2\frac{3}{4}''$ (6·98 cm)	AUC 1167
Green	12 oz (340·2 gm)	$3''$ (7·62 cm)	AUC 1170
Red and Green	$11\frac{1}{4}$ oz (318·9 gm)	$3\frac{7}{8}''$ (9·84 cm)	AUC 4826
Red and Light Blue	18 oz (510·3 gm)	$3\frac{7}{8}''$ (9·84 cm)	AUC 4818

CARBURETTER JET NEEDLES

On most carburetter specifications that appear in this Service Parts List the rich, standard, and weak jet needles have been listed. In some cases only the rich or weak needles have been listed together with the standard jet needle. The standard jet needle is fitted to all new S.U. carburetter assemblies and installations.

When ordering it is essential to quote the needle code letters and/or numbers together with the appropriate part number.

Example :   **Needle—jet**
Rich (RH)..AUD 1291
Standard (OA6) ....AUD 1276
Weak (OA7) ....AUD 1277

Extract from Part No. AKD 5036

B.M.C. SERVICE LIMITED
COWLEY · OXFORD · ENGLAND

Telephone —	—	—	—	—	Oxford 77777
Telex —	—	—	BMC Serv Oxford 83145 and 83146
Telegrams —	—	—	BMC Serv Telex, Oxford
Cables —	—	—	BMC Serv Telex Oxford, England
Codes —	—	Bentley's, Bentley's Second Phrase, A.B.C. (5th and 6th Editions), Western Union and Private

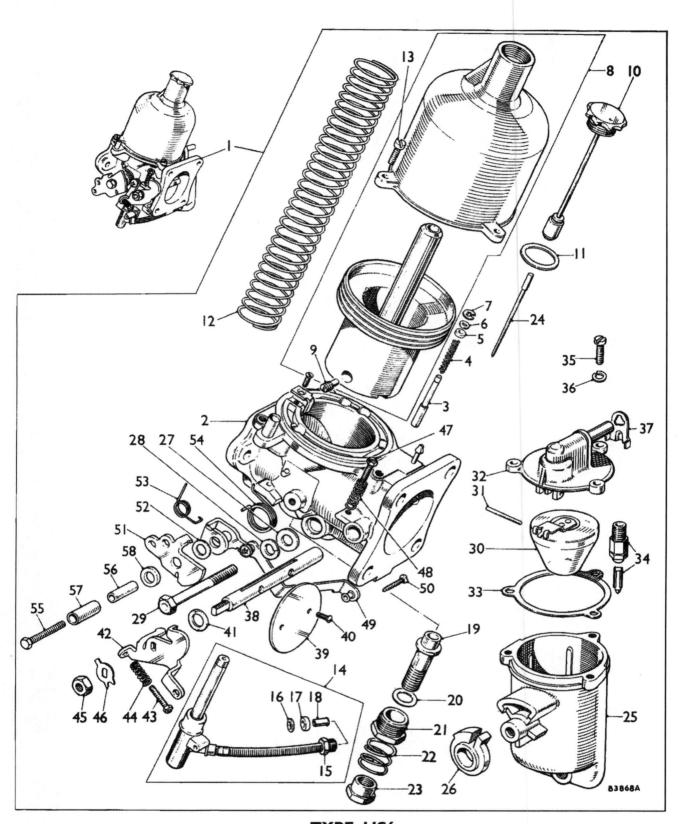

TYPE HS6

83868A

			DESCRIPTION	Part No.	Illus. No.	Quantity	Stock recoms. DIST. Exp.	UK	D	Change Point	REMARKS

CARBURETTERS—TYPE HS6

	Page	Plate
SINGLE ASSEMBLY		
AUD 147	SK 2	K 1
TWIN INSTALLATION		
AUC 981	SK 3–SK 5	K 2–K 4

TYPE HS6

SINGLE ASSEMBLY

Description	Part No.	Illus. No.	Quantity	Exp.	UK	D	Change Point	Remarks
Carburetter assembly	AUD 147	1	1	★	★			
Body	AUD 9540	2	1					
Pin—piston lifting	AUC 1249	3	1	★	★			
Spring—pin	AUC 1151	4	1	★	★			
Washer (neoprene)	AUC 4943	5	1					
Washer (brass)	AUC 4944	6	1					
Circlip—pin	AUC 1250	7	1					
Chamber and piston assembly	AUD 9502	8	1					
Screw—needle locking	AUC 2057	9	1					
Cap and damper	AUC 8103	10	1	★	★			
Washer (fibre)	AUC 4900	11	1	★	★			
Spring—piston—Yellow	AUC 1167	12	1	★	★			
Screw—chamber to body	AUC 5156	13	3					
Jet assembly	AUD 9148	14	1	★	★			
Nut	AUD 2129	15	1					
Washer	AUD 2193	16	1					
Gland	AUD 2194	17	1					
Ferrule	AUD 2195	18	1					
Bearing—jet	AUC 8460	19	1	★	★			
Washer—jet bearing (brass)	AUC 8478	20	1					
Screw—jet locking	AUC 2002	21	1					
Spring—jet locking	AUC 2114	22	1					
Screw—jet adjusting	AUC 8461	23	1					
Needle—jet								
Rich (SW)	AUD 1337	24	1	★	★			
Standard (TW)	AUD 1362	24	1	★	★			
Weak (CIW)	AUD 1117	24	1	★	★			
Chamber—float	AUC 1310	25	1					
Adaptor	AUD 2062	26	1	★	★			
Washer—plain	PWZ 104	27	1					
Washer—spring	LWZ 304	28	1					
Bolt—float chamber fixing	HCZ 0416	29	1					
Float	AUD 9202	30	1	★	★			
Pin—hinge—float to lid	AUC 1152	31	1					
Lid—float chamber	AUD 9203	32	1					
Washer—lid	AUC 8459	33	1	★	★			
Needle and seat	AUD 9096	34	1	★	★			
Screw—lid	AUC 2175	35	3					
Washer—spring	LWZ 303	36	3					
Plate—baffle—lid	AUC 1215	37	1					
Spindle—throttle	AUC 8494	38	1					
Disc—throttle	AUC 3280	39	1					
Screw—disc to spindle	AUC 1358	40	2					
Washer—spindle (brass)	AUC 2625	41	1					
Lever—throttle return	AUD 2769	42	1					
Screw—stop—cam	AUC 8488	43	1					
Spring—screw	AUC 2451	44	1					
Nut—spindle	AJD 8104 Z	45	1					
Washer—tab—nut	AUC 1206	46	1					
Screw—throttle stop	AUC 8483	47	1					
Spring—screw	AUC 2451	48	1					
Lever and link—pick-up	AUD 9492	49	1					
Screw—link to jet	PTZ 605	50	1					
Lever—cam	AUD 2398	51	1					
Washer—cam lever	AUD 2429	52	1					
Spring—cam lever	AUD 2431	53	1					
Spring—pick-up lever	AUC 8462	54	1					
Bolt—pivot	AUC 8400	55	1					
Tube—pivot bolt	AUC 8473	56	1					
Tube—outer	AUD 2430	57	1					
Washer—distance	AUD 2483	58	1					

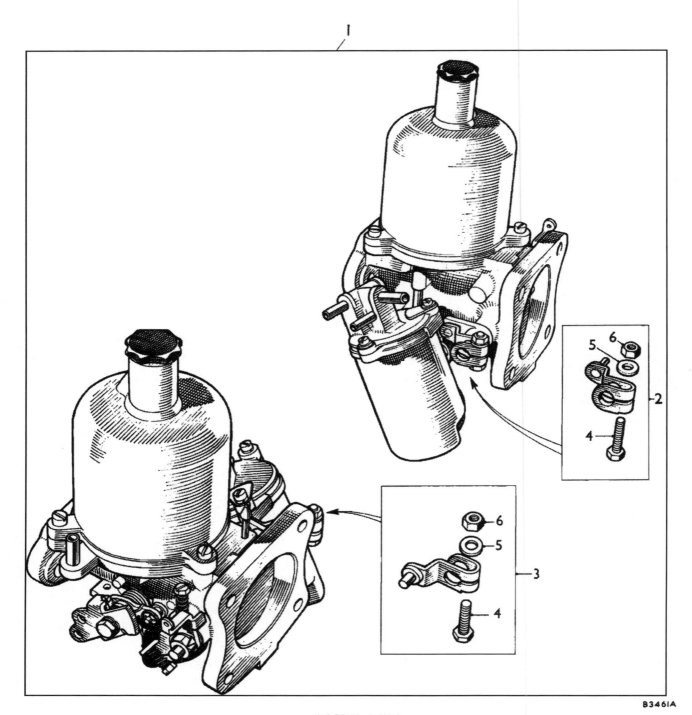

TYPE HS6

B3461A

DESCRIPTION	Part No.	Illus. No.	Quantity	Stock recoms. DIST. Exp.	UK	D	Change Point	REMARKS

Type HS6—*continued*

TWIN INSTALLATION

DESCRIPTION	Part No.	Illus. No.	Quantity	Exp.	UK	Change Point	REMARKS
Carburetter installation	AUC 981	1	1	★	★		
Lever and pin assembly—front	AUE 86	2	1				
Lever and pin assembly—rear	AUE 87	3	1			(C) 17551 to 25314	
Bolt—lever	AJD 1042	4	2				
Washer—plain—bolt	AUC 8396	5	2				
Nut—bolt	AJD 8012 Z	6	2				

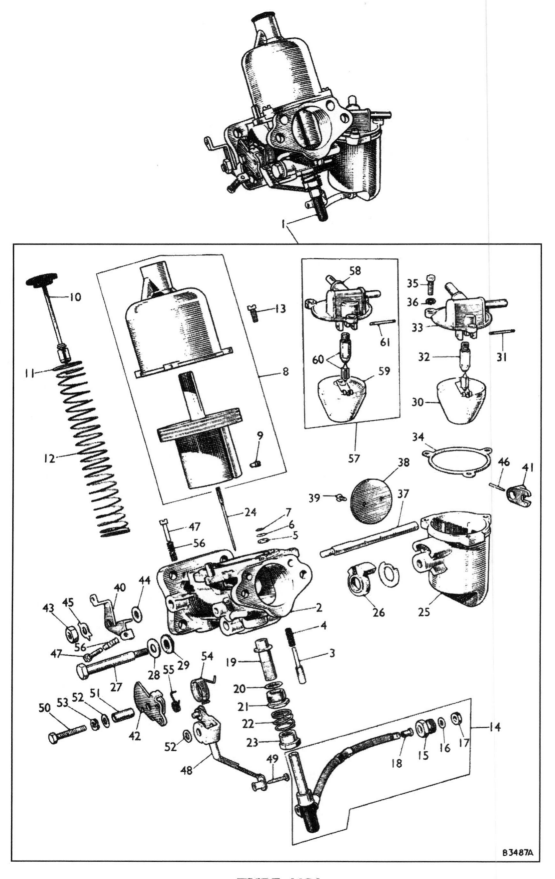

TYPE HS6

Type HS6—*continued*
Twin Installation—*continued*

DESCRIPTION	Part No.	Illus. No.	Quantity	Exp.	UK	D	Change Point	REMARKS
Carburetter assembly—front	AUC 9194	1	1					
Body	AUC 8753	2	1					
Pin—piston lifting	AUD 2160	3	1	★	★			
Spring—pin	AUC 2066	4	1	★	★			
Washer (neoprene)	AUC 4948	5	1					
Washer (brass)	AUC 4944	6	1					
Circlip	AUC 1250	7	1					
Chamber and piston assembly	AUD 9187	8	1					
Screw—needle locking	AUC 2057	9	1					
Cap and damper	AUC 8108	10	1	★	★			
Washer—cap (fibre)	AUC 4900	11	1	★	★			
Spring—piston—Green	AUC 1170	12	1	★	★			
Screw—chamber to body	AUC 5156	13	3					
Jet assembly	AUD 9149	14	1	★	★			
Nut	AUD 2129	15	1					
Washer	AUD 2193	16	1					
Gland	AUD 2194	17	1					
Ferrule	AUD 2195	18	1					
Bearing—jet	AUC 8460	19	1	★	★			
Washer—bearing (brass)	AUC 8478	20	1					
Screw—jet locking	AUC 2002	21	1					
Spring—jet locking	AUC 2114	22	1					
Screw—jet adjusting	AUC 8461	23	1					
Needle—jet								
Rich (RD)	AUD 1288	24	1	★	★			
Standard (BC)	AUD 1063	24	1	★	★			
Weak (TC)	AUD 1469	24	1	★	★			
Chamber—float	AUC 1310	25	1					
Adaptor	AUD 2179	26	1					
Bolt—float chamber to body	AUC 1319	27	1					
Washer—bolt (steel)	AUC 1317	28	1					
Washer—bolt (rubber)	AUC 1818	29	1					
Float	AUC 8667	30	1	★	★			
Pin—float hinge	AUC 1152	31	1					
Needle and seat	AUD 9096	32	1	★	★		(C) 17551 to 25314	
Lid—float chamber	AUD 9080	33	1					Not available; use AUE 273
Lid assembly—float chamber	AUE 273	57	1					
Lid	AUD 9204	58	1					
Float	AUD 9202	59	1	★	★			
Needle and seat	AUD 9096	60	1	★	★			
Pin—hinge	AUC 1152	61	1					
Washer—joint—lid	AUD 8459	34	1	★	★			
Screw—lid to float chamber	AUC 2175	35	3					
Washer—spring—screw	LWZ 303	36	3					Part No. change; was AUC 2246
Spindle—throttle	AUC 8494	37	1					
Disc—throttle	AUC 3280	38	1					
Screw—disc to spindle	AUC 1858	39	2					
Levers								
Throttle return	AUD 2197	40	1					
Lost motion	AUC 1421	41	1					
Cam	AUD 2164	42	1					
Nut—lever to throttle spindle	AJD 8104 Z	43	1					Part No. change; was AUC 1189
Washer (brass)	AUC 2625	44	1					
Washer—tab	AUC 1206	45	1					
Pin—taper—lever to throttle spindle	AUC 2106	46	1					
Screw—throttle stop	AUC 8483	47	2					
Lever and link—pick-up	AUD 9091	48	1					
Screw—link to jet	PTZ 605	49	1					
Bolt—pivot—lever	AUC 8400	50	1					
Tube—bolt	AUC 8473	51	1					
Washer—plain	AUC 5032	52	2					
Washer—spring	AUD 2076	53	1					
Springs								
Pick-up lever	AUC 1875	54	1					
Cam lever	AUD 2049	55	1					
Throttle stop screw	AUC 2451	56	2					

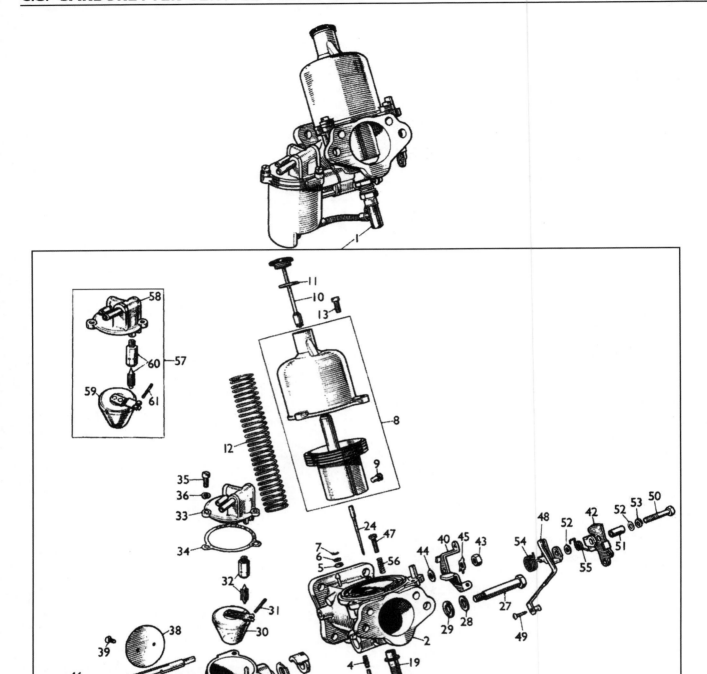

B.3488A

TYPE HS6

Type HS6—*continued*
Twin Installation—*continued*

				Stock recoms.				
DESCRIPTION	Part No.	Illus. No.	Quantity	DIST. Exp.	UK	D	Change Point	REMARKS
Carburetter assembly—rear	AUC 9195	1	1					
Body	AUC 8744	2	1					
Pin—piston lifting	AUD 2160	3	1	★	★			
Spring—pin	AUC 2066	4	1	★	★			
Washer—pin (neoprene)	AUC 4943	5	1					
Washer—pin (brass)	AUC 4944	6	1					
Circlip—pin	AUC 1250	7	1					
Chamber and piston assembly	AUD 9187	8	1					
Screw—needle locking	AUC 2057	9	1					
Cap and damper	AUC 8103	10	1	★	★			
Washer—cap (fibre)	AUC 4900	11	1	★	★			
Spring—piston—Green	AUC 1170	12	1	★	★			
Screw—chamber to body	AUC 5156	13	3					
Jet assembly	AUD 9148	14	1	★	★			
Nut	AUD 2129	15	1					
Washer	AUD 2193	16	1					
Gland	AUD 2194	17	1					
Ferrule	AUD 2195	18	1					
Bearing—jet	AUC 8460	19	1	★	★			
Washer—bearing (brass)	AUC 8478	20	1					
Screw—jet locking	AUC 2002	21	1					
Spring—jet locking	AUC 2114	22	1					
Screw—jet adjusting	AUC 8461	23	1					
Needles—jet								
Rich (RD)	AUD 1288	24	1	★	★			
Standard (BC)	AUD 1063	24	1	★	★			
Weak (TC)	AUD 1469	24	1	★	★			
Chamber—float	AUC 1810	25	1					
Adaptor	AUD 2178	26	1					
Bolt—float chamber to body	AUC 1819	27	1					
Washer—bolt (steel)	AUC 1317	28	1					
Washer—bolt (rubber)	AUC 1318	29	1					
Float	AUC 8667	30	1	★	★			
Pin—float hinge	AUC 1152	31	1					
Needle and seat	AUD 9096	32	1	★	★		(C) 17551 to 25814	
Lid—float chamber	AUD 9081	33	1					Not available; use AUE 274
Lid assembly—float chamber	AUE 274	57	1					
Lid	AUD 9205	58	1					
Float	AUD 9202	59	1	★	★			
Needle and seat	AUD 9096	60	1	★	★			
Pin—hinge	AUC 1152	61	1					
Washer—joint—lid	AUC 8459	34	1	★	★			
Screw—lid to float chamber	AUC 2175	35	3					
Washer—spring—screw	LWZ 203	36	3					Part No. change; was AUC 2246
Spindle—throttle	AUC 8494	37	1					
Disc—throttle	AUC 3280	38	1					
Screw—disc to spindle	AUC 1358	39	2					
Levers								
Throttle return	AUD 2196	40	1					
Lost motion	AUC 1421	41	1					
Cam	AUD 2163	42	1					
Nut—lever to throttle spindle	AJD 8104 Z	43	1					Part No. change; was AUC 1189
Washer (brass)	AUC 2625	44	1					
Washer—tab	AUC 1206	45	1					
Pin—taper—lever to throttle spindle	AUC 2106	46	1					
Screw—throttle stop	AUC 8483	47	2					
Lever and link—pick-up	AUD 9090	48	1					
Screw—link to jet	PTZ 605	49	1					
Bolt—pivot—lever	AUC 8400	50	1					
Tube—bolt	AUC 8473	51	1					
Washer—plain	AUC 5032	52	2					
Washer—spring	AUD 2076	53	1					
Springs								
Pick-up lever	AUC 8462	54	1					
Cam lever	AUD 2050	55	1					
Throttle stop screw	AUC 2451	56	2					

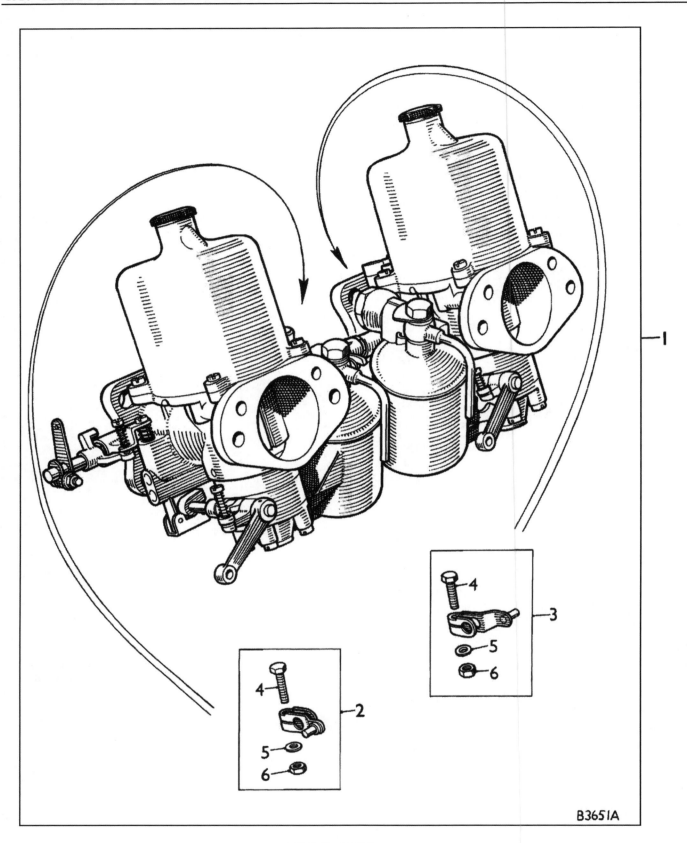

B3651A

TYPE HD8

DESCRIPTION	Part No.	Illus. No.	Quantity	Stock recoms. DIST. Exp.	UK	D	Change Point	REMARKS

CARBURETTERS—TYPE HD8

						Page	Plate
	TWIN INSTALLATION						
AUD 124	... ...					SG 2–SG 4	G 1–G 3

TYPE HD8

TWIN INSTALLATION

Description	Part No.	Illus. No.	Quantity			Change Point
Carburetter installation	AUD 124	1	1 pr. ★ ★			
Lever and pin assembly—front	AUE 86	2	1			
Lever and pin assembly—rear	AUE 87	3	1			(C) H–BJ8–25315 on
Bolt—lever	AJD 1042	4	2			
Washer—plain	AUC 8896	5	2			
Nut—bolt	AJD 8012 Z	6	2			

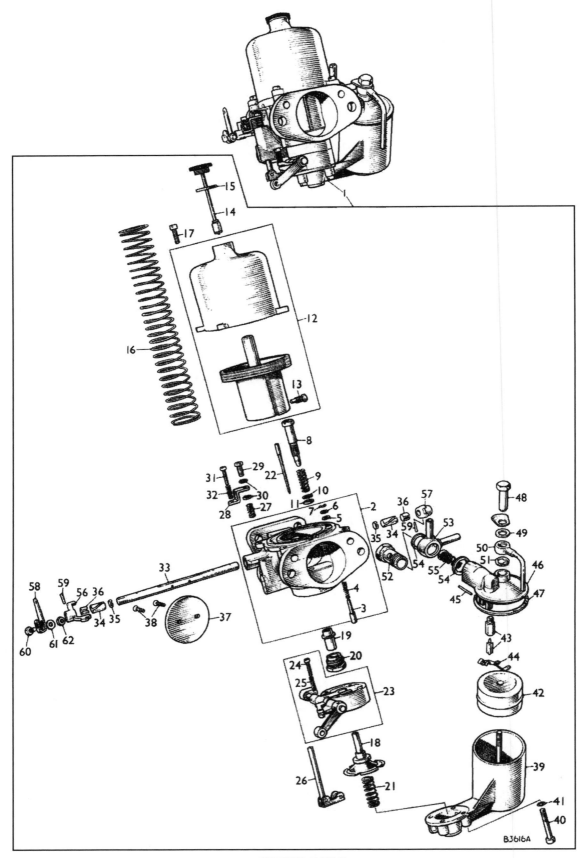

B3616A

TYPE HD8

DESCRIPTION	Part No.	Illus. No.	Quantity	Stock recoms. DIST. Exp.	UK	D	Change Point	REMARKS
Type HD8—*continued*								
Twin Installation—*continued*								
Carburetter assembly—front	AUC 9262	1	1					
Body assembly	AUD 9172	2	1					
Pin—piston lifting	AUC 2065	3	1	★	★			
Spring—pin	AUC 2066	4	1	★	★			
Washer (neoprene)	AUC 4943	5	1					
Washer (brass)	AUC 4944	6	1					
Circlip—pin	AUC 1250	7	1					
Valve—slow running	AUC 2028	8	1					
Spring—valve	AUC 2027	9	1					
Washer—dished (brass)	AUC 2080	10	1					
Washer—gland (neoprene)	AUC 2029	11	1					
Chamber and piston assembly	AUC 8078	12	1					
Screw—needle locking	AUC 2057	13	1					
Cap and damper	AUC 8112	14	1	★	★			
Washer (fibre)	AUC 4900	15	1	★	★			
Spring—piston—Red and Green	AUC 4826	16	1	★	★			
Screw—chamber to body	AUC 2175	17	4					
Jet	AUC 8156	18	1	★	★			
Bearing—jet	AUC 2001	19	1	★	★			
Screw—jet locking	AUC 2002	20	1					
Spring—jet return	AUD 2093	21	1					
Needle—jet								
Rich (UN)	AUD 1474	22	1	★	★			
Standard (UH)	AUD 1370	22	1	★	★			
Weak (UL)	AUD 1466	22	1	★	★			
Housing assembly	AUD 9392	23	1					
Screw—stop adjusting	AUC 2521	24	1					
Spring—screw	AUC 2451	25	1					
Cam shoe and rod	AUC 8962	26	1					
Spring—rod	AUD 2070	27	1				(C) H–BJ8–25315 on	
Plate—top	AUC 2019	28	1					
Screw—plate retaining	AUC 4790	29	1					
Washer—shakeproof	LWN 403	30	2					
Screw—stop adjusting	AUC 2521	31	1					
Spring—screw	AUC 2451	32	1					
Spindle—throttle	AUD 2675	33	1					
Bush—spindle	AUD 2424	34	2					
Ring—inner	AUD 2500	35	2					
Ring—outer	AUD 2243	36	2					
Disc—throttle	AUC 4890	37	1					
Screw—disc	AUC 1858	38	2					
Chamber—float	AUC 2062	39	1					
Bolt—float chamber to body	AUC 2110	40	4					
Washer—shakeproof	LWN 403	41	4					
Float	AUC 1123	42	1	★	★			
Needle and seat	AUD 9096	43	1	★	★			
Lever—hinged	AUD 2285	44	1					
Pin—hinge	AUC 1152	45	1					
Lid—float chamber	AUD 2284	46	1					
Washer—joint—lid	AUC 1147	47	1	★	★			
Nut—cap—lid	AUC 1867	48	1					
Washer (aluminium)	AUC 1557	49	1					
Pipe—air vent and overflow	AUC 3200	50	1					
Washer (fibre)	AUC 1928	51	1	★	★			
Bolt—banjo	AUC 2698	52	1					
Banjo—double	AUC 8397	53	1					
Washer (fibre)	AUC 2141	54	2	★	★			
Filter	AUC 2139	55	1					
Lever								
Throttle stop	AUD 2253	56	1					
Lost motion	AUC 1421	57	1					
Return spring	AUC 8209	58	2					
Pin—taper	AUC 2106	59	1					
Bolt—lever	AJD 1042	60	1					
Washer—plain	AUC 8396	61	1					
Nut—bolt	AJD 8012 Z	62	1					

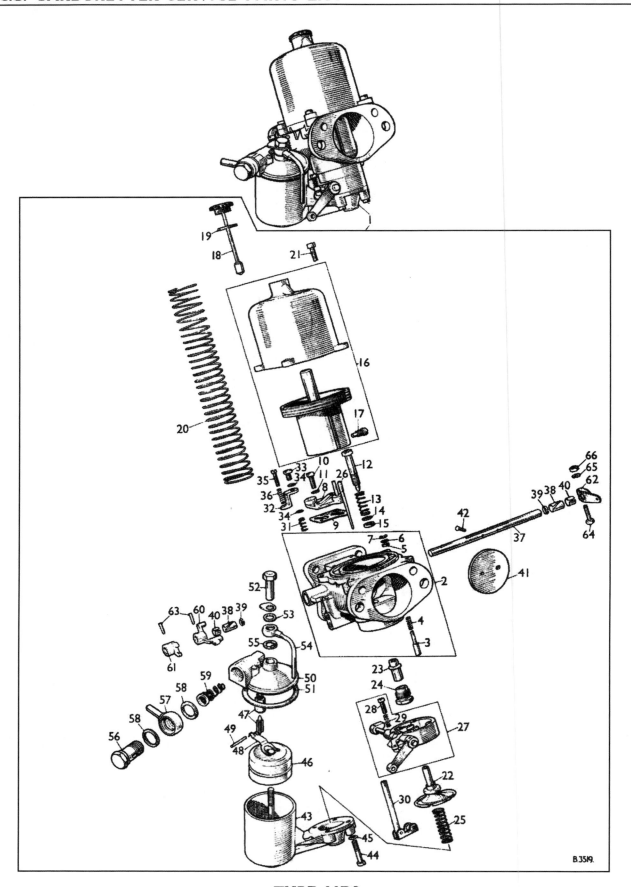

TYPE HD8

Type HD8—*continued*
Twin Installation—*continued*

DESCRIPTION	Part No.	Illus. No.	Quantity	Exp.	UK	D	Change Point	REMARKS
Carburetter assembly—rear	AUC 9263	1	1					
Body assembly	AUD 9171	2	1					
Pin—piston lifting	AUC 2065	3	1	★	★			
Spring—pin	AUC 2066	4	1	★	★			
Washer (neoprene)	AUC 4943	5	1					
Washer (brass)	AUC 4944	6	1					
Circlip—pin	AUC 1250	7	1					
Adaptor—auto ignition	AUC 1323	8	1					
Washer—joint—adaptor	AUC 2014	9	1	★	★			
Screw—adaptor	AUC 2175	10	2					
Washer—shakeproof	LWN 403	11	2					
Valve—slow running	AUC 2028	12	1					
Spring—valve	AUC 2027	13	1					
Washer—dished (brass)	AUC 2030	14	1					
Washer—gland (neoprene)	AUC 2029	15	1					
Chamber and piston assembly	AUC 8078	16	1					
Screw—needle locking	AUC 2057	17	1					
Cap and damper	AUC 8112	18	1	★	★			
Washer (fibre)	AUC 4900	19	1	★	★			
Spring—piston—Red and Green	AUC 4826	20	1	★	★			
Screw—chamber and body	AUC 2175	21	4					
Jet	AUC 8156	22	1	★	★			
Bearing—jet	AUC 2001	23	1	★	★			
Screw—jet locking	AUC 2002	24	1					
Spring—jet return	AUD 2093	25	1					
Needle—jet								
Rich (UN)	AUD 1474	26	1	★	★			
Standard (UH)	AUD 1370	26	1	★	★			
Weak (UL)	AUD 1466	26	1	★	★			
Housing assembly—jet	AUD 9392	27	1					
Screw—stop adjusting	AUC 2521	28	1					
Spring—screw	AUC 2451	29	1					
Cam shoe and rod	AUC 8962	30	1					
Spring—rod	AUD 2070	31	1				(C) H–BJ8–25815 on	
Plate—top	AUC 2019	32	1					
Screw—plate retaining	AUC 4790	33	1					
Washer—shakeproof	LWN 403	34	2					
Screw—stop adjusting	AUC 2521	35	1					
Spring—screw	AUC 2451	36	1					
Spindle—throttle	AUD 2257	37	1					
Bush—spindle	AUD 2424	38	2					
Ring—inner	AUD 2500	39	2					
Ring—outer	AUD 2243	40	2					
Disc—throttle	AUC 4890	41	1					
Screw—disc	AUC 1358	42	2					
Chamber—float	AUC 4067	43	1					
Bolt—float chamber to body	AUC 2110	44	4					
Washer—shakeproof	LWN 403	45	4					
Float	AUC 1123	46	1	★	★			
Needle and seat	AUD 9096	47	1	★	★			
Lever—hinged	AUD 2285	48	1					
Pin—hinged	AUC 1152	49	1					
Lid—float chamber	AUD 2283	50	1					
Washer—joint—lid	AUC 1147	51	1	★	★			
Nut—cap—lid	AUC 1867	52	1					
Washer (aluminium)	AUC 1557	53	1					
Pipe—air vent and overflow	AUC 3200	54	1					
Washer (fibre)	AUC 1928	55	1	★	★			
Bolt—banjo	AUC 2698	56	1					
Banjo	AUC 8398	57	1					
Washer (fibre)	AUC 2141	58	2	★	★			
Filter	AUC 2189	59	1					
Lever								
Throttle stop	AUD 2253	60	1					
Lost motion	AUD 1421	61	1					
Return spring	AUC 8209	62	2					
Pin—taper	AUC 2106	63	1					
Bolt—lever	AJD 1042	64	1					
Washer—plain	AUC 8396	65	1					
Nut—bolt	AJD 8012 Z	66	1					

© **Copyright British Motor Corporation Limited 1966
and Brooklands Books Limited 2014**

This book is published by Brooklands Books Limited and based upon text and
illustrations protected by copyright and first published in 1966 by
British Motor Corporation Limited and may not be reproduced
transmitted or copied by any means without the prior written permission
of British Motor Corporation Limited and Brooklands Books Limited.

Brooklands Books Ltd., PO Box 904, Amersham, Bucks,
HP6 9JA, England   www.brooklandsbooks.com

Extract from Part No. AKD 5036

AUSTIN-HEALEY

MK. 2 and MK. 3
SERIES BJ7 and BJ8
BODY
SERVICE PARTS LIST
AKD 3524

CONTENTS

Identification Data

AUSTIN HEALEY 3000   **Body Service Parts List AKD 3524**

MODEL		COMMENCING	FINISHING
Mark II (Series BJ7)	ENGINE No.	29F–101 29FF–101	29F–6188 29FF–164
	CAR No. BODY No.	H–BJ7–17551 17424	H–BJ7–25314 70760
Mark III (Series BJ8)	ENGINE No.	29K–101 29KF–101 29KFA–224	29K–17636 29KF–223 29KFA–399
	CAR No. BODY No.	H–BJ8–25315 70761	H–BJ8–43026 87903

Key to Body Exterior and Main Trim Colour Combinations, from Start of Vehicle Production

THE B.M.C. COLOUR CODE NUMBERS QUOTED IN THE FOLLOWING TEXT RELATE TO THE PAINT COLOUR SAMPLES IN THE 'B.M.C. SERVICE PAINT SCHEME' PUBLICATION REF.: AKD 1482.

IN THE CASE OF TWO-TONE BODY EXTERIOR COLOURS THE COLOUR BELOW THE BREAK LINE IS QUOTED FIRST.

IN THE CASE OF TWO-TONE BODY EXTERIOR COLOURS WHERE A PRINCIPAL COLOUR APPEARS ABOVE AND BELOW THE CENTRAL BAND OF ANOTHER COLOUR THIS ALSO IS SUITABLY INDICATED.

MODEL CODE
BJ7 — MARK II
BJ8 — MARK III

Body Exterior and B.M.C. Paint Code	Model	Seats	Seat Piping	Liners	Hood and Tonneau cover	Door Seals	Carpet/Mats
METALLIC GOLDEN BEIGE (BG19)	BJ8	Black	B Black	Black	Black	Black	Black
		Red	B Red	Red	,,	Red	Red
BLACK (BK1)	BJ7 BJ8	,,	A Black B Red	,,	,,	,,	,,
BLACK (BK1)/ COLORADO RED (RD2)	,,	,,	A Black B Red	,,	,,	,,	Black
		Grey	A Red B Grey	Grey	,,	Grey	Red
		Black	A Red B Black	Black	,,	Black	Black
BLACK (BK1)/ IVORY WHITE (WT3)	,,	Red	A Ivory White B Red	Red	,,	Red	Red
		Black	A Ivory White B Black	Black	,,	Black	Black
HEALEY BLUE (BU2)	,,	Blue	A Ivory White B Blue	Blue	Blue	Blue	Blue
FLORIDA GREEN (GN1)	,,	Grey	A Green B Grey	Grey	Grey	Grey	Green
BRITISH RACING GREEN (GN25 OR GN29)	,,	Black	Black	Black	Black	Black	Black
COLORADO RED (RD2)	,,	Red	A Black B Red	Red	,,	Red	Red
		Grey	A Red B Grey	Grey	Grey	Grey	,,
		Black	A Red B Black	Black	Black	Black	Black
COLORADO RED (RD2)/ BLACK (BK1)	,,	Red	A Black B Red	Red	Black	Red	Red
IVORY WHITE (WT3)	,,	,,	A Ivory White B Red	,,	,,	,,	,,
		Black	A Ivory White B Black	Black	,,	Black	Black
IVORY WHITE (WT3)/ HEALEY BLUE (BU2)	,,	Blue	A Ivory White B Blue	Blue	Blue	Blue	Blue

A — BJ7
B — BJ8

226

Key to Body Exterior and Main Trim Colour Combinations, from Start of Vehicle Production
—continued

Body Exterior and B.M.C. Paint Code	Model	Seats	Seat Piping	Liners	Hood and Tonneau cover	Door Seals	Carpet/Mats
IVORY WHITE (WT3)/ FLORIDA GREEN (GN1)	BJ7 BJ8	Grey	A Green B Grey	Grey	Grey	Grey	Green

A — BJ7
B — BJ8

Part Number Index

The following is a complete index of parts in this List, giving the page reference of each part number

Part Number	Page	Part Number	Page	Part Number	Page	Part Number	Page	Part Number	Page
1A 9203	BA 4	AHB 5550	BO 3	AHB 6201	BO 7	AHB 6746	BO 6	AHB 8844	BN 6
1A 9307	BK 2	AHB 5552	BO 3	AHB 6202	BO 7	AHB 6747	BO 6	AHB 8844	BN 11
1A 9308	BK 2	AHB 5553	BO 3	AHB 6203	BO 7	AHB 6748	BO 6	AHB 8859	BN 3
		AHB 5554	BO 3	AHB 6227	BA 7	AHB 6788	BP 3	AHB 8860	BN 3
		AHB 5556	BO 3	AHB 6229	BM 3	AHB 6798	BO 7	AHB 8861	BD 3
14A 366	BB 3	AHB 5557	BO 3	AHB 6230	BM 3	AHB 6799	BO 7	AHB 8861	BM 3
14A 2625	BG 3	AHB 5559	BO 3	AHB 6233	BN 8	AHB 6800	BO 7	AHB 8862	BO 4
14A 2641	BN 8	AHB 5560	BO 3	AHB 6234	BN 8	AHB 6801	BO 7	AHB 8864	BO 4
14A 3823	BH 2	AHB 5561	BO 3	AHB 6235	BN 8	AHB 6816	BA 5	AHB 8871	BN 3
14A 4497	BF 3	AHB 5563	BO 3	AHB 6236	BN 8	AHB 6837	BL 4	AHB 8872	BN 3
14A 4497	BL 2	AHB 5564	BO 3	AHB 6237	BN 8	AHB 6838	BL 4	AHB 8953	BA 5
14A 6586	BB 4	AHB 5566	BO 3	AHB 6238	BN 8	AHB 6839	BL 4	AHB 8954	BA 5
14A 6642	BG 2	AHB 5567	BO 3	AHB 6239	BN 8	AHB 6878	BN 10	AHB 8971	BP 3
		AHB 5568	BO 3	AHB 6240	BN 8	AHB 6879	BN 10	AHB 8973	BA 7
AAA 743	BN 12	AHB 5570	BO 3	AHB 6267	BN 8	AHB 6880	BN 10	AHB 8974	BA 7
AAA 2456	BA 7	AHB 5571	BO 3	AHB 6268	BN 8	AHB 6881	BN 10	AHB 8978	BK 2
		AHB 5573	BO 3	AHB 6269	BN 8	AHB 6882	BF 3	AHB 8999	BJ 2
ABZ 0404	BJ 2	AHB 5574	BO 3	AHB 6270	BN 8	AHB 6883	BF 3	AHB 9000	BJ 2
ABZ 0406	BC 2	AHB 5575	BO 3	AHB 6271	BN 8	AHB 6889	BF 2	AHB 9001	BJ 2
ABZ 0407	BC 2	AHB 5577	BO 3	AHB 6272	BN 8	AHB 6890	BF 2	AHB 9005	BB 3
ABZ 0407	BP 2	AHB 5578	BO 3	AHB 6273	BN 8	AHB 6903	BN 8	AHB 9008	BA 4
		AHB 5580	BO 3	AHB 6274	BN 8	AHB 6904	BN 8	AHB 9009	BA 4
ACA 5314	BB 4	AHB 5581	BO 3	AHB 6288	BN 9	AHB 6905	BN 8	AHB 9011	BJ 2
		AHB 5582	BO 3	AHB 6289	BN 9	AHB 6906	BN 8	AHB 9014	BB 2
ACH 9373	BM 3	AHB 5584	BO 3	AHB 6290	BN 9	AHB 6908	BN 8	AHB 9019	BJ 2
		AHB 5585	BO 3	AHB 6291	BN 9	AHB 6909	BN 8	AHB 9065	BA 7
ADA 458	BB 4	AHB 5748	BB 3	AHB 6292	BN 9	AHB 6910	BN 8	AHB 9074	BA 3
ADA 461	BB 4	AHB 6001	BA 3	AHB 6293	BN 9	AHB 6911	BN 8	AHB 9092	BJ 2
ADA 463	BB 4	AHB 6012	BB 2	AHB 6294	BN 9	AHB 6920	BH 3	AHB 9093	BJ 2
ADA 464	BB 4	AHB 6033	BM 3	AHB 6295	BN 9	AHB 6942	BM 3	AHB 9095	BB 2
ADA 466	BB 4	AHB 6034	BM 3	AHB 6333	BN 8	AHB 6948	BM 3	AHB 9169	BA 5
ADA 467	BB 4	AHB 6035	BM 3	AHB 6346	BN 8	AHB 6949	BM 3	AHB 9170	BA 5
ADA 2450	BB 4	AHB 6036	BM 3	AHB 6347	BN 8	AHB 6994	BN 9	AHB 9171	BA 5
ADA 2493	BA 7	AHB 6041	BM 3	AHB 6364	BM 3	AHB 6995	BN 9	AHB 9176	BA 6
ADA 2765	BN 6	AHB 6042	BM 3	AHB 6365	BM 3	AHB 6996	BN 9	AHB 9177	BA 7
ADA 2765	BN 10	AHB 6047	BM 3	AHB 6375	BN 8	AHB 6997	BN 9	AHB 9178	BA 6
ADA 3669	BB 4	AHB 6048	BM 3	AHB 6376	BN 8	AHB 6998	BN 9	AHB 9179	BA 6
ADA 6306	BN 8	AHB 6049	BM 3	AHB 6377	BN 8	AHB 6999	BN 9	AHB 9192	BA 6
		AHB 6050	BM 3	AHB 6378	BN 8	AHB 7000	BN 9	AHB 9209	BJ 2
ADB 837	BM 3	AHB 6061	BM 3	AHB 6387	BG 2	AHB 7001	BN 9	AHB 9210	BA 7
ADB 4811	BN 6	AHB 6063	BM 3	AHB 6388	BG 2	AHB 7028	BN 11	AHB 9211	BB 2
ADB 4811	BN 9	AHB 6064	BM 3	AHB 6389	BF 3	AHB 7029	BN 11	AHB 9245	BA 5
ADB 4811	BN 10	AHB 6072	BM 3	AHB 6390	BF 3	AHB 7030	BN 11	AHB 9249	BP 3
		AHB 6073	BM 3	AHB 6397	BN 8	AHB 7031	BN 11	AHB 9254	BB 2
ADE 539	BN 12	AHB 6074	BM 3	AHB 6398	BN 8	AHB 7105	BF 3	AHB 9268	BA 7
ADE 565	BN 12	AHB 6081	BN 8	AHB 6399	BN 8	AHB 7106	BF 3	AHB 9278	BN 5
		AHB 6091	BO 7	AHB 6400	BN 8	AHB 7111	BK 2	AHB 9278	BN 10
ADG 823	BM 3	AHB 6092	BO 7	AHB 6408	BA 4	AHB 7121	BD 2	AHB 9279	BN 5
		AHB 6093	BO 7	AHB 6410	BM 3	AHB 7144	BN 11	AHB 9279	BN 10
ADH 456	BB 4	AHB 6095	BO 7	AHB 6461	BM 3	AHB 7147	BN 10	AHB 9280	BN 5
ADH 2851	BF 3	AHB 6096	BO 7	AHB 6506	BB 4	AHB 7149	BN 10	AHB 9280	BN 10
ADH 5556	BM 3	AHB 6097	BO 7	AHB 6547	BM 3	AHB 7151	BN 10	AHB 9281	BN 5
ADH 5556	BN 8	AHB 6098	BO 7	AHB 6558	BM 3	AHB 7153	BN 10	AHB 9281	BN 10
		AHB 6130	BO 6	AHB 6565	BA 5	AHB 7155	BN 10	AHB 9286	BN 5
AFH 6772	BL 3	AHB 6131	BO 6	AHB 6575	BO 6	AHB 7165	BK 2	AHB 9287	BN 5
AFH 6773	BL 3	AHB 6132	BO 6	AHB 6576	BO 6	AHB 7179	BN 9	AHB 9288	BN 5
		AHB 6133	BO 6	AHB 6577	BO 6	AHB 7180	BN 9	AHB 9289	BN 5
AHA 5211	BK 2	AHB 6135	BO 6	AHB 6578	BO 6	AHB 7181	BN 9	AHB 9294	BN 5
		AHB 6136	BO 6	AHB 6579	BO 6	AHB 7182	BN 9	AHB 9295	BN 5
AHB 5406	BM 2	AHB 6137	BO 6	AHB 6580	BO 6	AHB 7183	BN 9	AHB 9296	BN 5
AHB 5407	BL 3	AHB 6138	BO 6	AHB 6581	BO 6	AHB 7184	BN 9	AHB 9297	BN 5
AHB 5434	BN 3	AHB 6140	BO 7	AHB 6582	BO 6	AHB 7185	BN 9	AHB 9302	BN 5
AHB 5435	BN 3	AHB 6141	BO 7	AHB 6584	BO 6	AHB 7186	BN 9	AHB 9302	BN 10
AHB 5436	BN 3	AHB 6142	BO 7	AHB 6585	BO 6	AHB 7188	BH 2	AHB 9303	BN 5
AHB 5438	BN 3	AHB 6143	BO 7	AHB 6586	BO 6	AHB 8548	BO 4	AHB 9303	BN 10
AHB 5439	BN 3	AHB 6145	BO 6	AHB 6587	BO 6	AHB 8549	BO 4	AHB 9304	BN 5
AHB 5440	BN 3	AHB 6146	BO 6	AHB 6589	BO 6	AHB 8550	BO 4	AHB 9304	BN 10
AHB 5450	BN 3	AHB 6147	BO 6	AHB 6590	BO 6	AHB 8641	BN 6	AHB 9305	BN 5
AHB 5451	BN 3	AHB 6148	BO 6	AHB 6591	BO 6	AHB 8641	BN 11	AHB 9305	BN 10
AHB 5452	BN 3	AHB 6150	BO 6	AHB 6592	BO 6	AHB 8653	BN 6	AHB 9310	BN 5
AHB 5454	BN 3	AHB 6151	BO 6	AHB 6594	BO 6	AHB 8653	BN 11	AHB 9310	BN 10
AHB 5455	BN 3	AHB 6152	BO 6	AHB 6595	BO 6	AHB 8665	BN 6	AHB 9311	BN 5
AHB 5456	BN 3	AHB 6153	BO 6	AHB 6596	BO 6	AHB 8665	BN 11	AHB 9311	BN 10
AHB 5538	BO 3	AHB 6155	BO 6	AHB 6597	BO 6	AHB 8692	BN 6	AHB 9312	BN 5
AHB 5539	BO 3	AHB 6156	BO 6	AHB 6598	BA 5	AHB 8692	BN 11	AHB 9312	BN 10
AHB 5540	BO 3	AHB 6157	BO 6	AHB 6627	BN 9	AHB 8693	BN 6	AHB 9313	BN 5
AHB 5542	BO 3	AHB 6158	BO 6	AHB 6628	BN 9	AHB 8693	BN 11	AHB 9313	BN 10
AHB 5543	BO 3	AHB 6186	BO 6	AHB 6629	BN 9	AHB 8696	BN 6	AHB 9318	BN 5
AHB 5545	BO 3	AHB 6187	BO 6	AHB 6630	BN 9	AHB 8782	BN 12	AHB 9318	BN 10
AHB 5546	BO 3	AHB 6188	BO 6	AHB 6717	BF 2	AHB 8783	BN 12	AHB 9319	BN 5
AHB 5547	BO 3	AHB 6189	BO 6	AHB 6718	BF 2	AHB 8837	BN 6	AHB 9319	BN 10
AHB 5549	BO 3	AHB 6200	BO 7	AHB 6745	BO 6			AHB 9320	BN 5

Part Number Index—*continued*

Part Number	Page	Part Number	Page	Part Number	Page	Part Number	Page	Part Number	Page	Part Number	Page
AHB 9320	BN 10	AHB 9692	BO 4	AHB 9871	BO 3	ALH 1896	BM 3	11B 5254	BA 3		
AHB 9321	BN 5	AHB 9693	BO 4	AHB 9872	BO 4	ANK 4646	BD 3	11B 5264	BA 4		
AHB 9321	BN 10	AHB 9696	BN 4	AHB 9873	BO 4	ANK 4646	BF 3	11B 5265	BA 4		
AHB 9334	BN 6	AHB 9697	BN 4	AHB 9874	BN 6	ARO 9166	BG 3	11B 5303	BK 2		
AHB 9335	BN 6	AHB 9698	BN 4	AHB 9877	BO 3	ARO 9399	BG 3	11B 5308	BK 2		
AHB 9336	BN 6	AHB 9699	BN 4	AHB 9878	BO 3	AWZ 105	BB 3	11B 5309	BK 2		
AHB 9337	BN 6	AHB 9702	BN 4	AHB 9884	BL 2	1B 8641	BA 3	11B 5312	BK 2		
AHB 9338	BN 6	AHB 9703	BN 4	AHB 9893	BG 3	1B 8648	BA 3	14B 766	BB 2		
AHB 9339	BN 6	AHB 9704	BN 4	AHB 9894	BG 3	1B 8658	BA 3	14B 766	BC 2		
AHB 9342	BN 6	AHB 9705	BN 4	AHB 9895	BK 2	1B 8670	BA 4	14B 766	BG 2		
AHB 9422	BG 3	AHB 9706	BN 4	AHB 9900	BL 4	1B 8672	BA 4	14B 1382	BO 3		
AHB 9424	BH 2	AHB 9707	BN 4	AHB 9904	BH 2	1B 8685	BA 3	14B 1383	BO 3		
AHB 9425	BG 2	AHB 9708	BN 4	AHB 9907	BD 3	1B 8688	BA 3	14B 1386	BO 3		
AHB 9426	BG 2	AHB 9709	BN 4	AHB 9914	BG 2	1B 8689	BA 3	14B 1387	BO 3		
AHB 9427	BG 3	AHB 9721	BG 2	AHB 9915	BL 3	1B 8693	BA 3	14B 1388	BO 3		
AHB 9428	BG 3	AHB 9722	BG 2	AHB 9916	BL 3	1B 8698	BA 3	14B 1708	BC 3		
AHB 9429	BA 5	AHB 9732	BN 3	AHB 9917	BL 3	1B 8699	BA 3	14B 1718	BD 2		
AHB 9434	BF 2	AHB 9733	BN 3	AHB 9918	BL 3	1B 8703	BA 4	14B 1719	BD 2		
AHB 9435	BF 2	AHB 9734	BN 3	AHB 9930	BF 2	1B 8731	BA 3	14B 1725	BD 2		
AHB 9436	BF 2	AHB 9735	BN 3	AHB 9931	BF 2	1B 8766	BA 4	14B 1726	BD 2		
AHB 9437	BF 3	AHB 9736	BN 3	AHB 9934	BL 2	1B 8777	BA 3	14B 1727	BC 3		
AHB 9438	BF 3	AHB 9737	BN 3	AHB 9935	BL 3	1B 8839	BA 4	14B 1728	BC 3		
AHB 9439	BF 2	AHB 9738	BN 3	AHB 9943	BL 2	1B 8840	BA 4	14B 1729	BM 2		
AHB 9440	BB 2	AHB 9739	BN 3	AHB 9951	BG 3	1B 8937	BK 2	14B 1815	BA 6		
AHB 9441	BD 2	AHB 9740	BN 3	AHB 9954	BG 3	1B 8940	BK 2	14B 1867	BH 3		
AHB 9442	BC 2	AHB 9741	BN 3	AHB 9955	BA 3	4B 1089	BB 3	14B 1916	BL 4		
AHB 9443	BC 2	AHB 9742	BN 3	AHB 9956	BA 3	4B 1090	BD 2	14B 1941	BK 2		
AHB 9470	BF 3	AHB 9743	BN 3	AHB 9972	BA 3	4B 1091	BC 2	14B 1963	BD 3		
AHB 9471	BF 3	AHB 9744	BN 3	AHB 9973	BA 3	4B 1092	BC 2	14B 1964	BD 3		
AHB 9472	BF 2	AHB 9745	BN 3	AHB 9979	BA 3	4B 3172	BN 3	14B 2005	BB 2		
AHB 9473	BF 2	AHB 9746	BN 3	AHB 9987	BA 3	4B 3200	BO 4	14B 2006	BB 2		
AHB 9481	BG 3	AHB 9747	BN 3	AHB 9988	BA 3	4B 3215	BN 3	14B 2016	BN 6		
AHB 9482	BG 3	AHB 9748	BN 4	AHB 9989	BA 4	4B 3223	BA 6	14B 2016	BN 11		
AHB 9483	BD 3	AHB 9749	BN 4	AHB 9990	BA 4	4B 3247	BN 3	14B 2038	BD 2		
AHB 9491	BG 2	AHB 9750	BN 4	AHB 9993	BA 4	4B 3248	BN 6	14B 2512	BA 6		
AHB 9492	BG 2	AHB 9751	BN 4	AHB 9999	BA 3	4B 3248	BN 11	14B 2513	BA 6		
AHB 9499	BG 2	AHB 9752	BN 4	AHH 5255	BM 3	4B 3249	BN 6	14B 2546	BC 3		
AHB 9510	BA 7	AHB 9753	BN 4	AHH 5388	BA 7	4B 3249	BN 11	14B 2549	BA 5		
AHB 9511	BA 6	AHB 9754	BN 4	AHH 5714	BP 3	4B 3253	BN 6	14B 2550	BA 5		
AHB 9512	BA 6	AHB 9755	BN 4	AHH 5714	BP 4	4B 3253	BN 11	14B 2685	BA 7		
AHB 9518	BG 2	AHB 9764	BB 2	AHH 5759	BM 2	4B 3255	BN 6	14B 2742	BK 2		
AHB 9519	BG 2	AHB 9765	BD 2	AHH 5759	BM 3	4B 3255	BN 11	14B 2749	BP 4		
AHB 9520	BG 2	AHB 9772	BH 2	AHH 6348	BG 2	4B 3479	BF 3	14B 2767	BO 4		
AHB 9521	BG 2	AHB 9773	BH 2	AHH 6349	BG 2	4B 3479	BL 2	14B 2767	BO 7		
AHB 9522	BG 2	AHB 9774	BH 2	AHH 6848	BH 3	4B 4124	BN 3	14B 2768	BO 4		
AHB 9524	BG 2	AHB 9775	BH 2	AHH 6856	BH 3	4B 4206	BO 3	14B 2768	BO 7		
AHB 9525	BG 2	AHB 9778	BH 2	AJD 1012	BP 2	4B 4207	BO 3	14B 2774	BO 4		
AHB 9531	BL 3	AHB 9779	BH 2	AJD 1203Z	BH 2	4B 6821	BO 7	14B 2774	BO 7		
AHB 9532	BF 3	AHB 9780	BH 2	AJD 3204Z	BP 2	4B 7427	BA 5	14B 2845	BB 2		
AHB 9533	BF 3	AHB 9781	BH 2	AJD 4243C	BH 2	4B 7428	BA 5	14B 2846	BB 4		
AHB 9537	BF 3	AHB 9784	BH 2	AJD 4243Z	BH 2	4B 8521	BM 3	14B 2877	BO 4		
AHB 9538	BF 3	AHB 9785	BH 2	AJD 7202	BA 6	4B 8646	BB 3	14B 2877	BO 7		
AHB 9541	BF 3	AHB 9786	BH 2	AJD 7202	BG 3	4B 9353	BA 5	14B 3462	BD 2		
AHB 9542	BF 3	AHB 9787	BH 2	AJD 7202	BM 3	4B 9364	BA 5	14B 3463	BD 2		
AHB 9554	BO 4	AHB 9788	BL 2	AJD 7202	BO 7	4B 9366	BA 5	14B 3500	BO 4		
AHB 9555	BO 4	AHB 9788	BN 4	AJD 7212	BA 7	11B 5117	BA 4	14B 3732	BF 2		
AHB 9556	BL 2	AHB 9788	BN 8	AJD 7282	BJ 2	11B 5119	BA 4	14B 4466	BF 2		
AHB 9569	BF 2	AHB 9789	BL 2	AJD 7612	BF 3	11B 5120	BA 4	14B 5711	BN 6		
AHB 9570	BF 2	AHB 9789	BN 4	AJD 7622	BN 6	11B 5123	BA 4	14B 5711	BN 11		
AHB 9571	BC 3	AHB 9789	BN 8	AJD 7622	BN 10	11B 5126	BA 4	14B 5723	BB 2		
AHB 9572	BC 3	AHB 9794	BH 2	AJD 7622	BN 11	11B 5128	BA 4	14B 5724	BB 2		
AHB 9576	BL 2	AHB 9803	BL 4	AJD 7712	BF 3	11B 5148	BA 3	14B 5725	BB 2		
AHB 9587	BL 2	AHB 9804	BL 4	AJD 8012 C	BF 3	11B 5202	BA 3	14B 5726	BB 2		
AHB 9588	BL 2	AHB 9805	BL 4	AJD 8012Z	BG 3	11B 5205	BA 3	14B 5727	BB 2		
AHB 9589	BH 2	AHB 9817	BL 4	AJD 8012Z	BH 3	11B 5208	BA 4	14B 5728	BB 2		
AHB 9591	BL 3	AHB 9818	BL 4	AKE 5199	BL 2	11B 5212	BA 3	14B 5735	BK 2		
AHB 9593	BL 2	AHB 9819	BL 4	AKE 5200	BL 2	11B 5213	BA 4	14B 5739	BD 2		
AHB 9594	BL 2	AHB 9820	BL 4	AKE 5201	BL 2	11B 5216	BA 4	14B 5749	BA 5		
AHB 9595	BL 2	AHB 9821	BL 4	AKE 5267	BO 3	11B 5218	BA 3	14B 5750	BA 5		
AHB 9596	BL 2	AHB 9822	BL 4	AKE 5268	BO 3	11B 5220	BA 3	14B 5775	BM 2		
AHB 9597	BL 2	AHB 9824	BL 4	AKE 5269	BO 3	11B 5225	BA 3	14B 5776	BM 2		
AHB 9653	BL 2	AHB 9825	BL 4	AKE 5270	BO 3	11B 5228	BA 3	14B 5777	BB 3		
AHB 9659	BH 2	AHB 9835	BL 3	AKE 5271	BO 3	11B 5231	BA 3	14B 5809	BA 5		
AHB 9656	BN 4	AHB 9836	BL 3	AKE 5272	BO 3	11B 5232	BA 3	14B 5810	BA 5		
AHB 9656	BN 8	AHB 9849	BL 4	AKE 5273	BO 3	11B 5236	BA 3	14B 5811	BA 5		
AHB 9662	BG 2	AHB 9852	BL 4	AKE 5274	BO 4	11B 5251	BA 3	14B 5812	BA 5		
AHB 9681	BL 3	AHB 9856	BL 3	AKE 5275	BO 4	11B 5252	BA 3	14B 5861	BB 4		
AHB 9682	BL 3	AHB 9857	BL 3	AKE 5276	BN 6			14B 5896	BF 2		
AHB 9683	BA 6	AHB 9858	BL 3					14B 6453	BC 2		
AHB 9688	BO 4	AHB 9867	BO 3					14B 6461	BA 5		
AHB 9689	BO 4	AHB 9868	BO 3					14B 6462	BA 5		
AHB 9690	BO 4	AHB 9869	BO 3					14B 6467	BD 2		
AHB 9691	BO 4	AHB 9870	BO 3	ALH 1879	BF 3						

Part Number Index—*continued*

Part Number	Page	Part Number	Page	Part Number	Page	Part Number	Page	Part Number	Page
14B 6597	BD 2	BHA 4082	BM 3	FNZ 103	BN 9	8G 9273	BA 5	17H 2840	BG 3
14B 6598	BP 2	BHA 4340	BG 2	FNZ 103	BO 4			17H 2841	BG 3
14B 6599	BP 2	BHA 4359	BF 2	FNZ 103	BO 7	14G 3499	BP 2	17H 2842	BG 3
14B 6600	BP 2	BHA 4361	BH 3	FNZ 103	BP 3	14G 3692	BB 3	17H 2843	BG 3
14B 6601	BP 3	BHA 4362	BH 3	FNZ 103	BP 4	14G 3693	BB 3	17H 2844	BG 3
14B 6602	BP 3	BHA 4371	BL 4	FNZ 104	BB 2	14G 3763	BF 3	17H 2845	BG 3
14B 6603	BP 3	BHA 4416	BM 3	FNZ 104	BB 3	14G 3764	BF 3	17H 2846	BG 3
14B 6729	BC 3	BHA 4453	BN 9	FNZ 104	BC 2	14G 3766	BB 4	17H 2847	BG 3
14B 6740	BM 2	BHA 4510	BH 3	FNZ 104	BC 3	14G 5507	BM 2	17H 2848	BG 3
14B 6754	BB 4			FNZ 104	BD 2	14G 5854	BP 2	17H 2849	BG 3
14B 6760	BA 7	BRP 1108	BC 2	FNZ 104	BD 3	14G 6451	BP 4	17H 2850	BG 3
14B 6761	BA 7	BRP 1108	BG 2	FNZ 104	BG 2	14G 6451	BG 2	17H 2851	BG 3
14B 6765	BF 2	BRP 1110	BB 2	FNZ 104	BH 2	14G 6503	BG 2	17H 2852	BG 3
14B 6766	BF 2			FNZ 104	BJ 2	14G 6505	BG 2	17H 2853	BG 3
14B 6805	BB 4	CLZ 0313	BB 4	FNZ 104	BK 2	14G 6506	BG 2	17H 2854	BG 3
14B 6806	BB 4	CLZ 0511	BB 3	FNZ 104	BM 2	14G 8736	BN 5	17H 2855	BG 3
14B 6817	BD 2			FNZ 104	BN 9	14G 8736	BN 6	17H 2871	BG 3
14B 6824	BC 3	CMZ 0206	BM 3	FNZ 104	BO 4	14G 8736	BN 10	17H 2872	BG 3
14B 6825	BC 3	CMZ 0208	BN 6	FNZ 104	BO 7			17H 2967	BH 2
14B 6828	BA 7	CMZ 0208	BN 10	FNZ 105	BA 5	18G 8470	BG 3	17H 3176	BG 3
14B 7458	BA 6	CMZ 0208	BN 11	FNZ 105	BA 6	18G 8471	BG 3	17H 6836	BP 2
14B 7466	BD 3	CMZ 0210	BG 3	FNZ 105	BL 3	18G 8516	BG 3	17H 6910	BH 2
14B 7544	BA 6	CMZ 0308	BB 2	FNZ 105	BK 2	18G 8517	BG 3	17H 8108	BP 2
14B 7545	BA 6	CMZ 0308	BB 3	FNZ 106	BB 4			17H 8146	BH 3
14B 7550	BP 3	CMZ 0308	BC 3	FNZ 206	BB 4	24G 1233	BG 2	17H 8147	BH 3
14B 7554	BF 2	CMZ 0308	BD 2			24G 1345	BD 3	17H 8148	BH 3
14B 7555	BF 2	CMZ 0308	BP 4	FWP 106	BN 8			17H 9699	BK 2
14B 7556	BF 2	CMZ 0310	BB 2	FWP 406	BN 3	2H 1046	BB 3	17H 9700	BK 2
14B 7557	BF 2	CMZ 0410	BC 3	FWP 406	BN 4	2H 1046	BD 2	17H 9701	BK 2
14B 7562	BF 2	CMZ 0412	BD 2	FWP 406	BN 8	2H 4185	BD 3	17H 9702	BK 2
14B 7563	BF 2	CMZ 0422	BN 9	FWP 406	BN 9	2H 6181	BL 4	17H 9932	BD 3
14B 7564	BF 2	CMZ 0424	BN 9	FWP 406	BO 4	2H 6182	BL 4		
14B 7565	BF 2	CMZ 0512	BF 3			2H 6183	BL 4	27H 602	BP 2
14B 7566	BF 2	CMZ 0516	BF 2	1G 9799	BK 2	2H 6184	BL 4	27H 1171	BP 2
14B 7579	BM 2			1G 9800	BA 3	2H 6961	BN 5	27H 1173	BP 2
14B 7661	BB 2	CNZ 102	BJ 2			2H 6961	BN 10	27H 1174	BP 2
14B 7662	BB 2	CNZ 102	BM 3	4G 1636	BG 2	2H 8041	BA 7	27H 1176	BP 2
14B 7711	BP 4	CNZ 102	BN 6	4G 2541	BA 7	2H 8041	BF 3	27H 1177	BP 2
14B 7712	BP 4	CNZ 102	BN 10	4G 3575	BA 7	2H 8041	BM 3	27H 1232	BP 2
14B 7776	BP 2	CNZ 102	BN 11	4G 4920	BA 7	2H 8445	BN 5	27H 1248	BP 2
14B 7777	BP 2			4G 6492	BA 7	2H 8445	BN 6	27H 2198	BF 3
14B 7779	BP 4	CTP 403	BN 8	4G 6575	BP 4	2H 9215	BN 10	27H 2199	BF 3
14B 7780	BP 2	CTP 605	BN 8	4G 7614	BC 3	2H 9215	BB 3	27H 2200	BF 3
14B 7781	BP 2			4G 8595	BD 3	2H 9215	BD 2	27H 2278	BF 3
14B 7782	BP 4	CTZ 403	BC 3			2H 9215	BO 4	27H 2787	BG 3
14B 7805	BM 2	CTZ 404	BM 3	8G 705	BD 3			27H 2788	BG 3
14B 7810	BP 2	CTZ 404	BN 4	8G 8753	BL 2	3H 2506	BA 7	27H 2863	BF 3
14B 7829	BN 6	CTZ 604	BM 3	8G 8754	BL 2			27H 2864	BF 3
14B 7829	BN 11	CTZ 605	BN 6	8G 8755	BL 2	7H 6836	BP 2	27H 2865	BF 3
14B 7830	BN 6	CTZ 605	BN 10	8G 8756	BL 2	7H 8379	BF 3	27H 2866	BF 3
14B 7830	BN 11			8G 8757	BL 2	7H 8380	BF 3	27H 2867	BF 3
14B 8692	BD 3	CZZ 404	BN 8	8G 8758	BL 2	7H 8382	BF 3	27H 2868	BF 3
14B 8699	BL 4			8G 8759	BL 2	7H 8383	BF 3	27H 2869	BF 3
14B 8708	BN 6	5D 4199	BN 12	8G 8826	BL 2	7H 8384	BF 3	27H 2870	BF 3
14B 8708	BN 11	5D 9363	BN 12	8G 8846	BL 2	7H 9866	BO 7	27H 9623	BH 3
14B 8780	BP 4			8G 8847	BL 2			27H 9625	BH 3
14B 8781	BP 4	DMP 0824	BL 2	8G 8848	BL 2	13H 59	BP 4	27H 9655	BH 3
14B 8812	BB 3	DMP 0835	BN 6	8G 8888	BM 3	13H 76	BP 2	27H 9671	BH 3
14B 8851	BL 4	DMP 0835	BN 11	8G 8890	BM 3	13H 77	BP 2	27H 9824	BH 3
14B 8875	BN 6	DMP 0840	BG 2	8G 9143	BA 5	13H 78	BA 5	27H 9833	BF 3
14B 9476	BF 3	DMP 0840	BL 2	8G 9149	BA 2	13H 227	BA 2	27H 9863	BH 3
14B 9484	BB 3	DMP 1239	BC 2	8G 9150	BA 2	13H 231	BA 2	27H 9985	BG 3
14B 9820	BA 7	DMP 2824	BJ 2	8G 9151	BA 5	13H 232	BA 5		
14B 9820	BP 3			8G 9152	BA 5			37H 537	BP 3
14B 9821	BP 3	DXR 0412	BL 3	8G 9153	BA 5			37H 2506	BF 2
				8G 9154	BA 5	17H 819	BP 2	37H 2988	BH 2
24B 601	BJ 2	3F 90	BB 4	8G 9155	BA 5	17H 1493	BP 4	37H 3228	BH 2
24B 632	BP 2			8G 9156	BA 5	17H 1494	BP 2	37H 9522	BH 3
24B 633	BP 2	FNZ 103	BA 5	8G 9157	BA 5	17H 1574	BP 2	37H 9523	BH 3
24B 697	BM 2	FNZ 103	BB 2	8G 9158	BA 5	17H 1591	BP 2	37H 9659	BK 2
24B 725	BM 2	FNZ 103	BB 3	8G 9159	BA 5	17H 1597	BP 2	37H 9708	BH 3
24B 726	BM 2	FNZ 103	BB 4	8G 9180	BA 2	17H 2531	BG 3	37H 9719	BL 4
24B 773	BB 2	FNZ 103	BC 3	8G 9196	BA 5	17H 2669	BH 3	37H 9729	BH 3
24B 880	BF 2	FNZ 103	BD 2	8G 9197	BA 5	17H 2670	BH 3	37H 9730	BH 3
24B 881	BF 2	FNZ 103	BF 3	8G 9198	BA 5	17H 2672	BH 3	37H 9732	BG 3
24B 1682	BA 5	FNZ 103	BG 2	8G 9204	BA 2	17H 2812	BG 3	37H 9871	BK 2
24B 1683	BA 5	FNZ 103	BG 3	8G 9205	BA 2	17H 2813	BG 3	37H 9946	BH 3
24B 1684	BA 5	FNZ 103	BJ 2	8G 9206	BA 2	17H 2814	BG 3	37H 9947	BH 3
24B 1712	BL 3	FNZ 103	BL 4	8G 9210	BA 2	17H 2815	BH 2	37H 9950	BN 4
24B 1714	BL 3	FNZ 103	BM 2	8G 9211	BA 2	17H 2816	BH 2	37H 9950	BN 8
24B 1715	BL 3	FNZ 103	BM 3	8G 9212	BA 2	17H 2817	BH 2	37H 9955	BN 4
		FNZ 103	BN 3	8G 9219	BA 2	17H 2838	BG 3	37H 9955	BN 8
BHA 4082	BD 3	FNZ 103	BN 4	8G 9272	BA 5	17H 2839	BG 3	37H 9956	BN 4

Part Number	Page	Part Number	Page	Part Number	Page	Part Number	Page	Part Number	Page
37H 9956	BN 8	1AL 252	BN 12	LWZ 403	BG 3	PWZ 102	BJ 2	RMZ 0308	BF 3
37H 9957	BN 4			LWZ 403	BH 2	PWZ 102	BM 3		
37H 9957	BN 8	1BL 107	BN 12	LWZ 403	BL 3	PWZ 102	BN 6	RTP 403	BC 3
37H 9967	BH 3	1BL 252	BN 12	LWZ 503	BB 2	PWZ 102	BN 11	RTP 604	BD 3
37H 9968	BH 3	1BL 452	BN 12	LWZ 503	BB 3	PWZ 103	BA 5	RTP 604	BN 4
37H 9970	BH 3	1BL 555	BN 12			PWZ 103	BB 2	RTP 606	BN 4
37H 9971	BH 3			MTP 402	BN 3	PWZ 103	BB 3	RTP 606	BN 9
37H 9972	BH 3	1KL 1113	BN 12	MTP 404	BF 2	PWZ 103	BB 4	RTP 808	BL 3
37H 9973	BH 3	1KL 1558	BN 12	MTP 404	BG 3	PWZ 103	BC 3		
37H 9974	BH 3	1KL 2113	BN 12			PWZ 103	BD 2	TFP 810	BO 4
		1KL 2260	BN 12	MTZ 603	BM 3	PWZ 103	BG 2	TFP 1006	BL 4
47H 9510	BH 3	1KL 2458	BN 12	MTZ 604	BL 3	PWZ 103	BG 3	TFP 1006	BN 4
		1KL 2558	BN 12	MTZ 604	BM 3	PWZ 103	BJ 2	TFP 1006	BN 9
97H 2542	BF 3	1KL 3114	BN 12			PWZ 103	BL 4		
97H 2679	BH 3	1KL 3259	BN 12	PCR 0307	BP 4	PWZ 103	BM 2	TFS 106	BL 4
		1KL 3457	BN 12			PWZ 103	BM 3		
HBZ 0408	BH 2	1KL 3559	BN 12	PFS 106	BD 3	PWZ 103	BN 3		
HBZ 0409	BH 2			PFS 106	BM 3	PWZ 103	BN 4		
HBZ 0611	BK 2	LFP 1004	BL 4	PFS 514	BC 2	PWZ 103	BN 9		
HBZ 0612	BK 2			PFS 528	BA 6	PWZ 103	BO 4		
		LFS 100	BL 4			PWZ 103	BP 3		
HCS 0507	BP 3	LFS 107	BL 4	PJZ 1004	BF 3	PWZ 103	BP 4		
HCS 0709	BA 7			PJZ 1004	BG 2	PWZ 104	BB 2		
HCS 2632	BP 3	LNZ 104	BA 7			PWZ 104	BB 3		
HCS 3036	BP 3	LNZ 203	BM 3	PMP 0308	BM 2	PWZ 104	BB 4		
HCS 3036	BP 4			PMP 0308	BN 3	PWZ 104	BC 2		
		LWN 403	BD 3	PMP 0310	BM 2	PWZ 104	BC 3		
HZS 0403	BK 2	LWN 403	BF 2	PMP 0310	BM 3	PWZ 104	BD 2		
HZS 0404	BK 2	LWN 406	BH 3	PMP 0312	BM 2	PWZ 104	BD 3		
HZS 0405	BB 2					PWZ 104	BF 2		
HZS 0405	BB 4	LWZ 103	BA 5	PMZ 0204	BG 3	PWZ 104	BG 2		
HZS 0405	BG 2	LWZ 202	BJ 2	PMZ 0306	BA 5	PWZ 104	BG 3		
HZS 0405	BJ 2	LWZ 202	BM 3	PMZ 0306	BD 3	PWZ 104	BH 2		
HZS 0405	BK 2	LWZ 203	BA 7	PMZ 0306	BG 2	PWZ 104	BJ 2		
HZS 0406	BB 3	LWZ 203	BB 2	PMZ 0307	BN 3	PWZ 104	BK 2		
HZS 0406	BC 2	LWZ 203	BB 3	PMZ 0308	BB 2	PWZ 104	BM 2		
HZS 0406	BC 3	LWZ 203	BB 4	PMZ 0308	BB 4	PWZ 104	BO 4		
HZS 0406	BF 2	LWZ 203	BC 3	PMZ 0308	BH 3	PWZ 105	BA 5		
HZS 0406	BH 2	LWZ 203	BD 2	PMZ 0308	BJ 2	PWZ 105	BA 6		
HZS 0406	BJ 2	LWZ 203	BF 3	PMZ 0308	BM 2	PWZ 105	BA 7		
HZS 0407	BB 4	LWZ 203	BG 2	PMZ 0308	BO 4	PWZ 105	BB 3		
HZS 0407	BD 2	LWZ 203	BG 3	PMZ 0308	BP 3	PWZ 105	BD 2		
HZS 0505	BA 6	LWZ 203	BH 3	PMZ 0308	BP 4	PWZ 105	BL 3		
HZS 0506	BF 2	LWZ 203	BJ 2	PMZ 0310	BA 7	PWZ 106	BK 2		
HZS 0508	BF 2	LWZ 203	BL 4	PMZ 0310	BB 4	PWZ 106	BO 4		
HZS 0606	BK 2	LWZ 203	BM 2	PMZ 0310	BC 3	PWZ 106	BO 7		
HZS 0608	BK 2	LWZ 203	BM 3	PMZ 0310	BG 2	PWZ 202	BB 2		
HZS 0610	BK 2	LWZ 203	BN 3	PMZ 0310	BM 3	PWZ 203	BB 2		
		LWZ 203	BN 4	PMZ 0310	BN 3	PWZ 203	BB 3		
2K 4936	BL 4	LWZ 203	BN 9	PMZ 0310	BP 3	PWZ 203	BB 4		
2K 9005	BF 2	LWZ 203	BO 4	PMZ 0310	BP 4	PWZ 203	BC 3		
2K 9051	BC 2	LWZ 203	BO 7	PMZ 0314	BA 7	PWZ 203	BF 3		
2K 9579	BO 4	LWZ 203	BP 3	PMZ 0328	BP 3	PWZ 204	BK 2		
2K 9993	BC 2	LWZ 203	BP 4	PMZ 0408	BG 2	PWZ 204	BM 2		
2K 9993	BC 3	LWZ 204	BB 2	PMZ 0408	BO 4	PWZ 204	BN 9		
		LWZ 204	BB 3	PMZ 0410	BD 3	PWZ 204	BO 4		
6K 9426	BD 3	LWZ 204	BB 4	PMZ 0410	BK 2	PWZ 204	BO 7		
6K 9433	BP 2	LWZ 204	BC 2			PWZ 404	BG 2		
6K 9817	BC 2	LWZ 204	BC 3	PTP 604	BN 6	PWZ 404	BN 9		
6K 9817	BJ 2	LWZ 204	BD 2	PTP 604	BN 11				
6K 9817	BP 2	LWZ 204	BD 3						
		LWZ 204	BG 2	PTZ 603	BA 6	RFN 204	BA 7		
51K 3132	BA 5	LWZ 204	BH 2	PTZ 603	BC 2	RFN 220	BA 7		
		LWZ 204	BJ 2	PTZ 603	BL 3	RFN 403	BA 7		
52K 2614	BM 2	LWZ 204	BK 2	PTZ 603	BP 4	RFN 403	BB 4		
		LWZ 204	BM 2	PTZ 604	BN 8				
53K 122	BF 2	LWZ 204	BN 9	PTZ 803	BA 6	RFR 205	BA 7		
53K 126	BG 2	LWZ 204	BO 4	PTZ 804	BN 3	RFR 208	BA 7		
53K 155	BP 2	LWZ 204	BO 7	PTZ 805	BC 3	RFR 216	BA 7		
53K 155	BP 4	LWZ 205	BA 5	PTZ 807	BA 6	RFR 220	BA 7		
53K 1191	BF 2	LWZ 205	BA 6	PTZ 808	BA 6				
53K 1302	BP 2	LWZ 205	BL 3	PTZ 1003	BP 4	RJP 603	BN 3		
53K 1661	BD 2	LWZ 206	BK 2	PTZ 1004	BB 4	RJP 604	BN 3		
53K 1662	BD 2	LWZ 206	BO 4	PTZ 1004	BP 2	RJP 604	BN 8		
53K 1712	BF 2	LWZ 206	BO 7			RJP 606	BN 3		
53K 3039	BF 3	LWZ 303	BP 2	PWN 104	BF 3	RJP 606	BN 8		
53K 3039	BG 3	LWZ 304	BF 2			RJP 606	BO 4		
53K 3151	BA 7	LWZ 304	BK 2	PWP 103	BL 4				
		LWZ 306	BK 2	PWP 103	BM 3	RMP 0203	BH 2		
54K 3024	BF 2	LWZ 402	BN 6	PWP 203	BM 2	RMP 0206	BG 3		
54K 3024	BN 4	LWZ 402	BN 10			RMP 0308	BF 3		
54K 3024	BN 8	LWZ 402	BN 11	PWZ 102	BC 2	RMP 0308	BH 2		
54K 3413	BF 3	LWZ 402	BN 11	PWZ 102	BG 2	RMP 0310	BF 2		
54K 3495	BF 2	LWZ 403	BG 2	PWZ 102	BG 3	RMP 0312	BH 3		

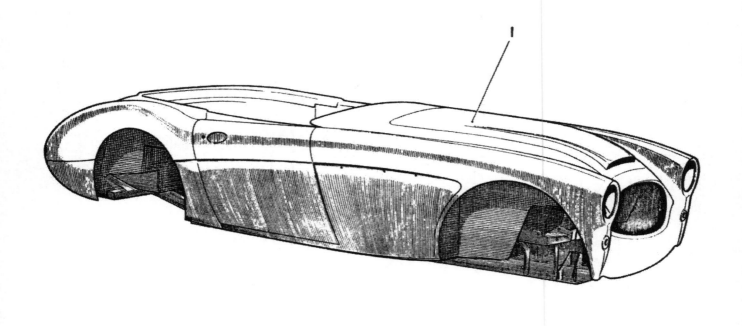

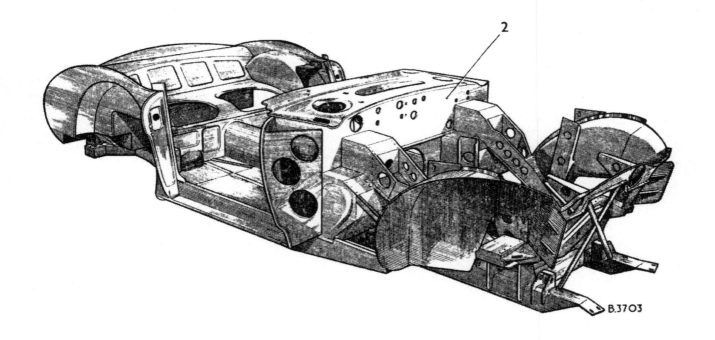

B.3703

		DESCRIPTION	Part No.	Illus. No.	Quantity	Stock recoms. DIST. Exp.	UK	D	Change Point	REMARKS

BODY SHELL

						Page	Plate
† BODY SHELL	...	...	...	...	...	BA 2	A 1
† FRAME—CHASSIS	...	...	...	...	...	BA 2, BA 3	A 1, A 2
† FRONT END ASSEMBLY	...	...	...	...	...	BA 5	A 3
† REAR END ASSEMBLY	...	...	...	...	...	BA 5	A 3

BODY SHELL

Shell Assembly—Primed

Description	Part No.	Illus. No.	Quantity	Change Point	Remarks
Except West Germany and Sweden	8G 9150	1	1	(C) H-BJ7-17551 to 25314	
West Germany and Sweden	8G 9180	1	1		
Except West Germany and Sweden	8G 9204	1	1	(C) H-BJ8-25315 to 26704	
West Germany and Sweden	8G 9205	1	1		
Except West Germany and Sweden	8G 9210	1	1	(C) H-BJ8-26705 to (B) H-BJ8-76137	Not available; use 8G 9219 together with 4 off BHA 4477 lamp-flasher (except Italy), 2 off BHA 4493 lamp-flasher front (Italy only), 2 off BHA 4477 lamp flasher-rear (Italy only), 2 off BHA 4148 reflector, 1 off AHB 8984 bracket reflector mounting RH, 1 off AHB 8985 bracket-reflector mounting LH, 1 off AHB7120—cable—main harness, 1 off AHB 7118 cable-chassis harness, 1 off AHB 7119 cable-boot harness and 2 off AHB 7136 plate-reinforcement-rear flasher lamp aperture.
West Germany and Sweden	8G 9211	1	1	(C) H-BJ8-26705 to (B) H-BJ8-75207 West Germany (C) H-BJ8-26705 to (B) H-BJ8-76137 Sweden	Not available; use 8G 9219 together with 2 off AHB7136 plate-reinforcement-rear flasher lamp aperture
	8G 9219	1	1	(B) H-BJ8-75208 on West Germany. (B) H-BJ8-76138 on except West Germany	

Panel

Description	Remarks
Bonnet	For details: see page BB2
Bonnet surround	For details: see page BB1.1
Front wing—RH	For details: see page BC1.1
Front wing—LH	
Door—RH	For details: see page BE1.1
Door—LH	
Rear quarter—RH	For details: see page BC1.1
Rear quarter—LH	
Tonneau	For details: see page BD2
Boot lid	For details: see page BD2

Frame assembly—chassis (with front and rear end assemblies)

Part No.	Illus. No.	Quantity	Change Point
8G 9149	2	1	(C) H-BJ7-17551 to 25314
8G 9206	2	1	(C) H-BJ8-25315 to 26704
8G 9212	2	1	(C) H-BJ8-26705 on

PLATE A 2

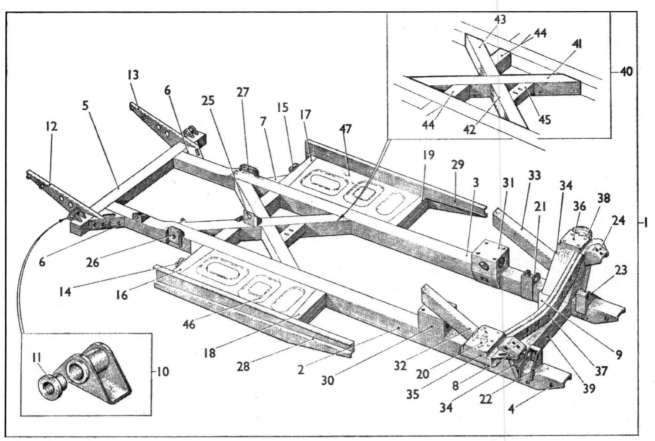

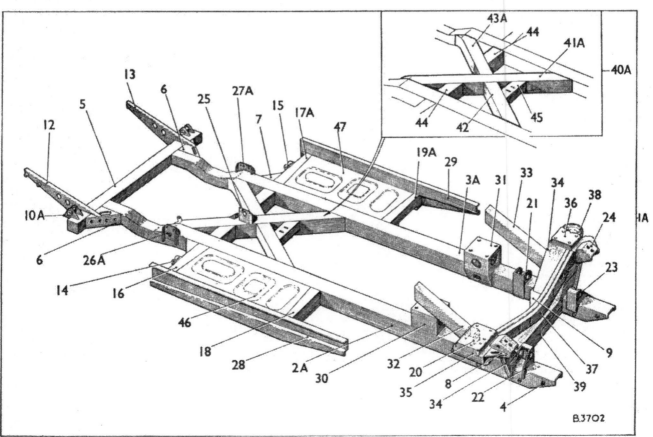

B.3702

	DESCRIPTION	Part No.	Illus. No.	Quantity	Stock recoms. DIST. Exp.	UK	D	Change Point	REMARKS
	Body Shell—*continued*								
	Frame—chassis	AHB 9074	1	1				(C) H-BJ7-17551 to 25314	Not available; use AHB 9999
		AHB 9999	1	1				(C) H-BJ8-25315 to 26704	
		AHB 9987	1A	1				(C) H-BJ8-26705 on	
	Side-member								
	Right hand	11B 5202	2	1				](C) H-BJ7-17551 to 25314	
	Left hand	11B 5205	3	1				](C) H-BJ8-25315 to 26704	
	Right hand	AHB 9955	2A	1				](C) H-BJ8-26705 on	
	Left hand	AHB 9956	3A	1				]	
	Tube—mounting—front bumper	11B 5212	4	4					
	Crossmember—rear	1B 8641	5	1					
	Gusset								
	Rear crossmember	1B 8658	6	2					
	Body mounting bracket—rear	1B 8693	7	2					
	Steering bracket	11B 5148	8	2					
	Front crossmember	1B 8777	9	2					
	Bracket—rear spring—rear	1B 8648	10	2				](C) H-BJ7-17551 to 25314	
	Bush—shackle pin	1G 9800	11	4	★	★		](C) H-BJ8-25315 to 26704	
	Bracket								
	Rear bumper—RH	11B 5252	12	1					
	Rear bumper—LH	11B 5254	13	1					
	Rear spring—rear	AHB 9979	10A	2				(C) H-BJ8-26705 on	
	Rear spring—front—RH	1B 8688	14	1					
	Rear spring—front—LH	1B 8689	15	1					
	Body mounting—rear—RH	11B 5225	16	1					
	Body mounting—rear—LH	11B 5228	17	1				(C) H-BJ7-17551 to 25314	Not available; use AHB 6001
	Body mounting—rear—LH	AHB 6001	17A	1				(C) H-BJ8-25315 on	
	Body mounting—front—RH	1B 8698	18	1					
	Body mounting—front—LH	1B 8699	19	1				(C) H-BJ7-17551 to 25314	Not available; use AHB 9988
	Body mounting—front—LH	AHB 9988	19A	1				(C) H-BJ8-25315 on	
	Front suspension lower link—rear—RH	11B 5251	20	1					
	Front suspension lower link—rear—LH	1B 8685	21	1					
	Front suspension lower link—front—RH	11B 5218	22	1					
	Front suspension lower link—front—LH	11B 5220	23	1					
	Steering	1B 8731	24	2					
	Handbrake	11B 5236	25	1					
	Rear shock absorber mounting—RH	11B 5231	26	1				(C) H-BJ7-17551 to 25314 (C) H-BJ8-25315 to 26704	
	Rear shock absorber mounting—RH	AHB 9972	26A	1				(C) H-BJ8-26705 on	
	Rear shock absorber mounting—LH	11B 5232	27	1				(C) H-BJ7-17551 to 25314 (C) H-BJ8-25315 to 26704	
	Rear shock absorber mounting—LH	AHB 9973	27A	1				(C) H-BJ8-26705 on	

† Revised Information.　　　　　　　　　　235　　　　　　　　　　Issue 3　　　　　　**BA 3**

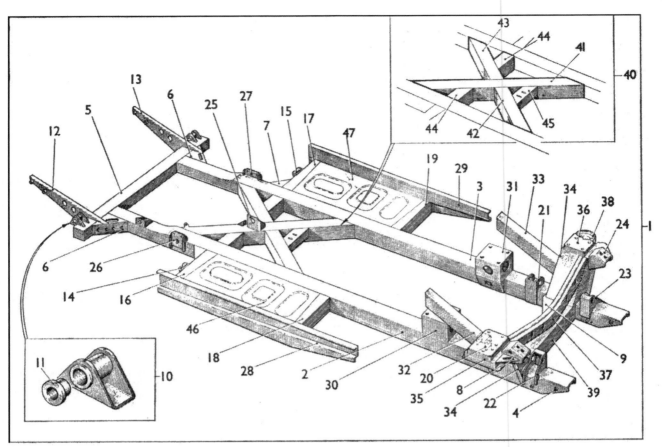

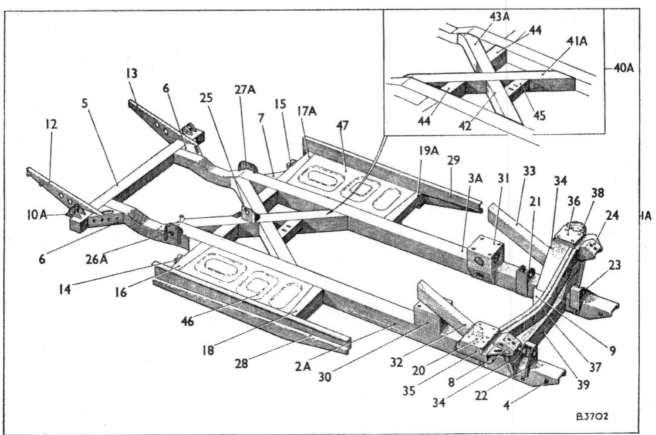

B.3702

	DESCRIPTION	Part No.	Illus. No.	Quantity	Stock recoms. DIST.			Change Point	REMARKS
					Exp.	UK	D		
Body Shell—*continued*									
	Sill—body—RH	11B 5264	28	1					
	Sill—body—LH	11B 5265	29	1					
	Platform—engine front mounting—RH	11B 5213	30	1					
	Platform—engine front mounting—LH	11B 5216	31	1					
	Strut—engine bearer—RH	1B 8670	32	1					
	Strut—engine bearer—LH	1B 8672	33	1					
	Housing—front suspension	1B 8766	34	2					
	Adaptor—suspension housing—RH	1B 8839	35	1					
	Adaptor—suspension housing—LH	1B 8840	36	1					
	Support—suspension housing	11B 5208	37	1					
	Cup—suspension bump rubber	1A 9203	38	2					
	Crossmember—front	1B 8703	39	1					
	Crossbrace assembly	11B 5119	40	1				(C) H-BJ7-17551 to 25314	
	Crossbrace assembly	AHB 9989	40A	1				(C) H-BJ8-2315 to 26704	
								(C) H-BJ8-26705 on	
	Beam—crossbrace								
	Main	11B 5120	41	1				(C) H-BJ7-17551 to 25314	
								(C) H-BJ8-25315 to 26704	
	Main	AHB 9990	41A	1				(C) H-BJ8-26705 on	
	Front half	11B 5123	42	1					
	Rear half	11B 5126	43	1				(C) H-BJ7-17551 to 25314	
								(C) H-BJ8-25315 to 26704	
	Rear half	AHB 9993	43A	1				(C) H-BJ8-26705 on	
	Stiffener	11B 5128	44	2					
	Support—rear engine mounting	11B 5117	45	1					
Panel—floor—side									
	Right hand	AHB 9008	46	1					
	Left hand	AHB 9009	47	1				(C) H-BJ7-17551 to 25314	
	Left hand	AHB 6408	47	1				(C) H-BJ8-25315 on	

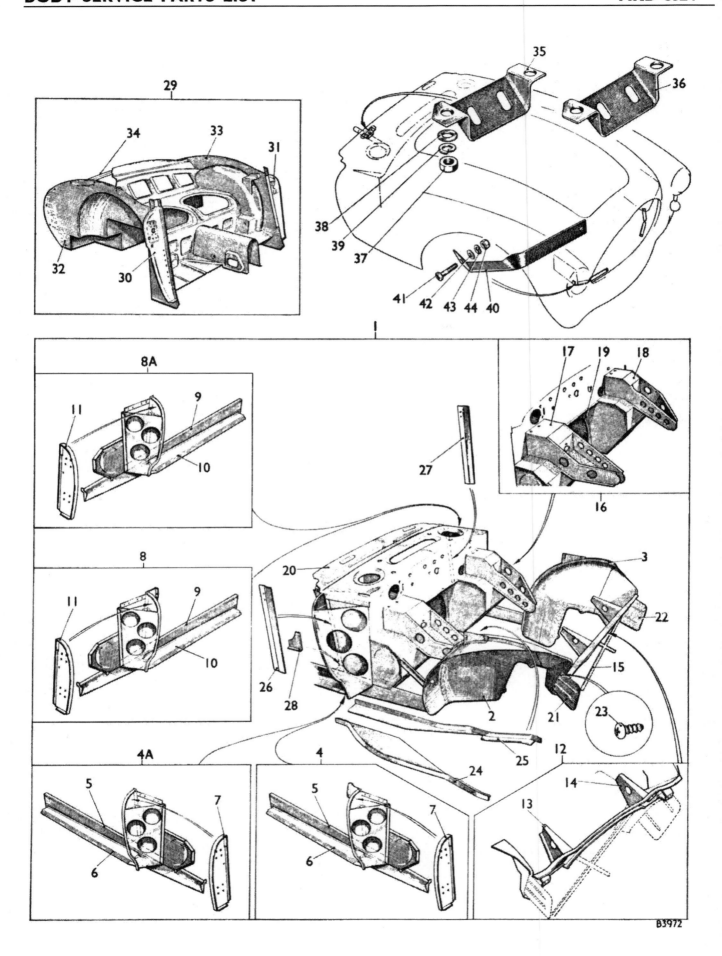

B3972

DESCRIPTION	Part No.	Illus. No.	Quantity	Stock recoms. DIST. Exp.	UK	D	Change Point	REMARKS
Body Shell—*continued*								
Front assembly	AHB 9429	1	1				(C) H-BJ7-17551 to 25314	
Front end assembly	AHB 6560	1	1				(C) H-BJ8-25315 on	
Wheelarch—RH	4B 7427	2	1					
Wheelarch—LH	4B 7428	3	1					
Panel assembly—scuttle side— RH	8G 9151	4	1				(C) H-BJ7-17551 to 25314	
Panel assembly—scuttle side—RH	8G 9197	4A	1				(C) H-BJ8-25315 on	
Panel—sill inner—RH	14B 5809	5	1					
Panel—sill outer—RH	14B 5749	6	1					
Pillar—door hinge—RH	8G 9153	7	1					
Panel assembly—scuttle side—LH	8G 9152	8	1				(C) H-BJ7-17551 to 25314	
Panel assembly—scuttle side—LH	8G 9198	8A	1				(C) H-BJ8-25315 on	
Panel—sill inner—LH	14B 5810	9	1					
Panel—sill outer—LH	14B 5750	10	1					
Pillar—door hinge—LH	8G 9154	11	1					
Cowl and crossbrace assembly	4B 9353	12	1					
Bracket—radiator steady—RH	14B 5811	13	1					
Bracket—radiator steady—LH	14B 5812	14	1					
Crossbrace—centre	4B 9366	15	1					
Dash and pedal box assembly	8G 9143	16	1				(C) H-BJ7-17551 to 25314	
Dash and pedal box assembly	8G 9196	16	1				(C) H-BJ8-25315 on	
Box—pedal accommodation—RH	AHB 8953	17	1					
Box—pedal accommodation—LH	AHB 8954	18	1					
Panel—reinforcement—pedal box sides	AHB 9169	19	1					
Panel								
Scuttle top—inner	†8G 9155	20	1				(C) H-BJ7-17551 to 25314	
Scuttle top—inner	†AHB 6622	20A	1				(C) H-BJ8-25315 on	
Wheelarch splash—RH	†14B 6461	21	1					
Wheelarch splash—LH	†14B 6462	22	1					
Screw—splash panel	51K 3132	23	8					
Flange—sealing—gearbox tunnel—RH	AHB 9170	24	1					
Flange—sealing—gearbox tunnel—LH	AHB 9171	25	1					
Plate—extension—scuttle side panel— RH	24B 1682	26	1					
Plate—extension—scuttle side panel— LH	24B 1683	27	1					
Gusset—scuttle side to sill	24B 1684	28	2					
Rear end assembly	AHB 9434	29	1				(C) H-BJ7-17551 to 25314 (C) H-BJ8-25315 to 26704	
Rear end assembly	AHB 6816	29	1				(C) H-BJ8-26705 on	
Pillar—door shut—RH	8G 9156	30	1					
Pillar—door shut—LH	8G 9157	31	1					
Panel—rear quarter—inner								
Right hand	8G 9158	32	1				] (C) H-BJ7-17551 to 52514	
Left hand	8G 9159	33	1				] (C) H-BJ8-25315 to 26704	
Right hand	8G 9272	32	1				] (C) H-BJ8-26705 on	
Left hand	8G 9273	33	1				]	
Rail—rear skirt	4B 9364	34	1					
Bracket—steering column fixing bracket **RHD**	14B 2549	35	1				]	
Bracket—steering column fixing bracket **LHD**	14B 2550	36	1					
Nut—bracket	FNZ 105	37	2				(C) H-BJ8-25315 on	
Washer—plain	PWZ 105	38	2					
Washer—spring	LWZ 205	39	2				]	
Bracket—steady—wheelarch splash panel	AHB 9245	40	2					
Screw—bracket	PMZ 0306	41	2					
Washer—plain	PWZ 103	42	2					
Washer—spring	LWZ 103	43	2					
Nut	FNZ 103	44	2					

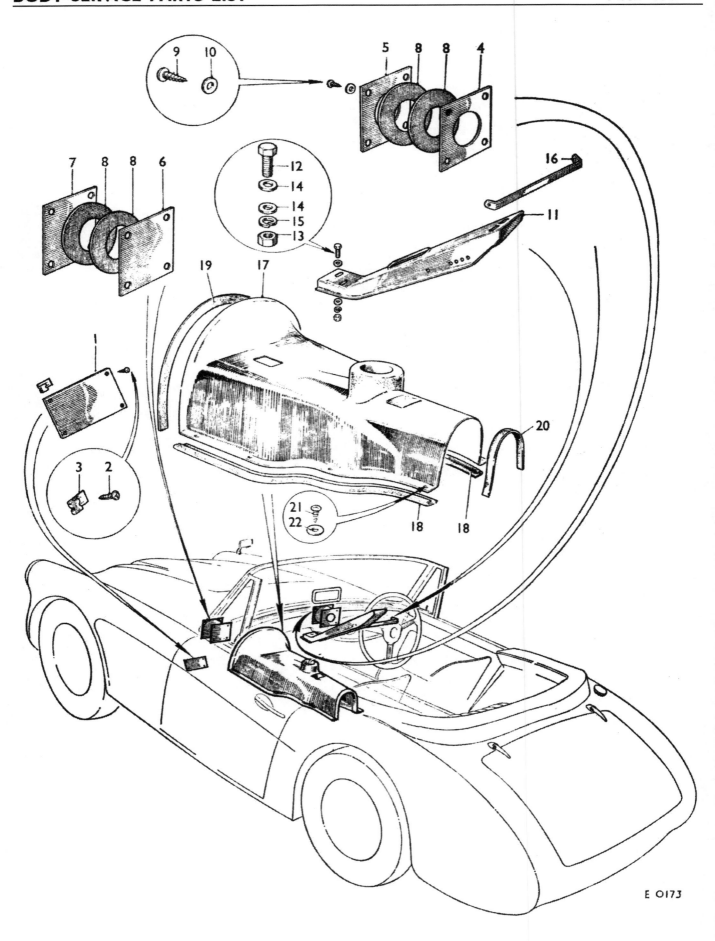

E 0173

	DESCRIPTION	Part No.	Illus. No.	Quantity	Change Point	REMARKS
Body Shell—*continued*						
	Plate—pedal box blanking	†4B 3223	1	1		
	Screw	†PTZ 803	2	4		
	Nut	†PFS 528	3	4		
Plate—steering column						
	Sealing—inner	†14B 1815	4	1		
	Sealing—outer	†14B 7544	5	1		
	Blanking—inner	†14B 2512	6	1		
	Blanking—outer	†14B 7545	7	1		
	Seal—plate (felt)	†14B 2513	8	4		
	Screw	†PTZ 603	9	16		
	Washer—screw	†AJD 7202	10	16		
	Bracket—steering column	AHB 9683	11	1		
	Screw	†HZS 0505	12	4		
	Nut	†FNZ 105	13	4		
	Washer—plain	†PWZ 105	14	6		
	Washer—spring	LWZ 205	15	4		
	Bracket—steering column steady	†14B 7458	16	1		
	Cover—gearbox	†AHB 9176	17	1		
Seal—cover						
	Mounting flange	†AHB 9192	18	2		
	Front	†AHB 9179	19	1	⎤(C) H–BJ7–17551 to 18022	Not available; use AHB 9512
	Rear	†AHB 9178	20	1	⎦	Not available; use AHB 9511
	Front	†AHB 9512	19	1	⎤(C) H–BJ7–18023 to 25314	
	Rear	†AHB 9511	20	1	⎦(C) H–BJ8–25315 on	
	Screw	†PTZ 807	21	6		
	Screw	†PTZ 808	21	2		
	Washer—plain	†AJD 7202	22	8		

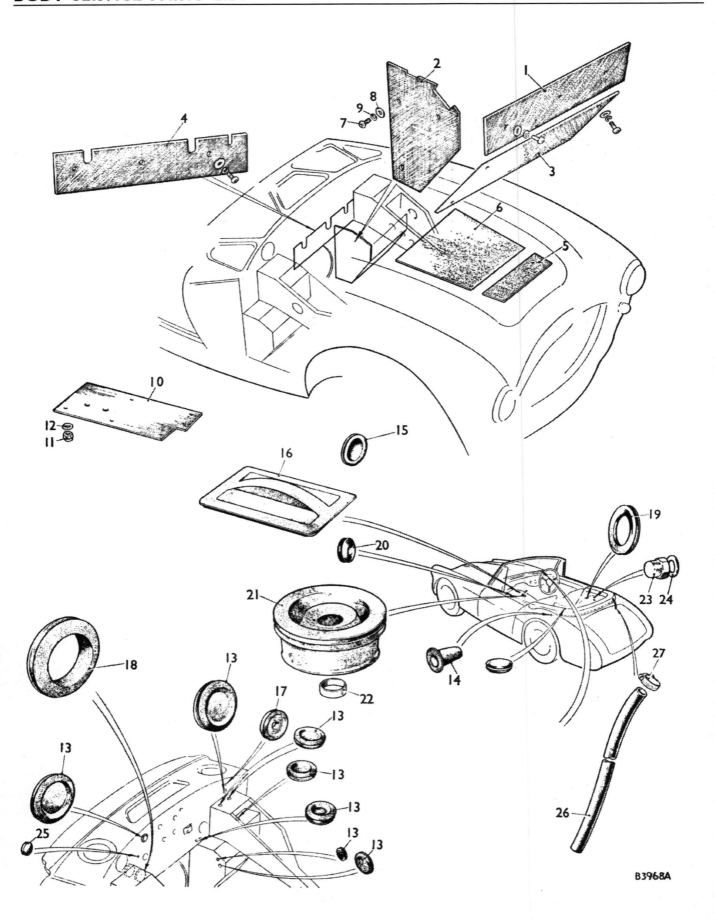

B3968A

		DESCRIPTION	Part No.	Illus. No.	Quantity	Change Point	REMARKS

Body Shell—*continued*

Pad—insulation

Description	Part No.	Illus. No.	Quantity	Change Point	Remarks
LH pedal box—front (asbestos)	14B 6760	1	1		
LH pedal box—side (asbestos)	14B 6761	2	1		
LH pedal box—lower front (asbestos)	14B 6828	3	1		
Dash—front (asbestos)	AHB 9210	4	1		
Bonnet—front (felt)]Not	AHB 8973	5	1		
Bonnet—rear (felt)]U.K.	AHB 8974	6	1		
Screw—insulation pad	PMZ 0310	7	6		
Screw—insulation pad	PMZ 0314	7	7		
Washer—plain	53K 3151	8	13		
Washer—spring	LWZ 203	9	13		
Heatshield—silencer	AHB 9065	10	1	(C) H–BJ7–17551 to 25314	
Heatshield—silencer	AHB 6227	10	1	(C) H–BJ8–25315 on	
Nut	LNZ 104	11	6		
Washer—plain	AJD 7212	12	6		

Plug—blanking

Description	Part No.	Illus. No.	Quantity	Change Point	Remarks
¼″ (6·35 mm.) dia of hole	RFN 204	13	2		
⁵⁄₁₆″ (7·93 mm.) dia of hole	RFR 205	13	4		
⅜″ (9·52 mm.) dia of hole	4G 6492	13	5		
½″ (12·7 mm.) dia of hole	RFR 208	13	1		
⅝″ (15·87 mm.) dia of hole	4G 2541	13	4/5		Quantity increased at (C) H–BJ8–25315
1″ (25·4 mm.) dia of hole	RFR 216	13	1		
1¼″ (31·75 mm.) dia of hole	RFN 220	13	2		
1⅜″ (34·92 mm.) dia of hole	4G 3575	13	1		
Safety strap hole in tunnel	ADA 2493	14	2		
Speedometer cable hole in gearbox cover	RFR 220	15	1		
Access holes in gearbox cover	4G 4920	16	2		

Grommet

Description	Part No.	Illus. No.	Quantity	Change Point	Remarks
Air intake control cable	RFN 403	17	1		
Steering column	3H 2506	18	1		
Drain tube	14B 9820	19	3	(C) H–BJ7–17551 to (B) H–BJ7–57499	
Drain tube through wheelarch	14B 9820	19	2	(C) H–BJ8–25315 on	
Gearbox cover fixings	AHB 9268	20	8		
Gear lever	AHB 9177	21	1	(C) H–BJ7–17551 to 20352	Not available; use AHB 9510
Gear—lever	AHB 9510	21	1	(C) H–BJ7–20353–25314 / (C) H–BJ8–25315 on	
Ring—gear lever grommet	AHH 5388	22	1	(C) H–BJ7–17551 to 20352	
Nut—dome—safety strap weld bolt	14B 2685	23	4		
Washer—plain—nut	PWZ 105	24	4		
Buffer—blanking hole in dash	2H 8041	25	1		
Tube—drain—cockpit water channel	AAA 2456	26	A/R		Supplied in 24″ (60·92cm.) lengths
Clip—drain tube	†HCS 0709	27	5	(B) H–BJ7–57500 to / (C) H–BJ7–25314 / (C) H–BJ8–25315 on	

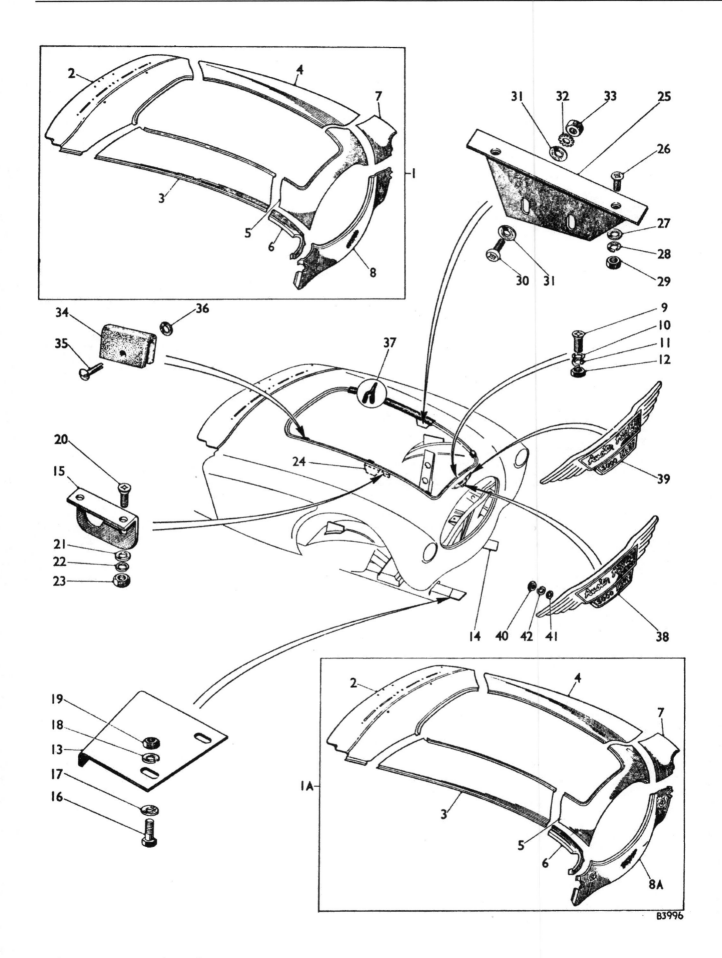

B3996

DESCRIPTION	Part No.	Illus. No.	Quantity	Exp.	UK	D	Change Point	REMARKS

†BONNET AND CONTROL DETAILS

	Page	Plate
† BONNET TOP ASSEMBLY	BB 3	B 2
† GRILLE—AIR INTAKE	BB 3	B 2
† HINGE—BONNET	BB 3	B 2
† MOTIF—BONNET SURROUND	BB 2	B 1
† ROD—BONNET LOCK REMOTE CONTROL	BB 4	B 3
† ROD—BONNET PROP	BB 3	B 2
† SURROUND ASSEMBLY—BONNET	BB 2	B 1

BONNET AND CONTROL DETAILS

DESCRIPTION	Part No.	Illus. No.	Quantity	Exp.	UK	D	Change Point	REMARKS
Surround assembly—bonnet except West Germany and Sweden	AHB 9440	1	1				(C) H-BJ7-17551 to 25314 / (C) H-BJ8-25315 to / (B) H-BJ8-76137	
Surround assembly—bonnet	AHB 9764	1A	1				(C) H-BJ7-17551 to 25314 / (C) H-BJ8-25315 on West Germany and Sweden / (B) H-BJ8-76138 on except West Germany and Sweden	
Panel								
Scuttle top	AHB 9254	2	1					
Wing inner—RH	14B 5723	3	1					
Wing inner—LH	14B 5724	4	1					
Cowl top	14B 5725	5	1					
Cowl side—RH	14B 5726	6	1					
Cowl side—LH	14B 5727	7	1					
Cowl bottom except West Germany and Sweden	14B 5728	8	1				(C) H-BJ7-17551 to 25314 / (C) H-BJ8-25315 to / (B) H-BJ8-76137	
Cowl bottom	AHB 9211	8A	1				(C) H-BJ7-17551 to 23514 / (C) H-BJ8-25315 on West Germany and Sweden / (B) H-BJ8-76138 on except West Germany and Sweden	
Screw	CMZ 0308	9	3					
Washer—plain	PWZ 103	10	3					
Washer—spring	LWZ 203	11	3					
Nut	FNZ 103	12	3					
Bracket								
Surround to chassis—RH	14B 7661	13	1					
Surround to chassis—LH	14B 7662	14	1					
Bonnet prop rod support	24B 773	15	1					†Included parts of body shell See page BA 2
Screw	HZS 0405	16	4					
Washer—plain	PWZ 104	17	8					
Washer—spring	LWZ 204	18	4					
Nut	FNZ 104	19	4					
Screw	CMZ 0310	20	2					
Washer—plain	PWZ 103	21	2					
Washer—shakeproof	LWZ 503	22	2					
Nut	FNZ 103	23	2					
Plate—support—bonnet opening—RH	14B 2005	24	1					
Plate—support—bonnet opening—LH	14B 2006	25	1					
Screw	CMZ 0308	26	4					
Washer—plain	PWZ 103	27	4					
Washer—spring	LWZ 203	28	4					
Nut	FNZ 103	29	4					
Screw	PMZ 0308	30	4					
Washer—plain	PWZ 203	31	8					
Washer—shakeproof	LWZ 503	32	4					
Nut	FNZ 103	33	4					
Buffer—bonnet (rubber)	14B 766	34	4					
Rivet	BRP 1110	35	4					
Washer—plain	PWZ 202	36	4					
Strip—sealing—bonnet surround—LH	AHB 9095	37	1					
Motif 'Austin-Healey 3000 Mk. II'	AHB 9014	38	1	★	★		(C) H-BJ7-17551 to 25314	
Motif 'Austin-Healey 3000 Mk. III'	AHB 6012	39	1	★	★		(C) H-BJ8-25315 on	
Nut	FNZ 103	40	2					
Washer—plain	PWZ 103	41	2					
Washer—spring	LWZ 203	42	2					

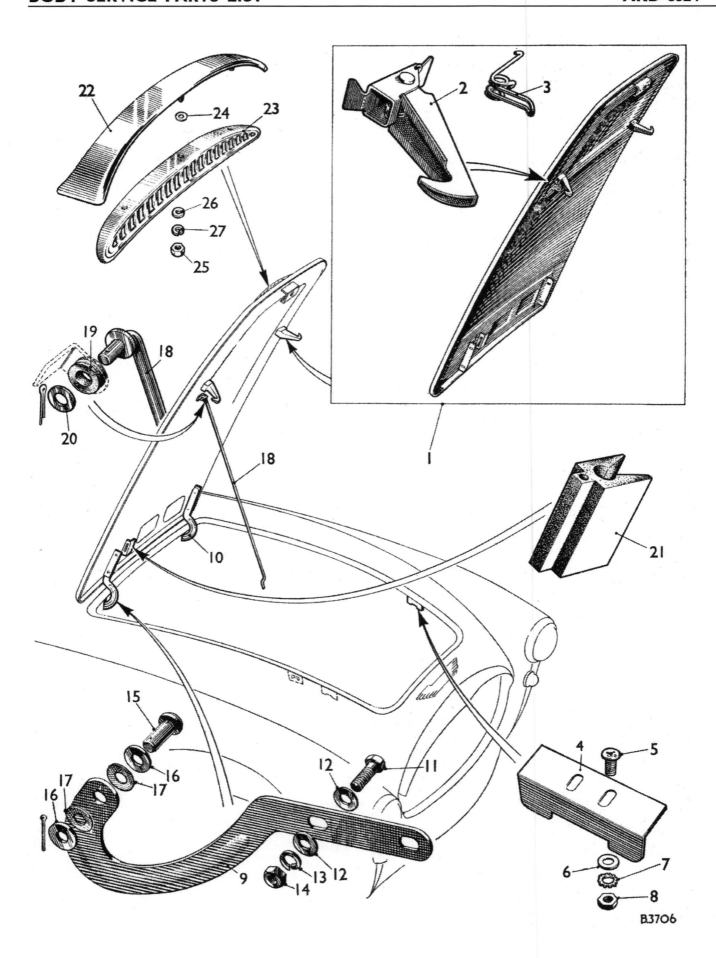

B.3706

	DESCRIPTION	Part No.	Illus. No.	Quantity	Stock recoms. DIST. Exp.	UK	D	Change Point	REMARKS

Bonnet and Control Details—*continued*

DESCRIPTION	Part No.	Illus. No.	Quantity		REMARKS
Bonnet top assembly	4B 1089	1	1	★	
Catch assembly—safety	14A 366	2	2		
Spring	4B 8646	3	2		
Striker—safety catch	14B 8812	4	2		
Screw—striker to bonnet surround	CMZ 0308	5	4		
Washer—plain	PWZ 203	6	4		
Washer—shakeproof	LWZ 503	7	4		
Nut—screw	FNZ 103	8	4		
Hinge—bonnet—RH	14G 3692	9	1		†Included parts of body shell See page BA 2
Hinge—bonnet—LH	14G 3693	10	1		
Screw—hinge to bonnet	HZS 0406	11	4		
Washer—plain	PWZ 104	12	8		
Washer—spring	LWZ 204	13	4		
Nut	FNZ 104	14	4		
Pin—clevis—hinge to body	CLZ 0511	15	2		
Washer—plain	PWZ 105	16	4		
Washer—anti-rattle	AWZ 105	17	4		
Rod—bonnet prop	AHB 5748	18	1		
Ferrule—prop rod (rubber)	2H 1046	19	1		
Washer—plain	PWZ 105	20	1		
Stop—prop rod (rubber)	2H 9215	21	1		
Surround—air intake	14B 5777	22	1		
Grille—air intake	AHB 9005	23	1		
Washer—packing—grille	14B 9484	24	3		
Nut—surround and grille to bonnet	FNZ 103	25	3		
Washer—plain	PWZ 103	26	3		
Washer—spring	LWZ 203	27	3		

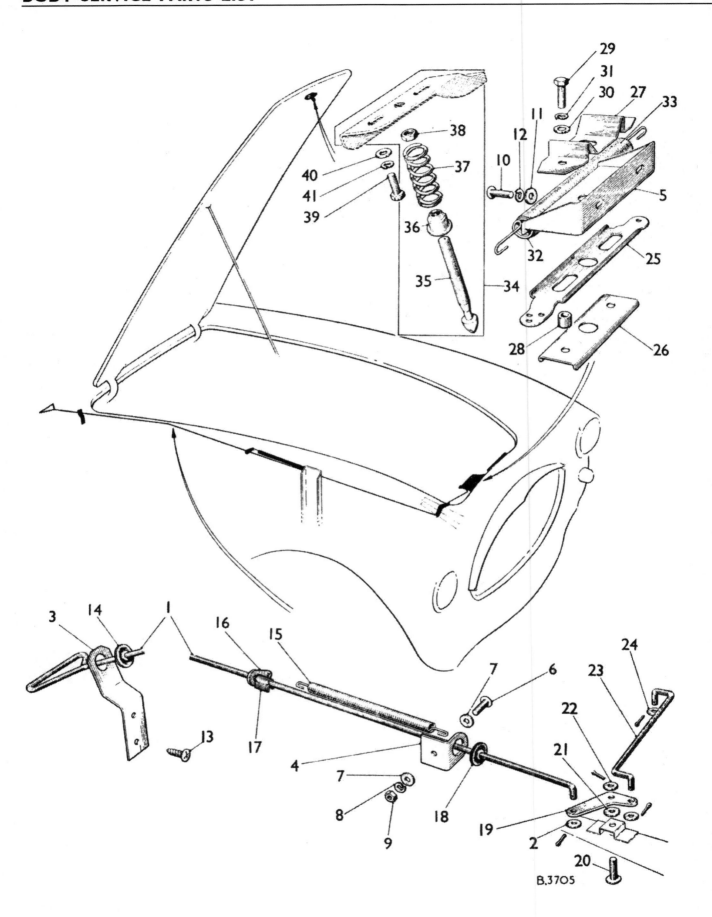

B.3705

DESCRIPTION	Part No.	Illus. No.	Quantity	Exp.	UK	D	Change Point	REMARKS
Bonnet and Control Details—*continued*								
Rod—bonnet lock remote control	14B 6805	1	1					
Washer—plain—rod	PWZ 103	2	1					
Bracket—support								
Remote control rod—rear	AHB 6506	3	1				†(C) H-BJ8-25315 on	
Remote control rod—front	14B 6806	4	1					
Bonnet lock	14B 5861	5	1					
Screw—remote control rod front support bracket	PMZ 0308	6	1					Included parts of body shell. See page BA 2
Washer—plain	PWZ 103	7	2				†(C) H-BJ7-17551 to 25314	
Washer—spring	LWZ 203	8	1					
Nut	FNZ 103	9	1					
Screw—bonnet lock support bracket	PMZ 0310	10	2					
Washer—plain	PWZ 103	11	2					
Washer—spring	LWZ 203	12	2					
Screw—remote control rod rear support bracket	PTZ 1004	13	2				†(C) H-BJ8-25315 on	
Grommet—control rod through dash panel	RFN 403	14	1					
Spring—anti-rattle—control rod	ADA 2450	15	1	★	★			
Bracket—anchor—spring	ACA 5314	16	1					
Clip—retaining—anchor bracket	14G 5507	17	1					
Grommet—control rod through support bracket	3F 90	18	1					
Lever—catch slider	ADA 3669	19	1					
Pin—clevis—lever	CLZ 0313	20	1					
Washer—plain	PWZ 203	21	1					
Washer—plain	PWZ 103	22	1					
Rod—connecting—lever to slider	14B 6754	23	1					
Washer—plain	PWZ 103	24	1					
Slider—bonnet catch	ADA 461	25	1					
Support—slider	ADH 456	26	1					
Plate—guide—striker pin	ADA 463	27	1					
Tube—distance—slider	ADA 464	28	2					
Screw—guide plate and slider to support	HZS 0407	29	2					
Washer—plain	PWZ 104	30	2					
Washer—spring	LWZ 204	31	2					
Spring—tension—bonnet catch	ADA 466	32	1	★	★			
Sleeve—spring (rubber)	ADA 467	83	1					
Pin assembly—striker—bonnet catch	14B 2845	34	1	★	★			
Pin	14A 6586	35	1					
Cup—spring retaining	ADA 458	36	1					
Spring	14B 2846	37	1					
Locknut	FNZ 206	38	1					
Screw—pin to bonnet	HZS 0405	39	2					
Washer—plain	PWZ 104	40	2					
Washer—spring	LWZ 204	41	2					

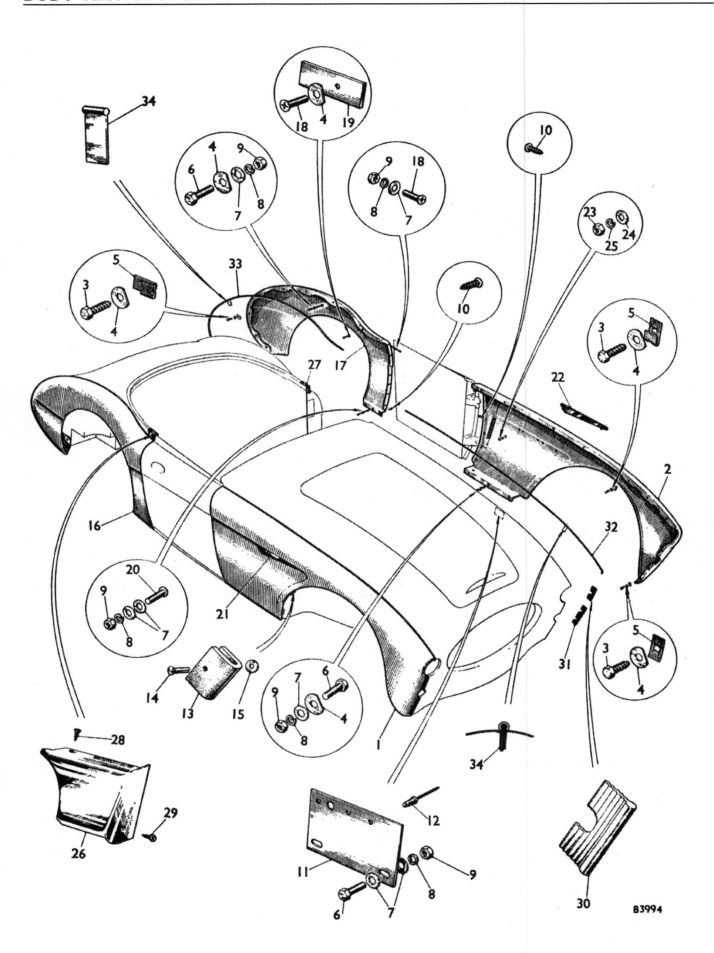

B3994

	DESCRIPTION	Part No.	Illus. No.	Quantity	Change Point	REMARKS

WING DETAILS

					Page	Plate
† FINISHER—REAR QUARTER PANEL	...	...	...		BC 3	C 1
† FLASH—FRONT WING	...	...	...	...	BC 3	C 1
† PANEL—REAR QUARTER	...	...	...	...	BC 2	C 1
† PIPING—WINGS	...	...	...	...	...	BC 3	C 1
† WINGS—FRONT	...	...	...	...	...	BC 2	C 1

WING DETAILS

Description	Part No.	Illus. No.	Quantity	Change Point	Remarks
Wing—front—RH	AHB 9442	1	1		
Wing—front—LH	AHB 9443	2	1		
Bolt	ABZ 0407	3	14		
Washer—'D'	2K 9993	4	14		
Nut—spring	6K 9817	5	14		
Bolt	ABZ 0406	3	6		
Washer—'D'	2K 9993	4	6		
Nut—spring	PFS 514	5	6		
Screw	HZS 0406	6	6		
Washer					
'D'	2K 9993	4	6		
plain	PWZ 104	7	6		
spring	LWZ 204	8	6		
Nut	FNZ 104	9	6		Included parts of body shell. See page BA 2
Screw	PTZ 603	10	14		
Bracket—wing support	14B 6453	11	2		
Screw	HZS 0406	6	4		
Washer—plain	2K 9051	7	8		
Washer—spring	LWZ 204	8	4		
Nut	FNZ 104	9	4		
Rivet	DMP 1239	12	6		
Buffer—wing (rubber)	14B 766	13	4		
Rivet	BRP 1108	14	4		
Washer—plain	PWZ 102	15	4		
Panel—rear quarter—RH	4B 1091	16	1		
Panel—rear quarter—LH	4B 1092	17	1		
Bolt	ABZ 0407	3	13/10		Quantities reduced, H-BJ7 at (B) 57499
Washer—'D'	2K 9993	4	13/10		
Nut—spring	6K 9817	5	13/10		

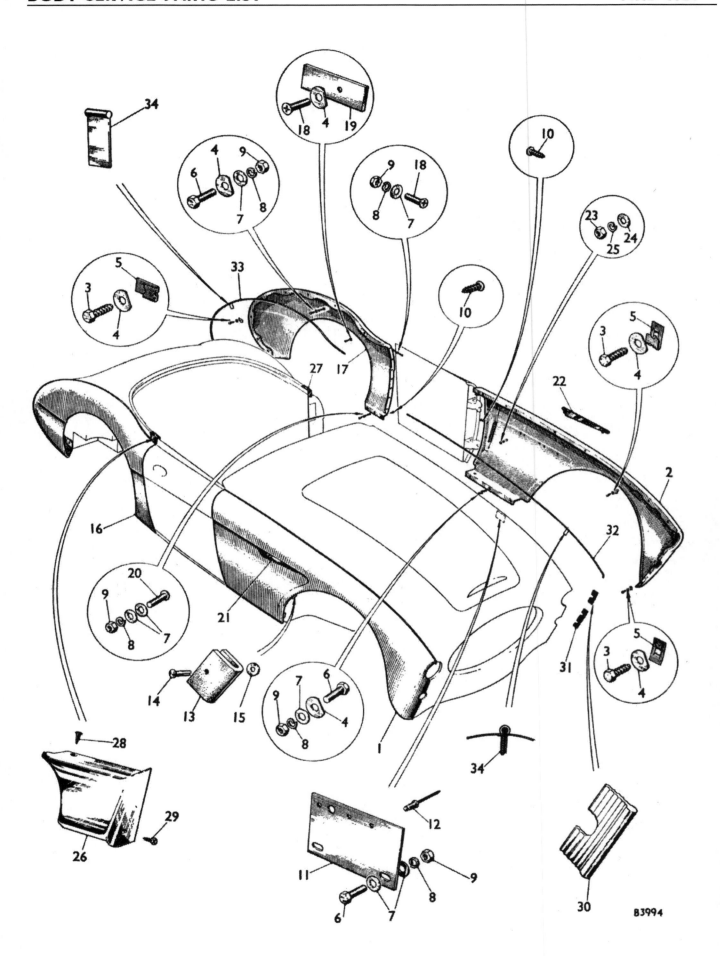

PLATE C 1

Issue 1

252

B3994

	DESCRIPTION	Part No.	Illus. No.	Quantity	Change Point	REMARKS
	Wing Details—*continued*					
	Screw	CMZ 0410	18	2		
	Washer—'D'	2K 9993	4	2	(B) H–BJ7–57500 on	
	Plate—tapped	†14B 2546	19	2		
	Screw	†HZS 0406	6	1/6		Quantities increased at (B) H–BJ7–57500
	Washer—'D'	†2K 9993	4	1/6		
	Washer—plain	†PWZ 104	7	1	(C) H–BJ7–17551 to (B) H–BJ7–57499	Included parts of body shell. see page BA 2
	Washer—spring	†LWZ 204	8	1/6		Quantities increased at (B) H–BJ7–57500
	Nut	†FNZ 104	9	1/2		
	Screw	†PMZ 0310	20	4		
	Washer—plain	†PWZ 103	7	8		
	Washer—spring	†LWZ 203	8	4		
	Nut	†FNZ 103	9	4		
	Screw	†PTZ 805	10	2		
	Screw	†CMZ 0308	18	16		
	Washer—plain	†PWZ 203	7	16		
	Washer—spring	†LWZ 203	8	16		
	Nut	†FNZ 103	9	16		
	Flash—front wing—RH	†14B 1727	21	1		
	Flash—front wing—LH	†14B 1728	22	1		
	Nut	†FNZ 103	23	6		
	Washer—plain	†PWZ 103	24	6		
	Washer—spring	†LWZ 203	25	6		
	Finisher—rear quarter panel—RH	†AHB 9571	26	1		
	Finisher—rear quarter panel—LH	†AHB 9572	27	1		
	Screw	†RTP 403	28	2		
	Screw	†CTZ 403	29	2		
	Piping					
	Front wing—upper (plastic)	†14B 6824	30	2		
	Front wing—lower (plastic)	†14B 6825	31	2		
	Front wing to bonnet surround	†14B 6729	32	2		
	Rear quarter panel to tonneau	†14B 1708	33	2		
	Tab—retaining—piping	†4G 7614	34	40		

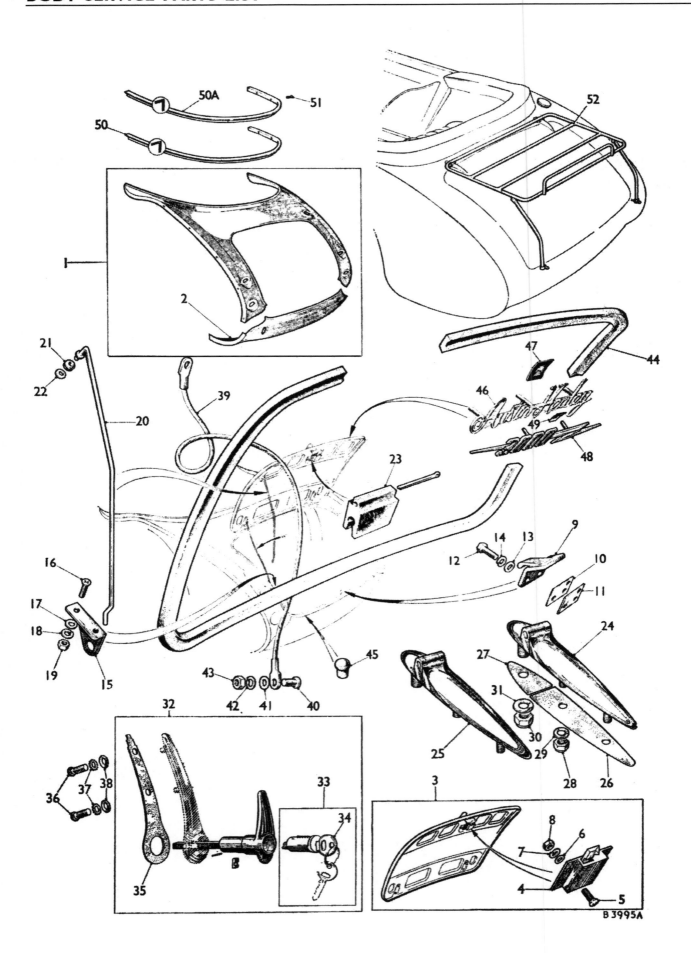

B 3995A

	DESCRIPTION	Part No.	Illus. No.	Quantity	Exp.	UK	D	Change Point	REMARKS

TONNEAU, BOOT LID AND FITTINGS

DESCRIPTION	Page	Plate
† CARRIER—LUGGAGE	BD 3	D 1
HANDLE—BOOT LID	BD 3	D 1
HINGE—BOOT LID	BD 2	D 1
LID—BOOT	BD 2	D 1
MOTIF—'3000'	BD 3	D 1
MOULDING—TONNEAU	BD 3	D 1
NAMEPLATE—'AUSTIN-HEALEY'	BD 3	D 1
TONNEAU ASSEMBLY	BD 2	D 1

TONNEAU, BOOT LID
AND FITTINGS

Description	Part No.	Illus. No.	Quantity	Exp.	UK	D	Change Point	REMARKS
Tonneau assembly except West Germany and Sweden	AHB 9441	1	1				(C) H-BJ7-17551 to 25314 (C) H-BJ8-25315 to (B) H-BJ8-76137	
West Germany and Sweden	AHB 9765	1	1				(C) H-BJ7-17551 to 25314 (C) H-BJ8-25315 to (B) H-BJ8-75207 West Germany (C) H-BJ8-25315 to (B) H-BJ8-76137 Sweden	
	AHB 7121	1	1				(B) H-BJ8-75208 on West Germany (B) H-BJ8-76138 on except West Germany	
Panel—rear skirt	14B 5739	2	1					†Included parts of body shell See page BA 2
Lid—boot	4B 1090	3	1					
Lock	14B 1718	4	1	★		★		
Screw	CMZ 0412	5	4					
Washer—plain	PWZ 104	6	4					
Washer—spring	LWZ 204	7	4					
Nut	FNZ 104	8	4					
Striker—lock	14B 1719	9	1					
Piece—packing	14B 6817	10	1					
Plate—tapped	14B 2038	11	1					
Screw	HZS 0407	12	3					
Washer—plain	PWZ 104	13	3					
Washer—spring	LWZ 204	14	3					
Bracket—prop rod support	14B 6467	15	1					
Screw	CMZ 0308	16	2					
Washer—plain	PWZ 103	17	2					
Washer—spring	LWZ 203	18	2					
Nut	FNZ 103	19	2					
Rod—boot lid prop	14B 6597	20	1					
Ferrule—prop rod (rubber)	2H 1046	21	1					
Washer—plain	PWZ 105	22	1					
Stop—prop rod (rubber)	2H 9215	23	1					
Hinge—boot lid—RH	14B 1725	24	1	★		★		
Hinge—boot lid—LH	14B 1726	25	1	★		★		
Washer—hinge to boot lid	14B 3462	26	2	★		★		
Washer—hinge to body	14B 3463	27	2	★		★		
Nut	53K 1661	28	4					
Washer—plain	PWZ 104	29	4					
Nut	53K 1662	30	2					
Washer—plain	PWZ 103	31	2					

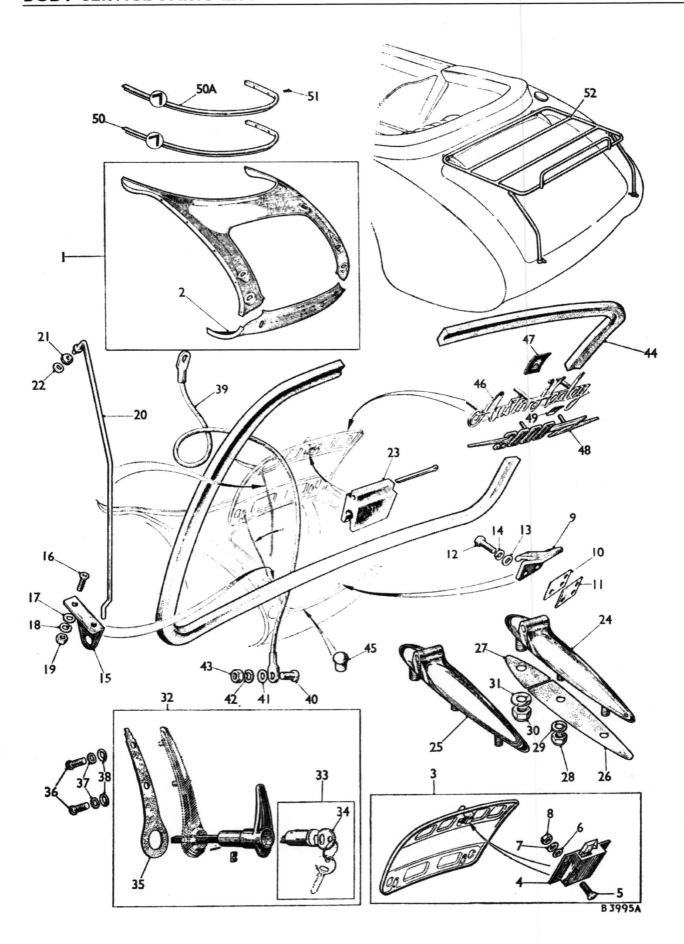

B 3995A

	DESCRIPTION	Part No.	Illus. No.	Quantity	Stock recoms. DIST. Exp.	UK	D	Change Point	REMARKS

Tonneau, Boot Lid and Fittings—*continued*

	DESCRIPTION	Part No.	Illus. No.	Quantity	Exp.	UK	D	Change Point	REMARKS
Handle assembly—locking		14B 1963	32	1	★	★			
Barrel—lock		2H 4185	33	1	★	★			Not available; use 24G 1345
Barrel—lock		24G 1345	33	1	★	★			
Key		ANK 4646	34	2					
Washer—seating		14B 1964	35	1	★	★			
Screw		PMZ 0306	36	2					
Washer—shakeproof		LWN 403	37	2					
Washer—cup		6K 9426	38	2					
Cable—boot lid control		14B 8692	39	1	★	★			
Screw		PMZ 0410	40	1					
Washer—plain		PWZ 104	41	1					
Washer—spring		LWZ 204	42	1					
Nut		FNZ 104	43	1					
Rubber—sealing—boot lid		14B 7466	44	1	★	★			
Buffer—boot lid		4G 8595	45	3					
Nameplate 'Austin-Healey'		8G 705	46	1	★	★			
Push-on-fix		PFS 106	47	3					
Motif '3000'		AHB 8861	48	1	★	★			
Push-on-fix		BHA 4082	49	2					
Moulding—tonneau		†AHB 9483	50	1				(C) H-BJ7-17551 to 22092	Not available; use AHB 9907
Moulding—tonneau		AHB 9907	50A	1				(C) H-BJ7-22093 to 25314 (C) H-BJ8-25315 on	
Screw		RTP 604	51	14/12					Quantity reduced at (B) H-BJ7-57500
Carrier—luggage		†17H 9932	52	1					Optional extra

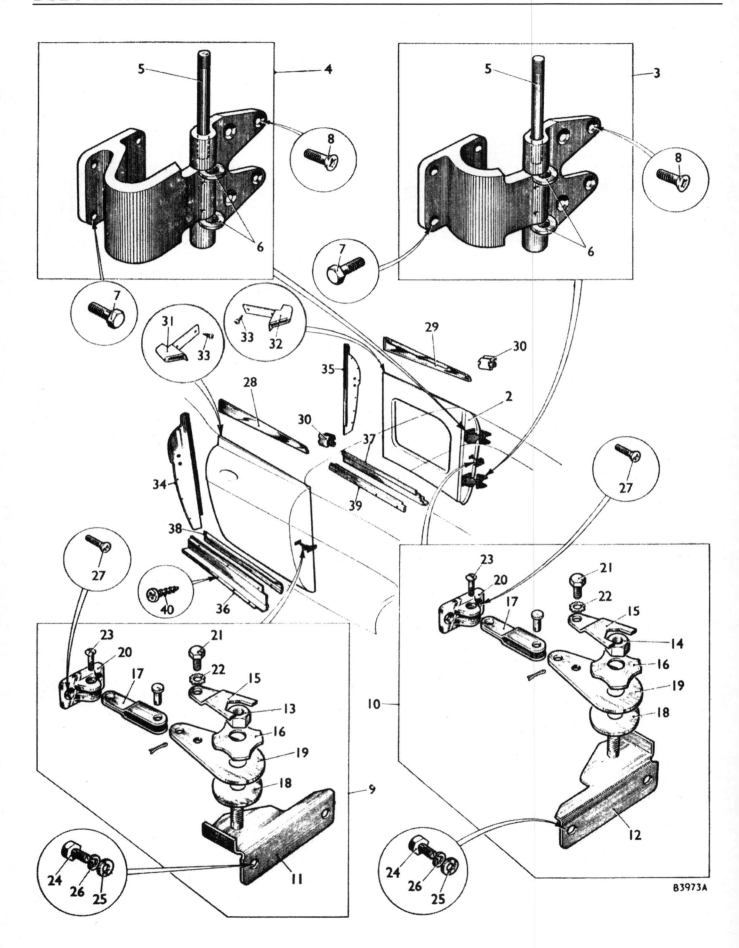

		DESCRIPTION	Part No.	Illus. No.	Quantity	DIST. Exp.	Stock recoms. UK	D	Change Point	REMARKS

DOORS AND FITTINGS

			Page	Plate
† CHECK ASSEMBLY	...	... ...	BF 2	F 1
† DOORS	...	... ...	BF 2	F 1
† HANDLE—DOOR ...	...	... ...	BF 3	F 2
† HANDLE—DOOR PULL ...	...	... ...	BF 3	F 2
† HANDLE—REMOTE CONTROL ...	...	... ...	BF 3	F 2
† HINGE—DOOR	...	... ...	BF 2	F 1
† LOCK AND REMOTE CONTROL ASSEMBLY ...		...	BF 3	F 2
† LOCK—DOOR	...	... ...	BF 3	F 2
† MOULDING—DOOR WAIST ...	...	... ...	BF 2	F 1

DOORS AND FITTINGS

Description	Part No.	Illus. No.	Quantity	Exp.	UK	D	Change Point	Remarks
Door								
Right-hand	AHB 9435	1	1				](C) H-BJ7-17551 to 25314]	
Left-hand	AHB 9436	2	1					
Right-hand	AHB 6717	1	1				](C) H-BJ8-25315 to 26704	
Left-hand	AHB 6718	2	1					
Right-hand	AHB 6889	1	1				](C) H-BJ8-26705 on	
Left-hand	AHB 6890	2	1					Included parts of body shell. See
Hinge assembly—lower	14B 5896	3	2	★	—	★		page BA 2
Hinge assembly—upper	AHB 9439	4	2	★	—	★		
Pin	14B 3732	5	4					
Washer—pin	2K 9005	6	8					
Screw								
Hinge to door—long	HZS 0508	7	12					
Hinge to door—short	HZS 0506	7	4					
Hinge to body	CMZ 0516	8	16				]	
Check assembly—RH	14B 7554	9	1					
Check assembly—LH	14B 7555	10	1					
Bracket and stud—RH	14B 7556	11	1					
Bracket and stud—LH	14B 7557	12	1					
Nut—stud—RHT	53K 1191	13	1					
Nut—stud—LHT	53K 1712	14	1					
Spanner—friction	14B 7562	15	2					
Washer—spring	14B 7563	16	2					
Link—connection	14B 7564	17	2					
Disc—friction	14B 7565	18	2					
Arm	14B 7566	19	2					
Bracket—strap to door	14B 4466	20	2					
Screw	53K 122	21	2					
Washer—shakeproof	LWN 403	22	2					
Screw	54K 3495	23	2					
Screw	HZS 0406	24	4					
Washer—plain	PWZ 104	25	4					
Washer—spring	LWZ 304	26	4					
Screw	RMP 0310	27	4					
Moulding—door waist—RH	AHB 9569	28	1					
Moulding—door waist—LH	AHB 9570	29	1					
Clip—moulding	BHA 4359	30	10/14					Quantity increased at (C) H-BJ8-25315
Seal—shut pillar—top—RH	AHB 9930	31	1				](B) H-BJ7-57500 to	
Seal—shut pillar—top—LH	AHB 9931	32	1				(C) H-BJ7-25314	
Screw	MTP 404	33	4				](C) H-BJ8-25315 on	
Plate—cover								
Shut pillar panel—RH	AHB 9472	34	1					
Shut pillar panel—LH	AHB 9473	35	1					
Sill panel—outer—RH	14B 6765	36	1					
Sill panel—outer—LH	14B 6766	37	1					
Sill panel—inner—RH	24B 880	38	1					
Sill panel—inner—LH	24B 881	39	1					
Screw—plate	54K 3024	40	36					
Tape-sealing 4½″ (11·5 cm.) wide	†37H 2506		A/R					Supplied in 50′ (15·2 m.) rolls

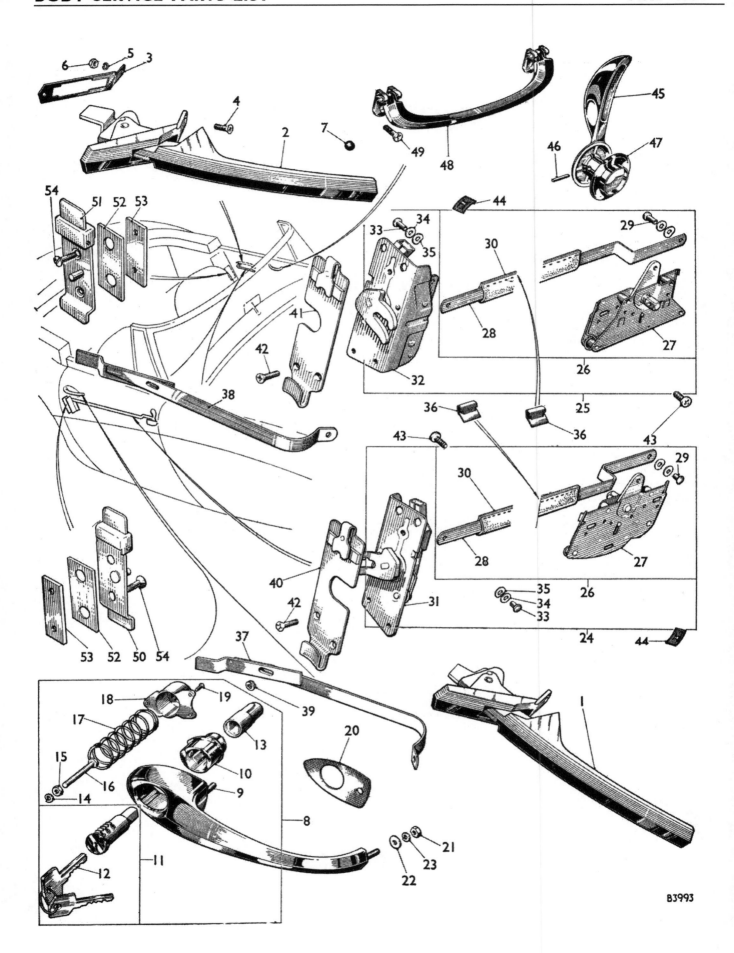

B3993

Doors and Fittings—*continued*

DESCRIPTION	Part No.	Illus. No.	Quantity	Exp.	UK	D	Change Point	REMARKS
Handle—door—RH	AHB 9537	1	1	★	★			
Handle—door—LH	AHB 9538	2	1	★	★			
Washer—seating	14B 9476	3	2				(C) H-BJ7-17551 to 25314	
Screw—handle to door	RMP 0308	4	2				(C) H-BJ8-25315 to 26704	
Washer—spring	LWZ 203	5	4					
Nut	FNZ 103	6	4					
Buffer—handle	2H 8041	7	2					
Handle—door—locking	AHB 6882	8	2	★	★			
Stud	27H 2863	9	4					
Button	27H 2864	10	2					
Lock barrel	27H 2865	11	2	★	★			
Key	ANK 4646	12	4					
Latch	27H 2866	13	2					
Washer—spring	†27H 2278	14	2					W.S.E. use AJD 7612
Washer—spring	AJD 7612	14	2				(C) H-BJ8-26705 on	
Locknut	†27H 2867	15	2					W.S.E. use AJD 8012 C
Locknut	†AJD 8012 C	15	2					
Bolt	†27H 2868	16	2					W.S.E. use 97H 2542
Bolt	†97H 2542	16	2					
Spring	27H 2869	17	2					
Plate—base	27H 2870	18	2					
Screw—retaining	ADH 2851	19	4					
Washer—handle seating	AHB 6883	20	2					
Nut—handle to door	FNZ 103	21	4					
Washer—plain	PWZ 203	22	4					
Washer—spring	LWZ 203	23	4					
Lock and remote control assembly								
Right hand	AHB 9437	24	1	★	★		(C) H-BJ7-17551 to 25314	
Left hand	AHB 9438	25	1	★	★			
Right hand	AHB 6389	24	1	★	★		(C) H-BJ8-25315 on	
Left hand	AHB 6390	25	1	★	★			
Remote control and connecting link assembly	7H 8379	26	2				(C) H-BJ7-17551 to 25314	
Control—remote	27H 2200	27	2				(C) H-BJ8-25315 on	
Link—connecting	7H 8382	28	2					
Rivet—link to remote control	27H 9833	29	2					
Sleeve—link—anti-rattle	7H 8383	30	2					
Lock								
Right hand	†7H 8380	31	1				(C) H-BJ7-17551 to 23514 W.S.E. use 27H 2198	
Left hand	7H 8384	32	1					
Right hand	27H 2198	31	1				(C) H-BJ8-25315 on	
Left hand	27H 2199	32	1					
Rivet—lock to link	27H 9833	33	2					
Washer—plain	PWN 104	34	2					
Washer—anti-rattle	ALH 1879	35	2					
Clip—anti-rattle sleeve	14A 4497	36	2					
Contactor—door lock—RH	AHB 7105	37	1					
Contactor—door lock—LH	AHB 7106	38	1				(C) H-BJ8-26705 on	
Washer—D/C spring	AJD 7712	39	2					
Plate—lock—RH	AHB 9532	40	1					
Plate—lock—LH	AHB 9533	41	1					
Screw—lock and plate to door	RMZ 0308	42	6					
Screw—remote control to door	PJZ 1004	43	6					
Nut—spire	53K 3039	44	6					
Handle—remote control	14G 3763	45	2	★	★			
Peg—handle	14G 3766	46	2					
Escutcheon—handle	14G 3764	47	2					
Handle—pull	4B 3479	48	2	★	★			
Screw—handle to door	54K 3413	49	4					
Striker—door lock—RH	AHB 9541	50	1	★	★			
Striker—door lock—LH	AHB 9542	51	1	★	★			
Plate—packing—striker	AHB 9470	52	2					
Plate—tapped—striker	AHB 9471	53	2					
Screw—striker	CMZ 0512	54	4					

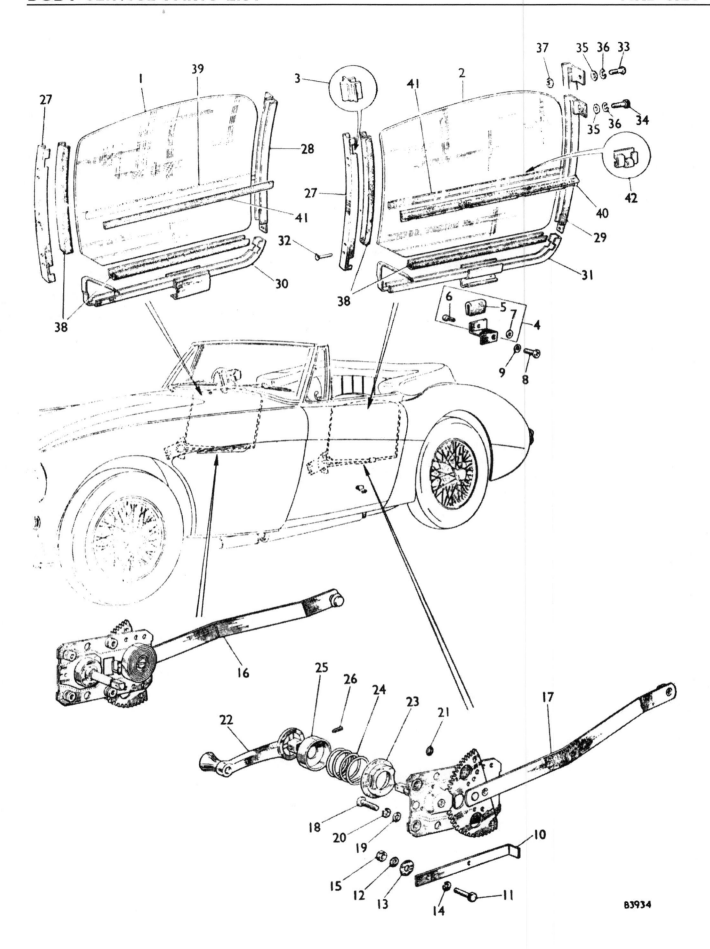

B3934

	DESCRIPTION	Part No.	Illus. No.	Quantity	Stock recoms. DIST. Exp.	UK	D	Change Point	REMARKS

WINDOWS AND WINDOW MECHANISM

	Page	Plate
† CHANNELS—GLASS	BG 2	G 1
† GLASS—DOOR	BG 2	G 1
† HANDLE—REGULATOR	BG 2	G 1
† REGULATOR—WINDOW	BG 2	G 1
† SEALS—DOOR WAIST	BG 2	G 1
† VENTILATOR ASSEMBLIES	BG 3	G 2

WINDOWS AND WINDOW MECHANISM

Description	Part No.	Illus. No.	Quantity	Stock	Change Point	Remarks
Glass—door—RH	AHB 9425	1	1			
Glass—door—LH	AHB 9426	2	1			
Runner—door glass (nylon)	AHB 9499	3	6			
Buffer stop assembly—door glass	AHB 9662	4	2			
Buffer	14B 766	5	2			
Rivet	BRP 1108	6	2			
Washer—plain	PWZ 102	7	2			
Screw—buffer stop to door	PMZ 0306	8	4			
Washer—shakeproof	LWZ 403	9	4			
Bracket—stop—door glass	AHB 9914	10	2			
Screw—bracket to door	HZS 0405	11	4			
Washer						
Plain	PWZ 104	12	2			
Plain	PWZ 404	13	2			
Spring	LWZ 204	14	4			
Nut	FNZ 104	15	8			
Regulator—window						
Right hand	AHB 9491	16	1	★—★	](C) H-BJ7-17551 to 25314	
Left hand	AHB 9492	17	1	★—★		
Right hand	AHB 6387	16	1	★—★	](C) H-BJ8-25315 on	
Left hand	AHB 6388	17	1	★—★		
Screw—regulator to door	PMZ 0408	18	8			
Washer—plain	PWZ 104	19	8			
Washer—spring	LWZ 204	20	8			
Ring—anti-rattle—regulator spindle	14A 6642	21	2			
Handle—regulator	14G 6503	22	2	★—★		
Escutcheon—handle	24G 1233	23	2			
Spring—handle	14G 6506	24	2	★—★		
Crown—handle	14G 6505	25	2			
Peg—handle	4G 1636	26	2	★—★		
Channel—glass						
Front	AHB 9522	27	2			
Rear—RH	AHB 9524	28	1			
Rear—LH	AHB 9525	29	1			
Lower—RH	AHB 9721	30	1			
Lower—LH	AHB 9722	31	1			
Rivet—front channel to lower channel	DMP 0840	32	4			
Screw—rear channel to door	PMZ 0310	33	4		(C) H-BJ7-17551 to (B) H-BJ7-57499	
Screw—rear channel to door	53K 126	34	4		(B) 57500 to (C) H-BJ7-25314 (C) H-BJ8-25315 on	
Washer—plain	PWZ 103	35	16/4			Quantity reduced at (B) H-BJ7-57500
Washer—spring	LWZ 203	36	4			
Nut	FNZ 103	37	4		(C) H-BJ7-17551 to (B) H-BJ7-57499	
Strip—glazing—glass						
Lower	†AHB 9519		2			]W.S.E. use
Front	†AHB 9518		2			AHB 9521
	AHB 9521	38	A/R			Supplied in multiples of feet
Seal—door waist						
Rubber—RH	AHH 6348	39	1	★—★		
Rubber—LH	AHH 6349	40	1	★—★		
Brush	AHB 9520	41	2			
Clip—brush seal to door	BHA 4340	42	8			

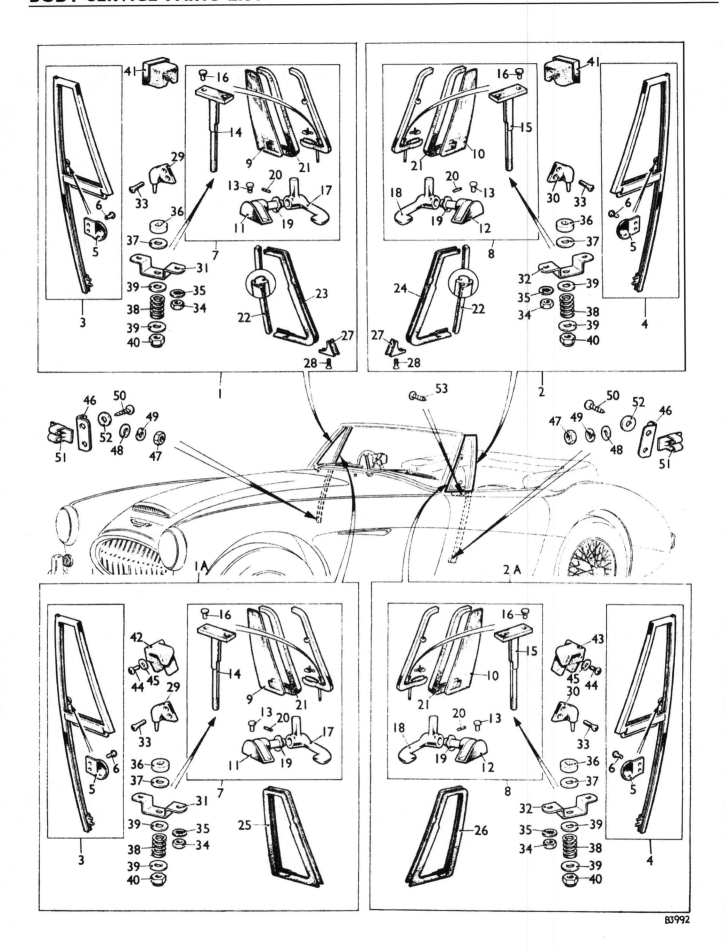

B3992

	DESCRIPTION	Part No.	Illus. No.	Quantity	Exp.	UK	D	Change Point	REMARKS
	Windows and Window Mechanism—*continued*								
	Ventilator assembly								
	Right hand	AHB 9481	1	1				⎤(C) H-BJ7-17551 to 20109	
	Left hand	AHB 9482	2	1					
	Right hand	AHB 9893	1A	1				⎤(C) H-BJ7-20110 to 25314	
	Left hand	AHB 9894	2A	1				(C) H-BJ8-25315 on	
	Right hand ⎤USA	†18G 8470	1A	1					
	Left hand	†18G 8471	1A	1				⎦	
	Frame assembly—outer—RH	17H 2837	3	1					⎤Prior to (C) H-BJ7-
	Frame assembly—outer—LH	17H 2838	4	1					20110 supply also 1 off top corner block AHB 9951 RH or AHB 9954 LH together with 1 off each PMZ 0204 screw, and PWZ 102 washer⎦
	Plate—handle locking	17H 2841	5	2					
	Rivet—plate to frame	ARO 9399	6	4					
	Frame assembly—inner								
	Right hand	†17H 2871	7	1					
	Left hand	†17H 2872	8	1					
	Right hand ⎤USA	†18G 8516	7	1					
	Left hand	†18G 8577	8	1					
	Glass—RH	AHB 9427	9	1					
	Glass—LH	AHB 9428	10	1					
	Bracket—handle—RH	17H 2844	11	1					
	Bracket—handle—LH	17H 2845	12	1					
	Rivet—bracket to frame	ARO 9166	13	4					
	Pivot—lower—RH	17H 2848	14	1					
	Pivot—lower—LH	17H 2849	15	1					
	Rivet—pivot to frame	ARO 9166	16	4					
	Handle—locking—RH	17H 2846	17	1	★	★			
	Handle—locking—LH	17H 2847	18	1	★	★			
	Washer—anti-rattle	27H 9985	19	2					Part No. change; was 37H 9731
	Pin—handle to bracket	37H 9732	20	2					W.S.E. use 14A 2625
	Pin—handle to bracket	14A 2625	20	2					
	Rubber—glazing	17H 2531	21	2					
	Rubber—sealing								
	Straight	17H 2812	22	1				⎤	W.S.E. use 27H 2787 RH or 27H 2788 LH
	Contoured—RH	17H 2814	23	1				(C) H-BJ7-17551 to 20109	W.S.E. use 27H 2787
	Contoured—RH	27H 2787	23	1					
	Contoured—LH	17H 2813	24	1					W.S.E. use 27H 2788
	Contoured—LH	27H 2788	24	1					
	Right hand	17H 2854	25	1	★	★		(C) H-BJ7-20110 to 25314	
	Left hand	17H 2855	26	1	★	★		(C) H-BJ8-25315 on	
	Block—front corner	17H 2852	27	2				(C) H-BJ7-17551 to 20109	
	Screw—block to outer frame	CMZ 0210	28	2				⎦	
	Bracket								
	Top pivot—outer—RH	17H 2839	29	1					
	Top pivot—outer—LH	17H 2840	30	1					
	Lower pivot—RH	17H 2842	31	1					
	Lower pivot—LH	17H 2843	32	1					
	Screw—top pivot bracket to outer frame	RMP 0206	33	4					
	Nut—lower pivot bracket to frame	AJD 8012Z	34	4					
	Washer—shakeproof	LWZ 403	35	4					
	Collar—lower pivot	17H 2850	36	2					
	Washer—distance	PWZ 104	37	2					
	Spring—lower pivot	17H 2851	38	2					
	Washer—plain	PWZ 104	39	4					
	Nut	17H 3176	40	2					
	Cover—top corner	17H 2853	41	2				(C) H-BJ7-17551 to 20109	
	Block—top corner—RH (rubber)	AHB 9951	42	1				⎤	
	Block—top corner—LH (rubber)	AHB 9954	43	1				(C) H-BJ7-20110 to 25314	
	Screw—block to frame	PMZ 0204	44	2				(C) H-BJ8-25315 on	
	Washer—plain	PWZ 102	45	2				⎦	
	Bracket—ventilator to door	AHB 9422	46	2					
	Nut—bracket	FNZ 103	47	4					
	Washer—plain	PWZ 103	48	4					
	Washer—spring	LWZ 203	49	4					
	Screw—ventilator to door	PJZ 1004	50	8					
	Nut—spire	53K 3039	51	8					
	Washer—plain	AJD 7202	52	8					
	Screw	MTP 404	53	4					

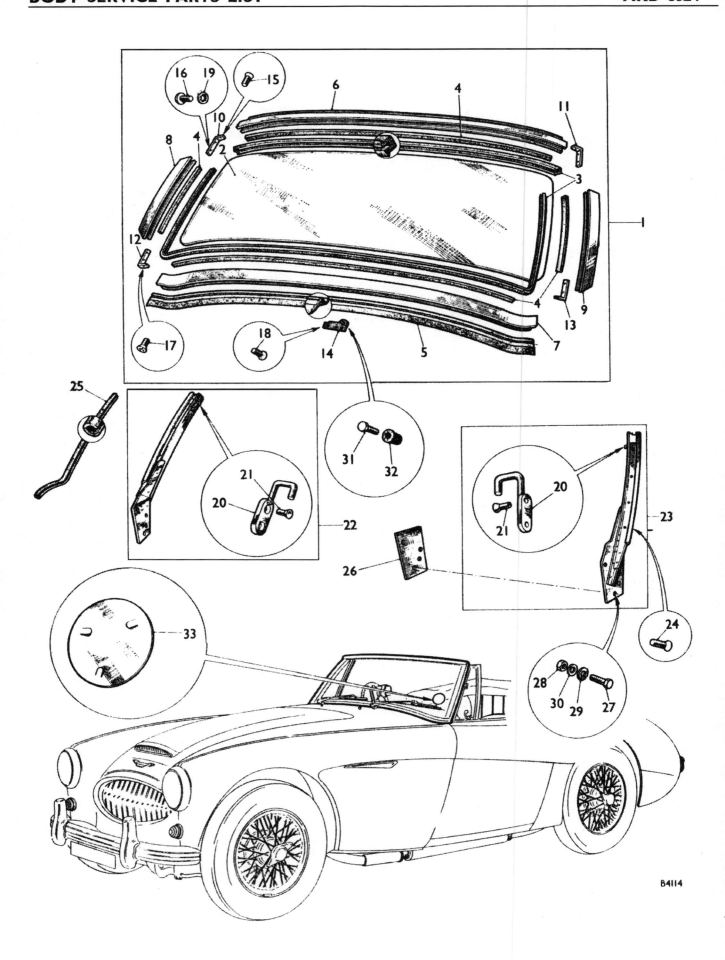

B4114

			DESCRIPTION	Part No.	Illus. No.	Quantity	Stock recoms. DIST. Exp.	UK	D	Change Point	REMARKS

†WINDSCREEN, WINDSCREEN WASHER AND MIRRORS

		Page	Plate
† GLASS—WINDSCREEN		BH 2	H 1
† HOLDER—LICENCE		BH 2	H 1
† PILLARS—WINDSCREEN		BH 2	H 1
† WINDSCREEN ASSEMBLY		BH 2	H 1
† WINDSCREEN WASHER		BH 3	H 2
MIRROR		BH 2	H 2

WINDSCREEN, WINDSCREEN WASHER AND MIRRORS

WINDSCREEN

Description	Part No.	Illus. No.	Qty	Exp.	UK	Change Point	Remarks
Windscreen assembly	17H 2815	1	1				
Windscreen assembly .... **USA**	37H 2988	1	1				
Glass	†AHB 9424	2	1	★	★		W.S.E. use AHB 7188
Glass .... **USA**	AHB 7188	2	1				
Rubber							
Glazing	AHB 9786	3	1	★	★		
Packing	17H 6910	4	1	★	★		Use 37H 3228 for this application
Packing	37H 3228		A/R				Supplied in multiples of feet
Sealing—windscreen to shroud panel	AHB 9787	5	1	★	★		W.S.E.; use AHB 9904
Sealing—windscreen to shroud panel	AHB 9904	5	1				
Channel							
Upper	AHB 9772	6	1				
Lower	AHB 9773	7	1				
Side—RH	AHB 9774	8	1				
Side—LH	AHB 9775	9	1				
Bracket							
Upper corner—RH	AHB 9778	10	1				
Upper corner—LH	AHB 9779	11	1				
Lower corner—RH	AHB 9780	12	1				
Lower corner—LH	AHB 9781	13	1				
Centre	AHB 9784	14	1				
Screw							
Bracket to top channel	AJD 4243C	15	2				
Bracket to side channel	AJD 1203Z	16	8				
Side bracket to lower channel	AJD 4243Z	17	2				
Centre bracket to lower channel	RMP 0203	18	2				
Washer—shakeproof—screw	LWZ 403	19	8				
Pillar assembly—side—RH	17H 2816	22	1				
Pillar assembly—side—LH	17H 2817	23	1				
Hook—toggle	AHB 9785	20	2				
Rivet—hook to reinforcement	17H 2967	21	4				
Screw—pillar to windscreen	RMP 0308	24	8				
Rubber—sealing—pillar—grey	AHB 9589	25	2	★	★		
Packing piece—foot	AHB 9659	26	A/R				
Bolt	HBZ 0408	27	6/1				Quantity reduced at (C) H-BJ8-25315
Screw	HZS 0406	27	2/5				Quantity increased at (C) H-BJ8-25315
Bolt	HBZ 0409	27	2			(C) H-BJ8-25315 on	
Nut—bolt and screw	FNZ 104	28	8				
Washer—plain	PWZ 104	29	8				
Washer—spring	LWZ 204	30	8				
Screw—bracket	HZS 0406	31	1				
Nut	AHB 9794	32	1				
Holder—licence	14A 3823	33	1				

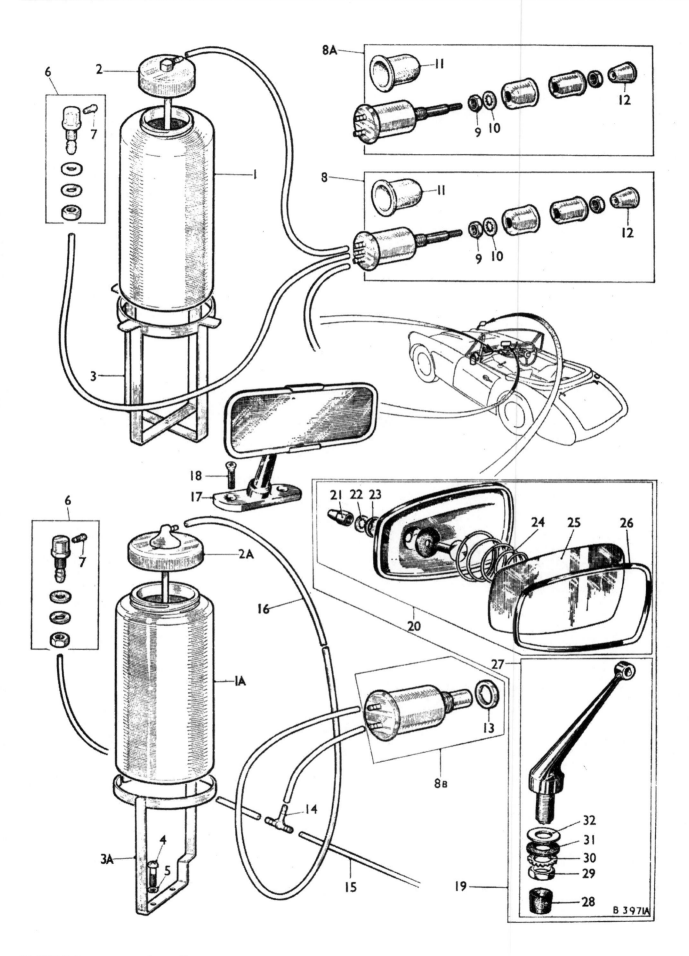

	DESCRIPTION	Part No.	Illus. No.	Quantity	Stock recoms. DIST. Exp.	UK	D	Change Point	REMARKS

Windscreen, Windscreen Washer and Mirrors—*continued*

WINDSCREEN WASHER

Description	Part No.	Illus. No.	Qty	Exp.	UK	D	Change Point	Remarks
Container	37H 9729	1	1	★	★			
Cap	17H 2670	2	1				(C) H-BJ7-17551 to 25314	
Bracket	27H 9671	3	1					
Container	13H 227	1A	1	★	★			
Cap assembly	AHH 6848	2A	1					
Bracket	†AHH 6856	3A	1				(C) H-BJ8-25315 on	W.S.E.; use 13H 232
Bracket	†13H 232	3A	1					
Screw—bracket	PMZ 0308	4	2					
Washer—spring	LWZ 203	5	2					
Jet assembly	13H 231	6	2	★	★			
Jet	27H 9623	7	2					
Washer (rubber)	†37H 9523		2					
Washer (brass)	†37H 9522		2					
Nut	†AJD 8012Z		2					
Control assembly	37H 9730	8	1				(C) H-BJ7-17551 to 20125	
Control assembly	17H 2672	8A	1				(C) H-BJ7-20126 to 25314	
Nut	27H 9655	9	2					
Washer—shakeproof	LWN 406	10	1				(C) H-BJ7-17551 to 25314	
Bulb (rubber)	27H 9824	11	1					
Knob	27H 9625	12	1					
Control assembly	†BHA 4362	8B	1				(C) H-BJ8-25315 on	W.S.E.; use BHA 4510
Control assembly	†BHA 4510	8B	1					
Ring—locking	17H 2669	13	1					
Connection—3-way	BHA 4361	14	1				(C) H-BJ7-20126 to 25314 (C) H-BJ8-25315 on	
Tubing—3/16″ (4·76mm.) OD	37H 9708	15	A/R	★	★			Supplied in multiples of feet
Tubing—1/4″ (6·35mm.) OD	97H 2679	16	A/R	★	★		(C) H-BJ7-20126 to 25314 (C) H-BJ8-25315 on	

MIRRORS

Description	Part No.	Illus. No.	Qty	Exp.	UK	D	Change Point	Remarks
Mirror—interior	†14B 1867	17	1	★	★		(C) H-BJ7-17551 to 25314 (C) H-BJ8-25315 to (B) H-BJ8-73213	W.S.E.; use AHB 6920
Mirror—interior	AHB 6920	17	1				(B) H-BJ8-73214 on	
Screw—mirror to scuttle	RMP 0312	18	2					
Mirror—wing—boomerang type	27H 9863	19	2					
Head assembly	37H 9947	20	2					
Nut—dome	37H 9967	21	2					
Washer—shakeproof	37H 9968	22	2					
Collar	47H 9510	23	2					
Spring	17H 8148	24	2					
Glass	17H 8146	25	2					Optional extra
Ring—glass retaining (plastic)	17H 8147	26	2					
Arm assembly	37H 9946	27	2					
Ferrule (rubber)	37H 9974	28	2					
Nut	37H 9970	29	2					
Washer—shakeproof	37H 9972	30	2					
Washer (rubber)	37H 9971	31	2					
Washer—plain	37H 9973	32	2					

† Revised Information.

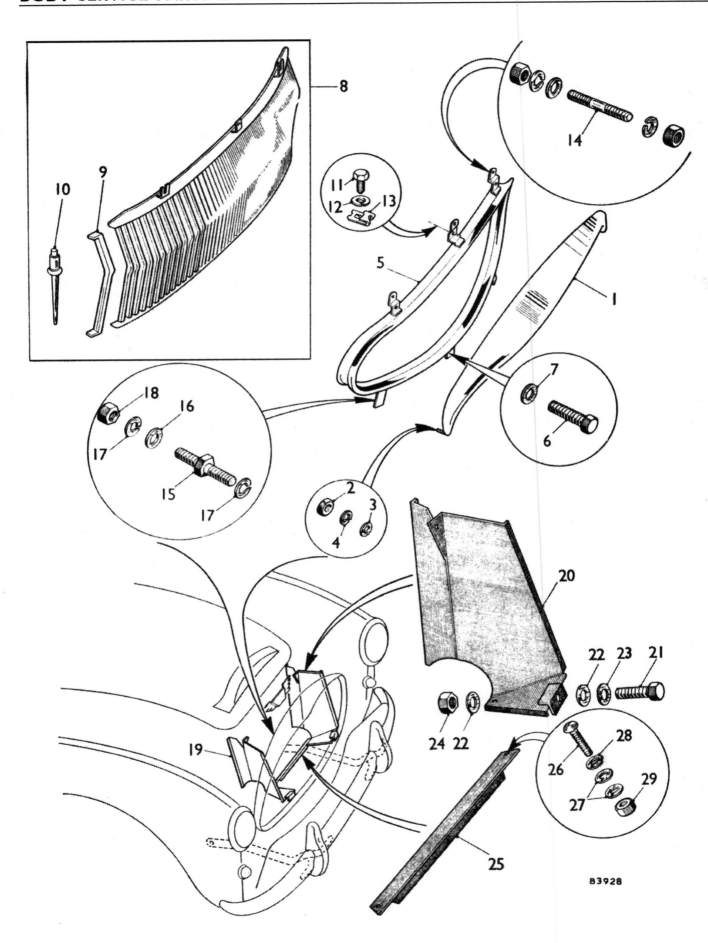

B3928

	DESCRIPTION	Part No.	Illus. No.	Quantity	Stock recoms. DIST. Exp.	UK	D	Change Point	REMARKS

†RADIATOR GRILLE

					Page	Plate
† DEFLECTOR—AIR INTAKE	...	...	...	...	BJ 2	J 1
† GRILLE—RADIATOR	...	...	...	...	BJ 2	J 1
† HOOD—RADIATOR GRILLE	...	...	...	...	BJ 2	J 1
† SURROUND—RADIATOR GRILLE		...	...	...	BJ 2	J 1

RADIATOR GRILLE

Description	Part No.	Illus. No.	Quantity	Exp.	UK	Change Point
Hood—radiator grille	AHB 9001	1	1			
Nut—hood to body	CNZ 102	2	2			
Washer—plain	PWZ 102	3	2			(C) H-BJ7-17551 to ▼
Washer—spring	LWZ 202	4	2			
Surround—radiator grille	AHB 8999	5	1	★	★	
Screw—surround to body	HZS 0405	6	1			
Washer—spring	LWZ 204	7	1			
Slat assembly—radiator grille	AHB 9000	8	1	★	★	
Slat	AHB 9011	9	39			
Rivet—slat to rail	DMP 2824	10	156			
Bolt—slat to surround—centre	ABZ 0404	11	2			
Washer—spring	LWZ 204	12	2			
Nut—spring	6K 9817	13	2			
Stud—hood, surround and slat to body—top	AHB 9209	14	3			
Stud—surround and slat to body—bottom	AHB 9019	15	2			
Washer—plain	PWZ 104	16	7			
Washer—spring	LWZ 204	17	10			
Nut	FNZ 104	18	7			
Deflector—air intake—RH	AHB 9092	19	1			
Deflector—air intake—LH	AHB 9093	20	1			
Screw—deflector to body	HZS 0406	21	2			
Washer—plain	AJD 7282	22	4			
Washer—spring	LWZ 204	23	2			
Nut	FNZ 104	24	2			
Tie-bar—deflector	24B 601	25	1			
Screw—tie-bar to deflector	PMZ 0308	26	2			
Washer—plain	PWZ 103	27	4			
Washer—spring	LWZ 203	28	2			
Nut	FNZ 103	29	2			

▼ Change point not available

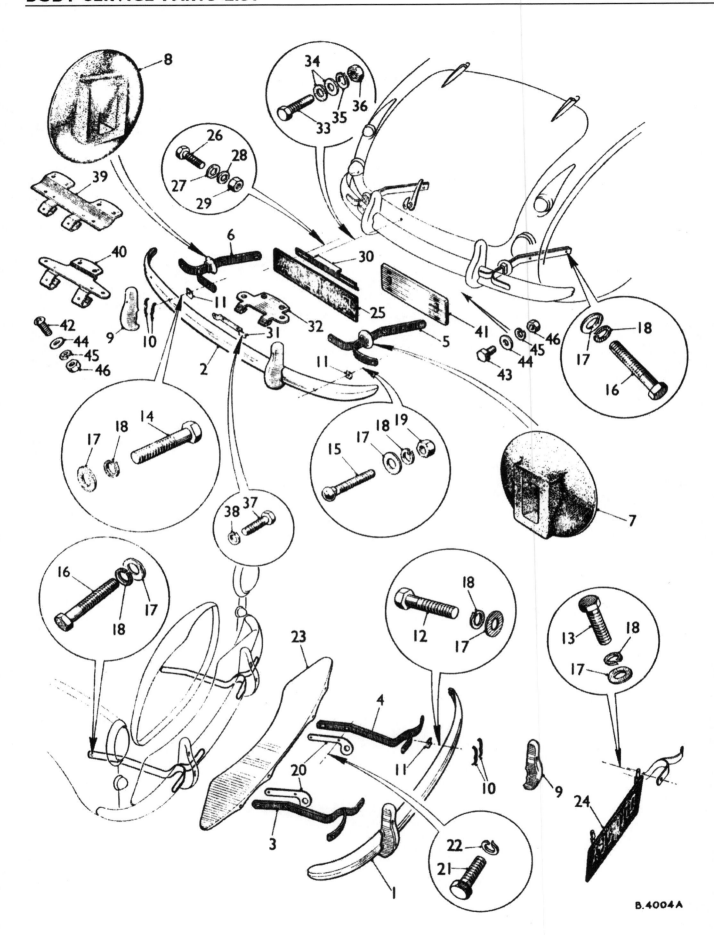

B.4004A

	DESCRIPTION	Part No.	Illus. No.	Quantity	DIST. Exp.	Stock recoms. UK	D	Change Point	REMARKS

†BUMPERS AND NUMBER-PLATE

						Page	Plate
† BUMPERS ...	...	...	...	...	...	BK 2	K 1
† NUMBER PLATES ...	...	...	...	...	...	BK 2	K 1
† OVER-RIDERS ...	...	...	...	...	...	BK 2	K 1

BUMPERS AND NUMBER-PLATE

Description	Part No.	Illus. No.	Qty	Dist.	Change Point	Remarks
Bar—bumper—front	11B 5303	1	1	★ ★		
Bar—bumper—rear	11B 5312	2	1	★ ★		
Spring—bumper bar						
Front—RH	17H 9701	3	1			
Front—LH	17H 9702	4	1			
Rear—RH	17H 9699	5	1			
Rear—LH	17H 9700	6	1			
Grommet—rear spring—RH	1A 9307	7	1	★ ★		
Grommet—rear spring—LH	1A 9308	8	1	★ ★		
Overrider	11B 5308	9	4	★ ★		
Seating—overrider	†37H 9871		A/R			Supplied in multiples of feet W.S.E. 37H 9871
5" (13 cm.)	†11B 5309	10	8			
Piece—packing—front overrider and rear spring	1G 9799	11	6			
Screw	HZS 0610	12	2			
Screw	HZS 0608	13	4			
Bolt	HBZ 0612	14	2			
Bolt	37H 9659	15	2			
Screw	HBZ 0611	16	8			
Washer—plain	PWZ 106	17	18			
Washer—spring	LWZ 306	18	18			
Nut	FNZ 106	19	2			
Eye—towing	AHB 9895	20	2		(C) H-BJ7-20880 to 25314	
Screw ⎤ Canada	HZS 0606	21	4		(C) H-BJ8-25315 on	
Washer—spring ⎦	LWZ 206	22	4			
Panel—front apron	14B 5735	23	1	★ ★		

NUMBER-PLATES

Description	Part No.	Illus. No.	Qty	Dist.	Change Point	Remarks
Number-plate—front ⎤	1B 8937	24	1			
Number-plate—rear ⎥	1B 8940	25	1			
Screw ⎥ U.K.	HZS 0404	26	2			
Washer—plain ⎥ only	PWZ 204	27	2			
Washer—spring ⎥	LWZ 204	28	2			
Nut ⎦	FNZ 104	29	2			
Bracket—mounting						
Rear number-plate ⎤ Except	14B 2742	30	1			
Number-plate illumination lamp ⎥ Europe and USA	14B 1941	31	1			
Rear number-plate and illumination lamp　Europe	AHB 8978	32	1		(C) H-BJ7-17551 to 25314 (C) H-BJ8-25315 to (B) H-BJ8-75207 West Germany (C) H-BJ8-25315 to (B) H-BJ8-76137 except West Germany	
Rear number-plate and illumination lamp　Europe	AHB 7111	39	1		(B) H-BJ8-75208 on West Germany (B) H-BJ8-76138 on except West Germany	
Rear number-plate and illumination lamp ⎤ USA	AHB 7165	40	1		(B) H-BJ8-79900 on	
Support—number-plate ⎥ and	AHA 5211	41	1		(B) H-BJ8-79900 on	
Screw ⎦ Canada	HZS 0405	33	2			
Washer—plain	PWZ 104	34	4			
Washer—spring	LWZ 204	35	2			
Nut	FNZ 104	36	2			
Screw	HZS 0405	37	2			
Washer—spring	LWZ 304	38	2			
Screw ⎤	PMZ 0410	42	2			
Screw ⎥ USA	HZS 0403	43	2			
Washer—plain ⎥ and	PWZ 104	44	4		(B) H-BJ8-79900 on	
Washer—spring ⎥ Canada	LWZ 204	45	4			
Nut ⎦	FNZ 104	46	4			

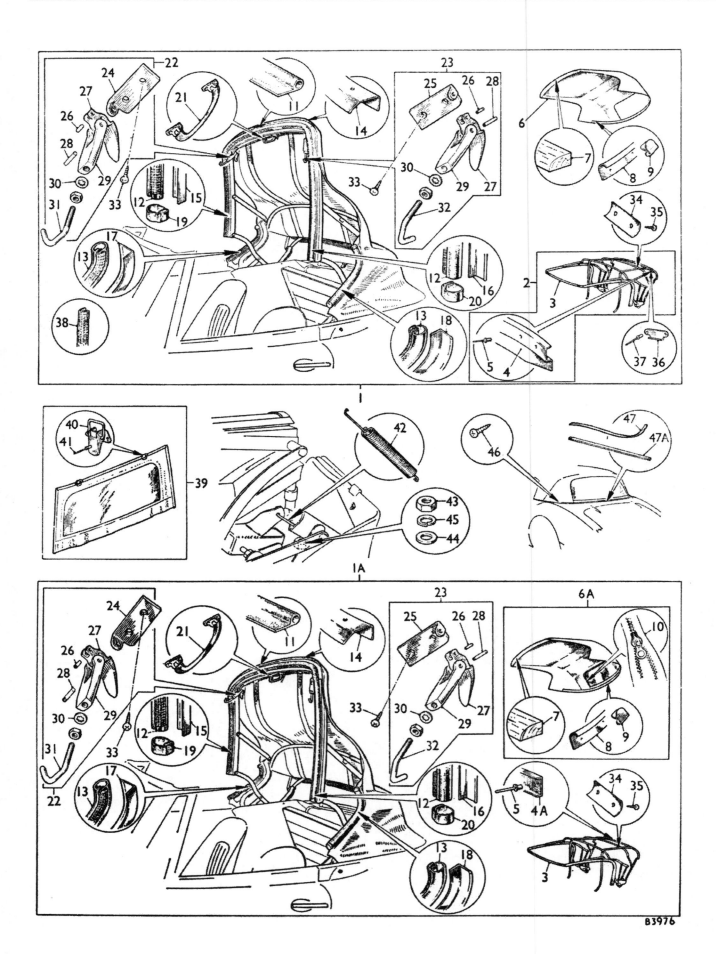

B3976

PLATE L 1   Issue 2   274

	DESCRIPTION	Part No.	Illus. No.	Quantity	Exp.	UK	D	Change Point	REMARKS
					Stock recoms. DIST.				

HOOD AND TONNEAU COVER

		Page	Plate
† BACKLIGHT ASSEMBLY		BL 3	L 1
† BAGS—STOWAGE		BL 4	L 2
† CANOPY—HOOD		BL 2	L 1
† CLAMP ASSEMBLY—HOOD		BL 3	L 1
† COVER—HOOD STOWAGE COMPARTMENT ...		BL 4	L 2
† COVER—TONNEAU		BL 4	L 2
† FRAME—HOOD		BL 2	L 1
† RAILS—TONNEAU COVER SUPPORT		BL 4	L 2

HOOD AND TONNEAU COVER

Description	Part No.	Illus. No.	Qty	Exp.	UK	D	Change Point	Remarks
Hood assembly (less backlight)								
Blue	8G 8753	1	1				(C) H-BJ7-17551 to	
Black	8G 8755	1	1				(B) H-BJ7-59371	
Grey	8G 8756	1	1					W.S.E. use AKE 5201
Hood assembly (with backlight)								
Blue	AKE 5199	1A	1				(B) H-BJ7-59372 to	
Black	AKE 5200	1A	1				(C) H-BJ7-25314	
Grey	AKE 5201	1A	1				(C) H-BJ8-25315 on	
Frame assembly	†8G 8754	2	1				(C) H-BJ7-17551 to (B) H-BJ7-59371	W.S.E. use 8G 8826 together with 1 off rail AHB 9653 and 10 off rivet DMP 0824
Frame	8G 8826	3	1					
Rail—trim—upper	AHB 9653	4	1				(C) H-BJ7-17551 to	
Rivet—rail	DMP 0824	5	10				(B) H-BJ7-59371	
Rail—trim—upper	AHB 9943	4A	1				(B) H-BJ7-59372 to	
Rivet—trim—upper	DMP 0840	5	8				(C) H-BJ7-25314 (C) H-BJ8-25315 on	
Canopy (less backlight)								
Blue	†8G 8757	6	1					W.S.E. use 8G 8846
Black	†8G 8758	6	1					W.S.E. use 8G 8847
Grey	†8G 8759	6	1				(C) H-BJ7-17551 to	W.S.E. use 8G 8848
Rail—header	AHB 9576	7	1				(B) H-BJ7-59371	
Rail—trim—rear	AHB 9556	8	1					
Clip—canopy to rear trim rail	14A 4497	9	36					
Canopy assembly (with backlight)								
Blue	8G 8846	6A	1					
Black	8G 8847	6A	1					
Grey	8G 8848	6A	1				(B) H-BJ7-59372 to	
Rail—header	AHB 9576	7	1				(C) H-BJ7-25314	
Rail—trim—rear	AHB 9556	8	1				(C) H-BJ8-25315 on	
Clip—canopy to rear trim rail	14A 4497	9	44					
Fastener—zip	AHB 9934	10	2					
Weatherstrip—front	AHB 9884	11	1	★	★			
Rubber—sealing—header rail and side cantrail	AHB 9587	12	1	★	★			
Rubber—sealing—rear cantrail	AHB 9588	13	2	★	★			
Retainer—sealing rubber								
Header rail	AHB 9593	14	1					
Side cantrail—RH	AHB 9594	15	1					
Side cantrail—LH	AHB 9595	16	1					
Rear cantrail—RH	AHB 9596	17	1					
Rear cantrail—LH	AHB 9597	18	1					
Cap—end—sealing rubber—RH	AHB 9788	19	3					
Cap—end—sealing rubber—LH	AHB 9789	20	3					
Handle—header rail	4B 3479	21	1					

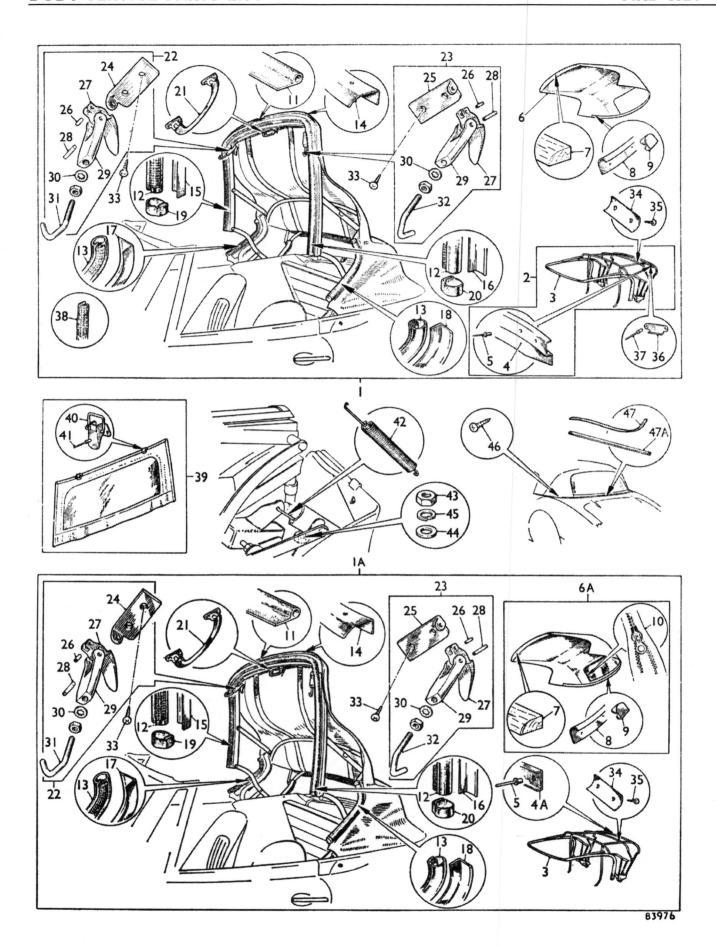

B3976

PLATE L 1   Issue 2   276

DESCRIPTION	Part No.	Illus. No.	Quantity	Exp.	UK	D	Change Point	REMARKS
				Stock recoms. DIST.				

Hood and Tonneau Cover—*continued*

DESCRIPTION	Part No.	Illus. No.	Quantity	Change Point	REMARKS
Clamp assembly—toggle—RH	AHB 9915	22	1		
Clamp assembly—toggle—LH	AHB 9916	23	1		
Base—RH	AHB 9681	24	1		
Base—LH	AHB 9682	25	1		
Pin—base to clamp	24B 1715	26	2		
Handle	AHB 9917	27	2		
Pin—handle to body	24B 1714	28	2		
Body	24B 1712	29	2		
Washer—shakeproof	LWZ 403	30	2		
Hook—RH	AHB 9835	31	1		
Hook—LH	AHB 9836	32	1		
Screw—clamp to frame	RTP 808	33	4		
Clip—retaining—webbing	AHB 5407	34	2		
Screw—clip to frame	PTZ 603	35	4		
Catch—toggle fastener—backlight	AFH 6773	36	2		
Rivet—catch to hood	DXR 0412	37	4		
Closure—upper trim rail	AHB 9591	38	1		
Backlight assembly					
Blue	AHB 9856	39	1	†(C) H-BJ2-17551 to	
Black	AHB 9857	39	1	(B) H-BJ7-59371	
Grey	AHB 9858	39	1		
Fastener—toggle	AFH 6772	40	2		
Rivet—fastener	DXR 0412	41	4		
Spring—assistance—hood linkage	AHB 9531	42	2		
Nut—hood to wheelarch	FNZ 105	43	6		
Washer—plain	PWZ 105	44	6		
Washer—spring	LWZ 205	45	6		
Screw—hood to body	MTZ 604	46	10		
Sealer—hood to water channel 75" (192cm.) long	AHB 9918	47	A/R	(C) H-BJ7-17551 to (B) H-BJ7-59371	Available in multiples of feet
Seal—hood to water channel	AHB 9935	47A	1	(B) H-BJ7-59372 on	

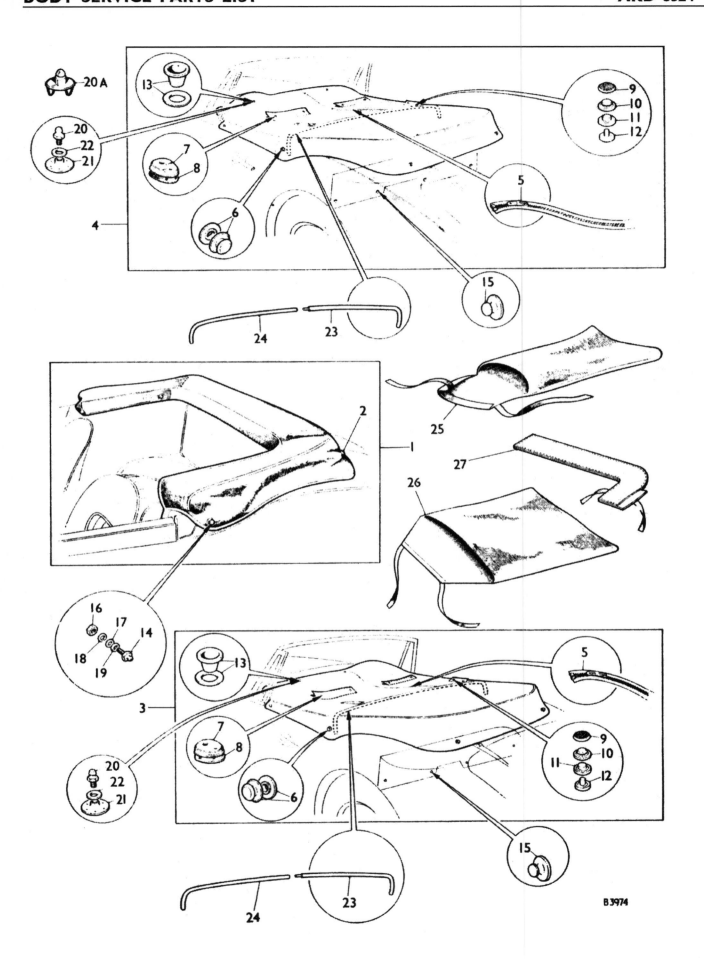

B 3974

PLATE L 2   Issue 2   278

BODY SERVICE PARTS LIST

	DESCRIPTION	Part No.	Illus. No.	Quantity	Stock recoms. DIST. Exp.	UK	D	Change Point	REMARKS
	Hood and Tonneau Cover—*continued*								
	TONNEAU COVER								
	Cover assembly—hood stowage compartment								
	Blue	AHB 9803	1	1					
	Black	AHB 9804	1	1				(C) H-BJ7-17551 to 25314	
	Grey	AHB 9805	1	1					
	Blue	AHB 6837	1	1					
	Black	AHB 6838	1	1				(C) H-BJ8-25315 on	
	Grey	AHB 6839	1	1					
	Fastener—cover to body	TFS 106	2	10					
	Cover assembly—tonneau								
	Blue	AHB 9817	3	1					
	Black RHD	AHB 9818	3	1					
	Grey	AHB 9819	3	1					
	Blue	AHB 9820	4	1					
	Black LHD	AHB 9821	4	1					
	Grey	AHB 9822	4	1					
	Fastener								
	Zip	14B 8699	5	1					
	Cover to tonneau	TFS 106	6	4					
	Lift-the-dot	LFS 107	7	10					
	Plate—clinch—lift-the-dot fastener	LFS 100	8	10					
	Button—socket	2H 6181	9	4	★	★			
	Socket	2H 6182	10	4	★	★			
	Stud	2H 6183	11	4	★	★			
	Fastener—stud	2H 6184	12	4	★	★			
	Eyelet and ring	BHA 4371	13	2	★	★			
	Fastener—cover to tonneau	TFP 1006	14	4					
	Fastener—cover to heelboard	14B 1916	15	4					
	Nut—fastener	FNZ 103	16	4					
	Washer								
	Plain	PWZ 103	17	8					
	Spring	LWZ 203	18	8					
	Fastener (leather)	2K 4936	19	8					
	Fastener—cover to door and fascia top	37H 9719	20	6				(C) H-BJ7-17551 to (C) ▼	
	Fastener—cover to door and fascia top	LFP 1004	20A	6				(C) ▼ on	
	"T" nut—fastener	14B 8851	21	4					
	Washer—plain	PWP 103	22	6					
	Rail—support—tonneau cover—RH	AHB 9824	23	1					
	Rail—support—tonneau cover—LH	AHB 9825	24	1					
	Bags—stowage								
	Hood stowage compartment cover	AHB 9849	25	1					
	Tonneau cover	AHB 9900	26	1					
	Tonneau cover support rails	AHB 9852	27	1					

▼ Change point not available

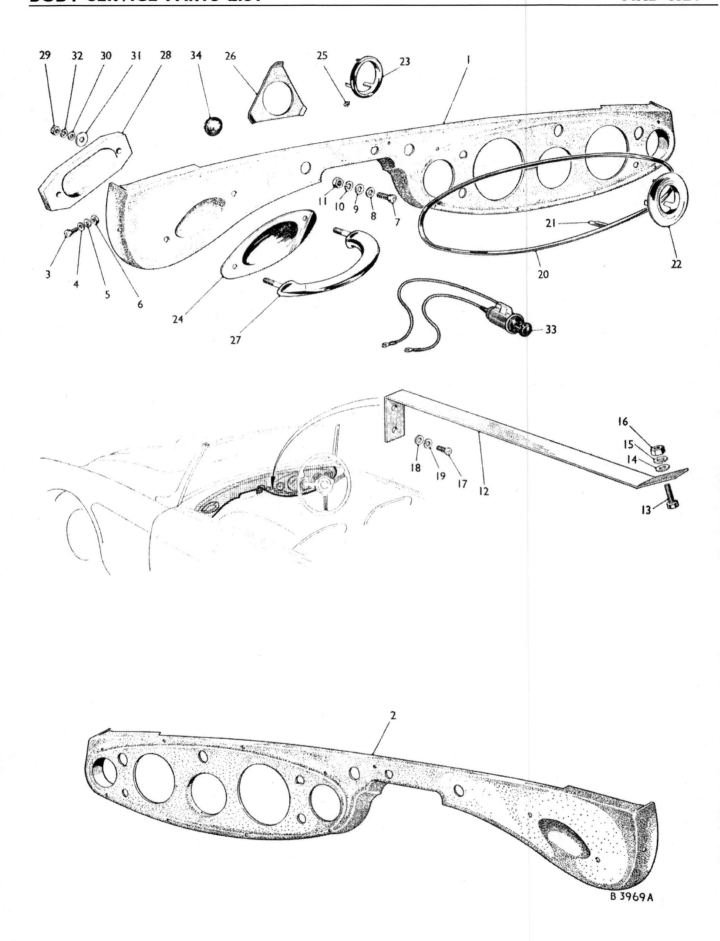

B 3969A

		DESCRIPTION	Part No.	Illus. No.	Quantity	Stock recoms. DIST. Exp.	UK	D	Change Point	REMARKS

FASCIA DETAILS

			Page	Plate
† BEZEL—SWITCHES	}		BM 3	M 2
† BOARD ASSEMBLY—FASCIA			BM 3	M 2
† FINISHERS—FASCIA AND CONSOLE PANEL...	(BJ8)		BM 3	M 2
† GLOVEBOX	}		BM 3	M 2
† HANDLE—GRAB ... ... (BJ 7)			BM 2	M 1
† LOCK—GLOVEBOX LID	} (BJ 8)		BM 3	M 2
† PANEL—CONSOLE			BM 3	M 2
† PANEL—FASCIA ... ... (BJ 7)			BM 2	M 1

FASCIA DETAILS

(BJ7)

Description	Part No.	Illus. No.	Qty	Remarks
Panel—fascia **RHD**	24B 697	1	1	
Panel—fascia **LHD**	24B 726	2	1	
Screw—panel to end fixing bracket	PMP 0312	3	4	
Washer—plain	PWZ 103	4	4	
Washer—spring	LWZ 203	5	4	
Nut	FNZ 103	6	4	
Screw—panel to centre support bracket	PMP 0310	7	1	
Washer—chrome	PWP 203	8	1	
Washer—plain	PWZ 204	9	1	
Washer—spring	LWZ 204	10	1	
Nut	FNZ 103	11	1	
Bracket—panel support	14B 7579	12	1	
Screw—bracket to panel	PMP 0308	13	1	
Washer—plain	PWZ 103	14	1	
Washer—spring	LWZ 203	15	1	
Nut	FNZ 103	16	1	
Screw—bracket to body	PMZ 0308	17	2	
Washer—plain	PWZ 103	18	2	
Washer—spring	LWZ 203	19	2	
Moulding—instrument panel	14B 6740	20	1	
Clip—moulding	14G 5854	21	8	
Escutcheon				
Steering column aperture	24B 725	22	1	
Steering column aperture	14B 7805	23	1	Adjustable steering
Grab handle	14B 5775	24	1	
Screw—retaining—steering column aperture escutcheon	52K 2614	25	1	Adjustable steering
Plate—retaining—steering column aperture escutcheon	AHB 5406	26	1	
Handle—grab	14B 1729	27	1	
Strip—packing—handle	14B 5776	28	1	
Nut—handle to panel	FNZ 104	29	2	
Washer				
Plain	†PWZ 104	30	2	
Plain	†PWZ 204	31	2	
Spring	†LWZ 204	32	2	
Lighter—cigar	†AHH 5759	33	1	
Button—blanking—fascia panel	†BHA 4416	34	2/1	For use when steering lock is fitted. Quantity reduced at (C) H-BJ8-25315

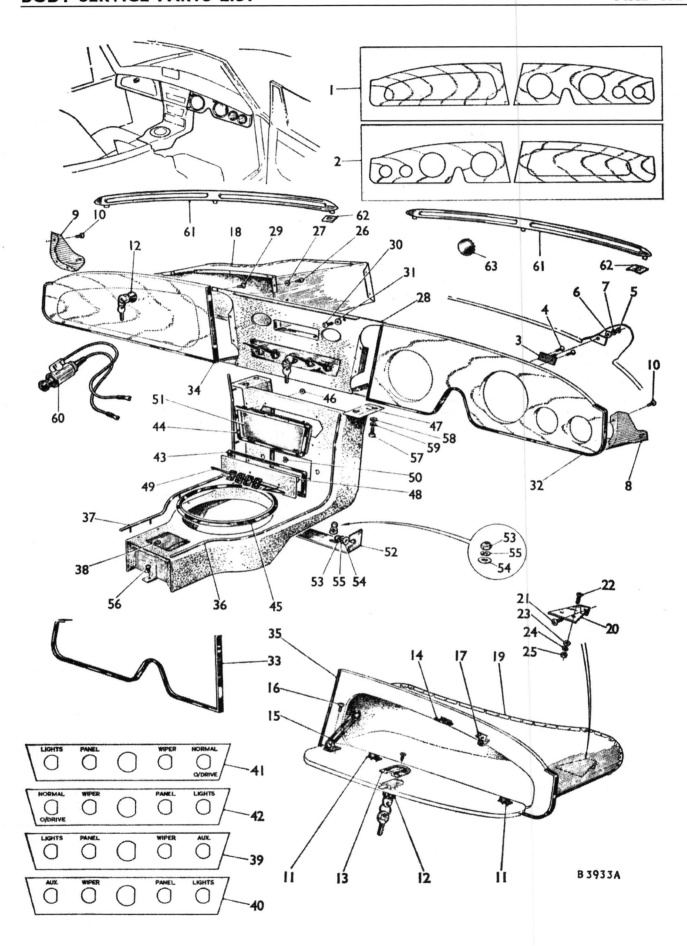

	DESCRIPTION	Part No.	Illus. No.	Quantity	Stock recoms. DIST. Exp.	UK	D	Change Point	REMARKS

FASCIA DETAILS

(BJ8)

Description		Part No.	Illus. No.	Quantity	Exp.	UK	D	Change Point	REMARKS
Board assembly—fascia	**RHD**	8G 8888	1	1 set					⎤Serviced in sets only
Board assembly—fascia	**LHD**	8G 8890	2	1 set					⎢due to difficulty in
Board—driver's side		NSP		1					⎢matching veneer if
Board—passenger's side		NSP		1					⎢components were
Lid—glove box		NSP		1					⎦serviced separately
Plate—stud		ADG 823	3	2					
Screw—plate to fascia		CTZ 404	4	4					
Nut—plate to bracket		FNZ 103	5	2					
Washer—plain		PWZ 103	6	2					
Washer—spring		LWZ 203	7	2					
Bracket—end—RH		AHB 6035	8	1					
Bracket—end—LH		AHB 6036	9	1					
Screw—bracket to fascia		MTZ 604	10	6					
Hinge—glove box lid		ADH 5556	11	2					
Lock—glove box lid		ALH 1896	12	1					
Plate—cover—lock		AHB 6047	13	1					
Striker—lock		AHB 6048	14	1					
Quadrant—glove box lid		ADB 837	15	1					
Screw—quadrant to glove box		MTZ 603	16	2					
Buffer—lid		2H 8041	17	1					
Glove box	**RHD**	AHB 6050	18	1					
Glove box	**LHD**	AHB 6049	19	1					
Bracket—glove box support		AHB 6558	20	1					
Screw—bracket to dash		MTZ 604	21	1					
Screw—glove box to bracket		CMZ 0206	22	2					
Washer—plain		PWZ 102	23	2					
Washer—spring		LWZ 202	24	2					
Nut		CNZ 102	25	2					
Screw—glove box to fascia		MTZ 604	26	12					
Washer—plain		PWZ 202	27	12					
Panel—centre—fascia		AHB 6061	28	1					
Screw—centre panel to outer panels		MTZ 604	29	8					
Screw—centre panel to bracket		PMP 0310	30	2					
Washer—plain		PWP 103	31	2					
Finisher									
Instrument panel	**RHD**	AHB 6033	32	1					
Instrument panel	**LHD**	AHB 6034	33	1					
Glove box panel	**RHD**	AHB 6042	34	1					
Glove box panel	**LHD**	AHB 6041	35	1					
Console—RH		AHB 6364	36	1					⎤(C) H-BJ8-25315 to 26704
Console—LH		AHB 6365	37	1					⎦
Console—RH		AHB 6948	36	1					⎤(C) H-BJ8-26705 on
Console—LH		AHB 6949	37	1					⎦
Washer—plain		PWZ 102	38	14					
Bezel									
Switch	**RHD**	AHB 6063	39	1					
Switch	**LHD**	AHB 6064	40	1					
Switch	**RHD**	AHB 6410	41	1					⎤For use when
Switch	**LHD**	AHB 6411	42	1					⎦overdrive is fitted
Radio aperture surround		AHH 5255	43	1					
Speaker fret		AHB 6229	44	1					
Gear lever surround		AHB 6073	45	1					
Washer—plain		PWZ 102	46	4					
Panel—console		AHB 6072	47	1				(C) H-BJ8-25315 to 26704	
Panel—console		AHB 6942	47	1				(C) H-BJ8-26705 on	
Cover—radio aperture		AHB 6074	48	1					
Motif '3000'		AHB 8861	49	1	★	★			
Push-on-fix—motif		BHA 4082	50	2					
Fret—speaker		AHB 6230	51	1					
Plate—console to gearbox cover		AHB 6547	52	1					
Locknut—console to gearbox cover		LNZ 203	53	4					
Washer—plain		AJD 7202	54	4					
Washer—spring		LWZ 203	55	4					
Screw—console to gear box cover		CTZ 604	56	1					
Screw—console to fascia centre		PMZ 0310	57	4					
Washer—plain		AJD 7202	58	4					
Washer—spring		LWZ 203	59	4					
Lighter—cigar		AHH 5759	60	1					Optional extra
Mask—demister		4B 8521	61	2					
Push-on-fix—mask		PFS 106	62	6					
Button—blanking—fascia panel		†BHA 4416	63	A/R					W.S.E. use ACH 9373
Button—blanking—fascia panel		†ACH 9373	63	A/R					

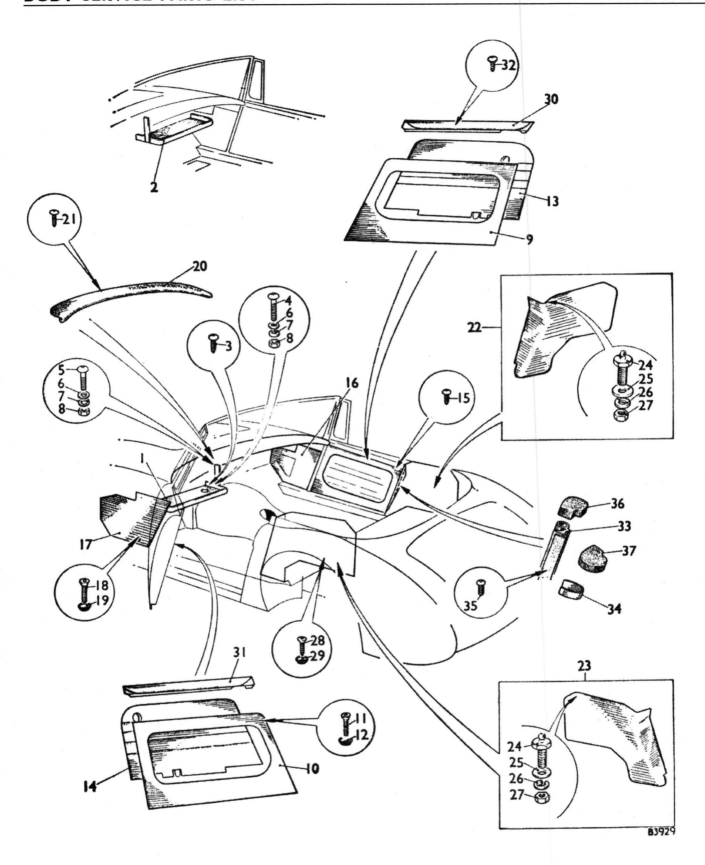

	DESCRIPTION	Part No.	Illus. No.	Quantity	Change Point	REMARKS

TRIMMING DETAILS

Pages

† BJ 7 ... ...   BN 2 to BN 6, BN 12

BJ7

	Page	Plate
† ASHTRAY	BN 6	N 2
† BULK MATERIALS	BN 12	—
† CARPETS	BN 5, BN 6	N 2
† COVERS—BOOT	BN 6	N 2
† DRAUGHT EXCLUDERS—DOOR	BN 4	N 1
† LINERS—TRIM	BN 3, BN 4	N 1
† TRAY—PARCEL	BN 3	N 1
† TRIM ROLLS—DOOR	BN 4	N 1

TRIMMING DETAILS (BJ7)

LINERS, DOOR SEALS

Description			Part No.	Illus. No.	Qty	Remarks
Tray parcel	Red with Red carpet		†4B 3172	1	1	
	Red with Black carpet		†AHB 8860	1	1	
	Blue with Blue carpet	RHD	†AHB 5434	1	1	
	Black with Black carpet		†AHB 5435	1	1	
	Grey with Green carpet		†AHB 5436	1	1	
	Grey with Red carpet		†AHB 8859	1	1	
	Red with Red carpet		†4B 4124	2	1	
	Red with Black carpet		†AHB 8871	2	1	
	Blue with Blue carpet	LHD	†AHB 5438	2	1	
	Black with Black carpet		†AHB 5439	2	1	
	Grey with Green carpet		†AHB 5440	2	1	
	Grey with Red carpet		†AHB 8872	2	1	
Screw	Tray fixing		PTZ 804	3	7	Correction; was PTZ 2804
	Tray to bracket		†PMP 0308	4	1	
	Bracket fixing		†PMZ 0307	5	1	
Washer—plain			†PWZ 103	6	2	
Washer—spring			†LWZ 203	7	2	
Nut			†FNZ 103	8	2	
Liner—door—outer	Red	RH	†AHB 9732	9	1	
		LH	†AHB 9736	10	1	
	Blue	RH	†AHB 9733	9	1	
		LH	†AHB 9737	10	1	
	Black	RH	†AHB 9734	9	1	
		LH	†AHB 9738	10	1	
	Grey	RH	†AHB 9735	9	1	
		LH	†AHB 9739	10	1	
Screw—liner			†RJP 603	11	18	
Screw—liner			†RJP 604	11	8	
Washer—cup			†FWP 406	12	26	
Liner—door—inner	Red	RH	†AHB 9740	13	1	
		LH	†AHB 9744	14	1	
	Blue	RH	†AHB 9741	13	1	
		LH	†AHB 9745	14	1	
	Black	RH	†AHB 9742	13	1	
		LH	†AHB 9746	14	1	
	Grey	RH	†AHB 9743	13	1	
		LH	†AHB 9747	14	1	
Screw—liner			†MTP 402	15	16	
Liner—scuttle	Red	RH	†4B 3215	16	1	
		LH	†4B 3247	17	1	
	Blue	RH	†AHB 5450	16	1	
		LH	†AHB 5454	17	1	
	Black	RH	†AHB 5451	16	1	
		LH	†AHB 5455	17	1	
	Grey	RH	†AHB 5452	16	1	
		LH	†AHB 5456	17	1	
Screw—liner			†RJP 604	18	8	
Screw—liner			†RJP 606	18	2	
Washer—cup			†FWP 406	19	10	

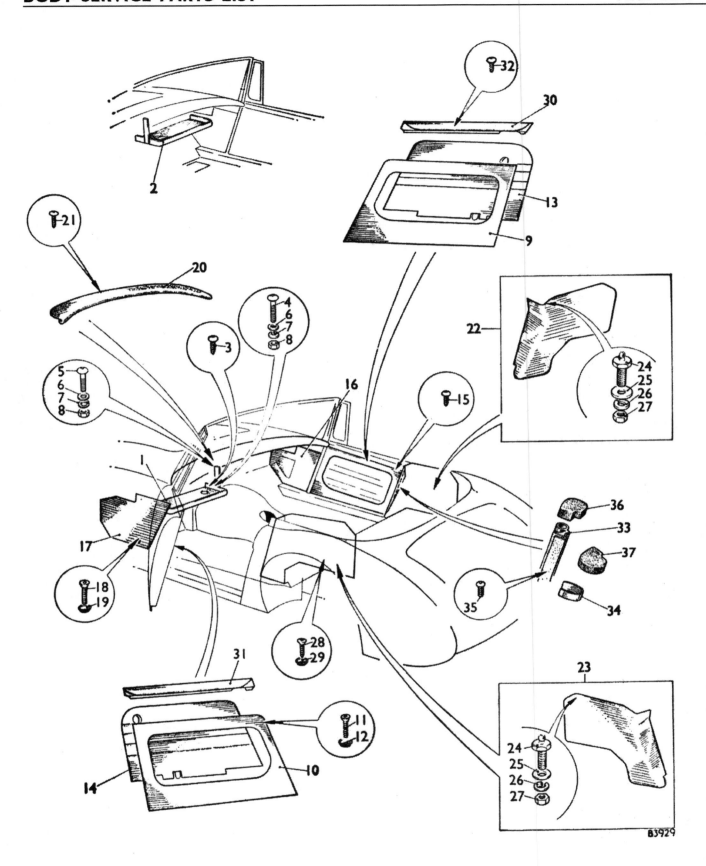

BODY SERVICE PARTS LIST

DESCRIPTION	Part No.	Illus. No.	Quantity	Change Point	REMARKS
Trimming Details (BJ7)—*continued*					
Liner—scuttle top					
Red	†AHB 9696	20	1		
Blue	†AHB 9697	20	1		
Black	†AHB 9698	20	1		
Grey	†AHB 9699	20	1		
Screw—liner	†54K 3024	21	1		
Liner assembly—rear quarter					
Red RH	†AHB 9702	22	1		
LH	†AHB 9706	23	1		
Blue RH	†AHB 9703	22	1		
LH	†AHB 9707	23	1		
Black RH	†AHB 9704	22	1		
LH	†AHB 9708	23	1		
Grey RH	†AHB 9705	22	1		
LH	†AHB 9709	23	1		
Peg—fastener—hood compartment cover	†TFP 1006	24	4		
Washer—plain	PWZ 103	25			
Washer—spring	LWZ 203	26	4		
Nut	†FNZ 103	27	4		
Screw—liner	†RTP 604	28	2		
Screw—liner	†RTP 606	28	6		
Washer—cup—screw	†FWP 406	29	8		
Roll—Door top					
Red RH	†AHB 9748	30	1		
LH	†AHB 9752	31	1		
Blue RH	†AHB 9749	30	1		
LH	†AHB 9753	31	1		
Black RH	†AHB 9750	30	1		
LH	†AHB 9754	31	1		
Grey RH	†AHB 9751	30	1		
LH	†AHB 9755	31	1		
Screw—roll	†CTZ 404	32	10		
Draught excluder—door 13″ (185·42cm.)					
Red	†37H 9956	33	A/R		Supplied in multiples of yards
Blue	†37H 9957	33	A/R		
Black	†37H 9955	33	A/R		
Grey	†37H 9950	33	A/R		
Clip—draught excluder	AHB 9656	34	2		
Screw—clip	†CTZ 404	35	2		
Cap—end—excluder—RH	†AHB 9788	36	1		
Cap—end—excluder—LH	†AHB 9789	37	1		

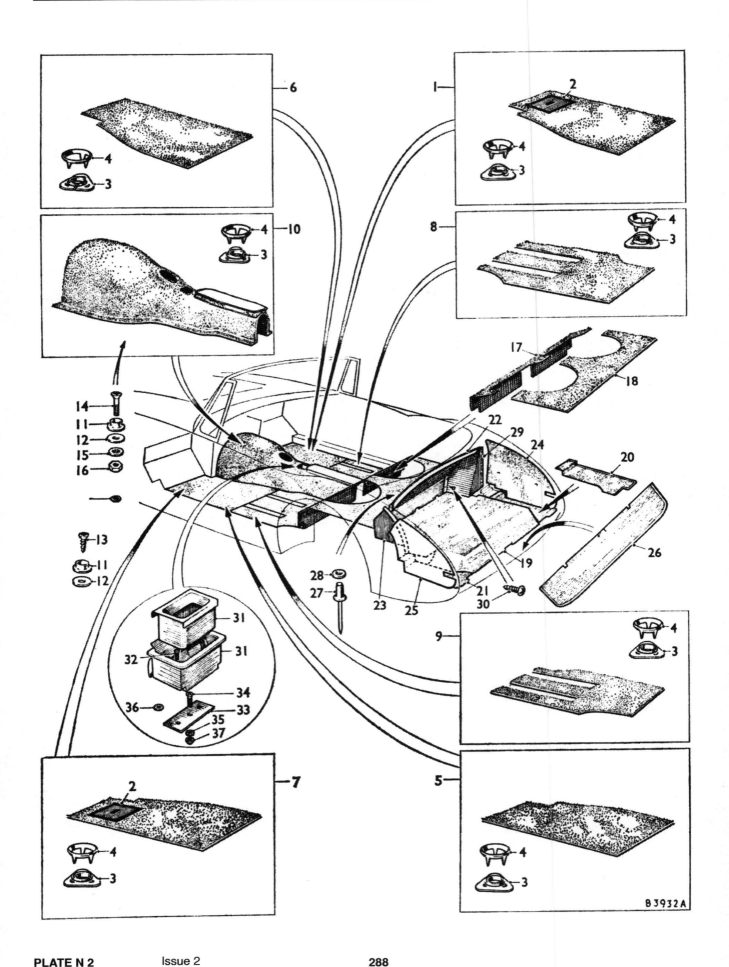

B 3932A

DESCRIPTION	Part No.	Illus. No.	Quantity	Change Point	REMARKS

Trimming Details (BJ7)—*continued*

FLOOR FITTINGS

Carpet assembly—front

DESCRIPTION			Part No.	Illus. No.	Quantity	Change Point	REMARKS
Red	RH		†AHB 9278	1	1		
	LH		†AHB 9286	5	1		Not available; use AHB 9302
Blue	RH		†AHB 9279	1	1		
	LH	RHD	†AHB 9287	5	1		Not available; use AHB 9303
Black	RH		†AHB 9280	1	1		
	LH		†AHB 9288	5	1		Not available; use AHB 9304
Green	RH		†AHB 9281	1	1		
	LH		†AHB 9289	5	1		Not available; use AHB 9305
Red	RH		†AHB 9294	6	1		Not available; use AHB 9278
	LH		†AHB 9302	7	1		
Blue	RH		†AHB 9295	6	1		Not available; use AHB 9279
	LH	LHD	†AHB 9303	7	1		
Black	RH		†AHB 9296	6	1		Not available; use AHB 9280
	LH		†AHB 9304	7	1		
Green	RH		†AHB 9297	6	1		Not available; use AHB 9281
	LH		†AHB 9305	7	1		
Pad—heel (rubber)			†2H 6961	2	1		
Fastener			†2H 8445	3	12		
Ring—spiked			†14G 8736	4	16		

Carpet assembly—rear

DESCRIPTION		Part No.	Illus. No.	Quantity	Change Point	REMARKS
Red	RH	†AHB 9310	8	1		
	LH	†AHB 9318	9	1		
Blue	RH	†AHB 9311	8	1		
	LH	†AHB 9319	9	1		
Black	RH	†AHB 9312	8	1		
	LH	†AHB 9320	9	1		
Green	RH	†AHB 9313	8	1		
	LH	†AHB 9321	9	1		
Fastener		†2H 8445	3	4		
Ring—spiked		†14G 8736	4	4		

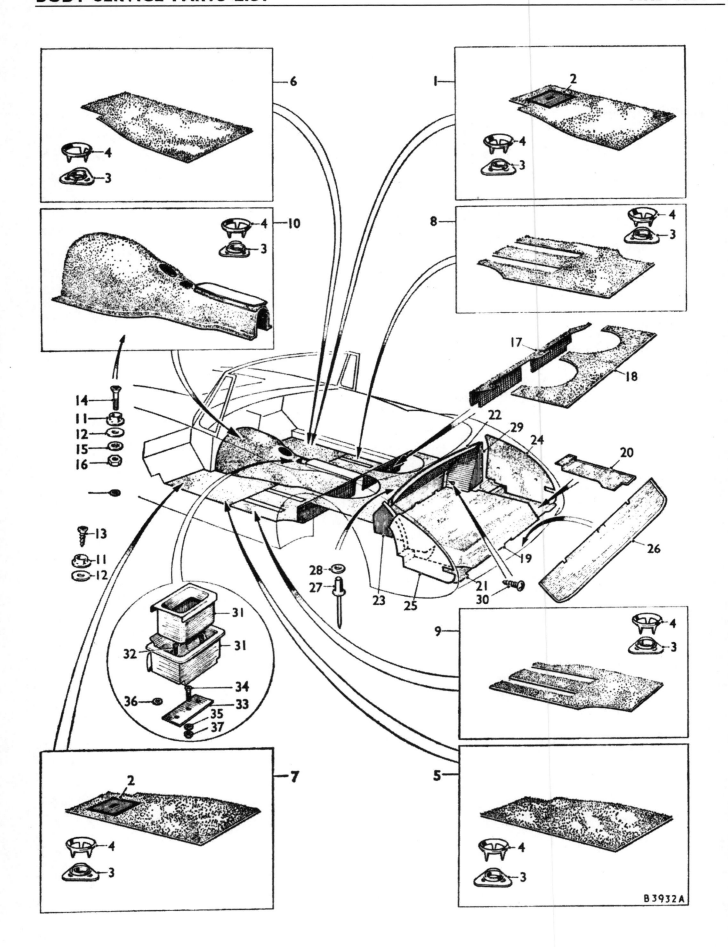

B3932A

DESCRIPTION	Part No.	Illus. No.	Quantity	Exp.	UK	D	Change Point	REMARKS

Trimming Details (BJ7)—*continued*

Floor Fittings—*continued*

Carpet assembly—gearbox

Description	Part No.	Illus. No.	Quantity					Remarks
Red with red and black armrest	AHB 9334	10	1					
Red with grey and red armrest	AHB 9335	10	1					
Red with red and white armrest	AHB 9336	10	1					
Blue with blue and white armrest	AHB 9337	10	1					
Black with red and black armrest	AHB 9338	10	1					
Black with black and white armrest	AHB 9339	10	1					
Black with black and red armrest	AHB 9874	10	1					
Black with black and black armrest	AKE 5276	10	1					
Green with grey and green armrest	AHB 9342	10	1					
Fastener	2H 8445	3	12					
Ring—spiked	14G 8736	4	12					
Stud—fastener	ADB 4811	11	24					
Washer—stud	ADA 2765	12	24					
Screw—stud to floor	CTZ 605	13	16					
Screw—stud to gearbox cover	CMZ 0208	14	8					
Washer—shakeproof	†AJD 7622	15	8					Not available; use LWZ 402
Washer—shakeproof	†LWZ 402	15	8					
Nut	CNZ 102	16	8					

Carpet—heelboard

Black	AHB 8693	17	1					Not available; use bulk material. See page BN12
Red	14B 7830	17	1					
Blue	AHB 8692	17	1					
Green	AHB 8844	17	1					

Carpet—seat pan surround

Blue	AHB 8696	18	1					
Green	AHB 8837	18	1					
Red	14B 8875	18	1					
Black	†AHB 8697	18	1					Correction; was AHB 8679

Cover—boot

Main floor	4B 3255	19	1					
Side floor—RH	4B 3248	20	1					
Side floor—LH	4B 3249	21	1					
Rear axle panel	4B 3253	22	1					
Wheelarch—LH	14B 7829	23	1					
Rear quarter—RH	AHB 8641	24	1					
Rear quarter—LH	AHB 8653	25	1					
Rear skirt	AHB 8665	26	1					
Rivet—rear axle panel cover	DMP 0835	27	6					
Washer—plain—rivet	PWZ 102	28	6					
Liner—boot—fuel pipe	14B 8708	29	1					
Screw—liner	PTP 604	30	6					
Ashtray	†14B 2016	31	1					
Screw	†CMZ 0208	32	2					
Plate—tapped—ashtray	†14B 5711	33	1					
Screw	†CMZ 0208	34	1					
Washer—shakeproof	†AJD 7622	35	1					Not available; use LWZ 402
Washer—shakeproof	†LWZ 402	35	1					
Nut	†CNZ 102	36	1					

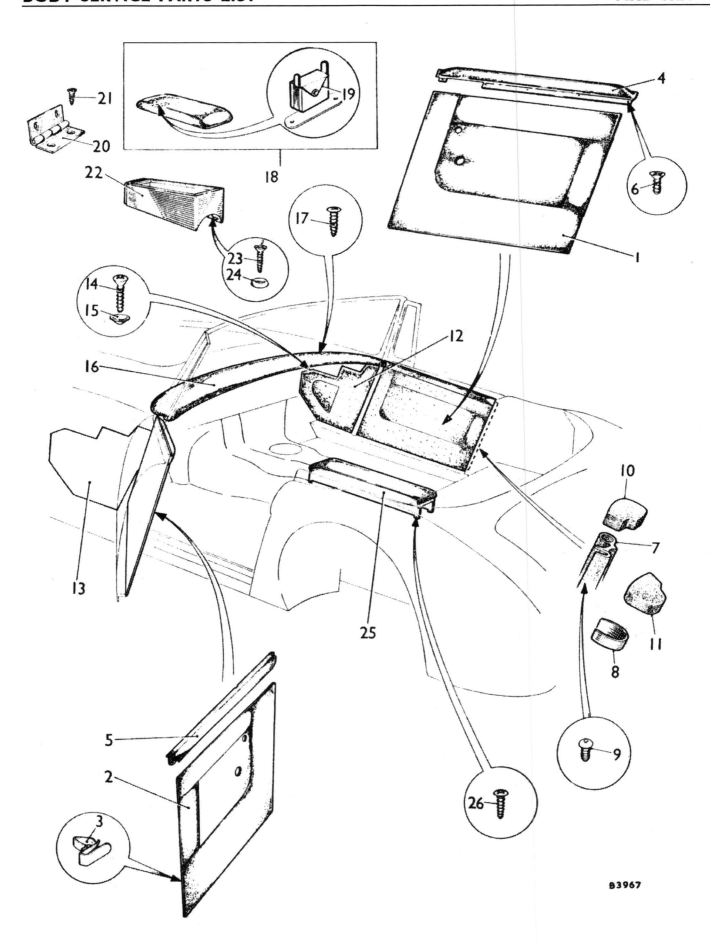

B3967

	DESCRIPTION	Part No.	Illus. No.	Quantity	Stock recoms. DIST. Exp.	UK	D	Change Point	REMARKS

TRIMMING DETAILS   *Pages*

| † BJ 8 | ... | ... | ... | ... | ... | ... | ... | BN 7 to BN 11, BN 12 |

BJ8

							Page	*Plate*
ARMREST	...	...	...	...	...	...	BN 8	N 3
† ASHTRAY	...	...	...	...	...	...	BN 11	N 5
BULK MATERIAL	...	...	...	...	...	...	BN 12	—
CARPETS	...	...	...	...	...	...	BN 10, BN 11	N 5
COVER—BOOT	...	...	...	...	...	...	BN 11	N 5
DRAUGHT EXCLUDER—DOOR	...	...	...	...	...	BN 8	N 3
LINER—TRIM	...	...	...	...	...	...	BN 8, BN 9	N 3, N 4
PANEL—HOOD PROTECTION	...	...	...	...	...	BN 9	N 4
TRIM ROLL—DOOR	...	...	...	...	...	...	BN 8	N 3

TRIMMING DETAILS (BJ8)

LINERS, DOOR SEALS

DESCRIPTION	Part No.	Illus. No.	Quantity	UK	Change Point	REMARKS
Liner—door Red RH	†AHB 6233	1	1			
LH	†AHB 6237	2	1			
Blue RH	†AHB 6234	1	1			
LH	†AHB 6238	2	1			
Black RH	†AHB 6235	1	1			
LH	†AHB 6239	2	1			
Grey RH	†AHB 6236	1	1			
LH	†AHB 6240	2	1			
Cup—liner to door	14A 2641	3	18			
Roll—door top—RH—black	AHB 6346	4	1			
Roll—door top—LH—black	AHB 6347	5	1			
Screw—roll to door	CZZ 404	6	10			
Draught excluder— Red	37H 9956	7	A/R			Supplied in
door 73″ (185·42cm.) Blue	37H 9957	7	A/R			multiples of yards
Black	37H 9955	7	A/R			
Grey	37H 9950	7	A/R			
Clip—draught excluder	AHB 9656	8	2			
Screw—draught excluder	CZZ 404	9	2			
Cap—end—draught excluder—RH	AHB 9788	10	1			
Cap—end—draught excluder—LH	AHB 9789	11	1			
Liner—scuttle Red RH	†AHB 6267	12	1			
LH	†AHB 6271	13	1			
Blue RH	†AHB 6268	12	1			
LH	†AHB 6272	13	1			
Black RH	†AHB 6269	12	1			
LH	†AHB 6273	13	1			
Grey RH	†AHB 6270	12	1			
LH	†AHB 6274	13	1			
Screw—liner	RJP 604	14	8			
Screw—liner	RJP 606	14	2			
Washer—cup—screw	FWP 406	15	10			
Liner—scuttle top—black	AHB 6333	16	1			
Screw—liner	54K 3024	17	4			
Lid—armrest Red	AHB 6375	18	1			
Blue	AHB 6376	18	1			
Black	AHB 6377	18	1			
Grey	AHB 6378	18	1			
Red	AHB 6397	18	1			
Blue Leather	AHB 6398	18	1		(C) H-BJ8-25315 to 26704	Optional extra
Black	AHB 6399	18	1			
Grey	AHB 6400	18	1			
Catch—magnetic	ADA 6306	19	1			
Hinge—lid	ADH 5556	20	2			
Screw—hinge	CTP 403	21	8			
Box—armrest	AHB 6081	22	1			
Screw—armrest to tunnel	CTP 605	23	1			
Washer—cup—screw	FWP 106	24	1			
Armrest Red	AHB 6903	25	1			
Blue	AHB 6904	25	1			
Black	AHB 6905	25	1			
Grey	AHB 6906	25	1			
Red	AHB 6908	25	1		(C) H-BJ8-26705	
Blue Leather	AHB 6909	25	1			Optional extra
Black	AHB 6910	25	1			
Grey	AHB 6911	25	1			
Screw—armrest to tunnel	PTZ 604	26	4			

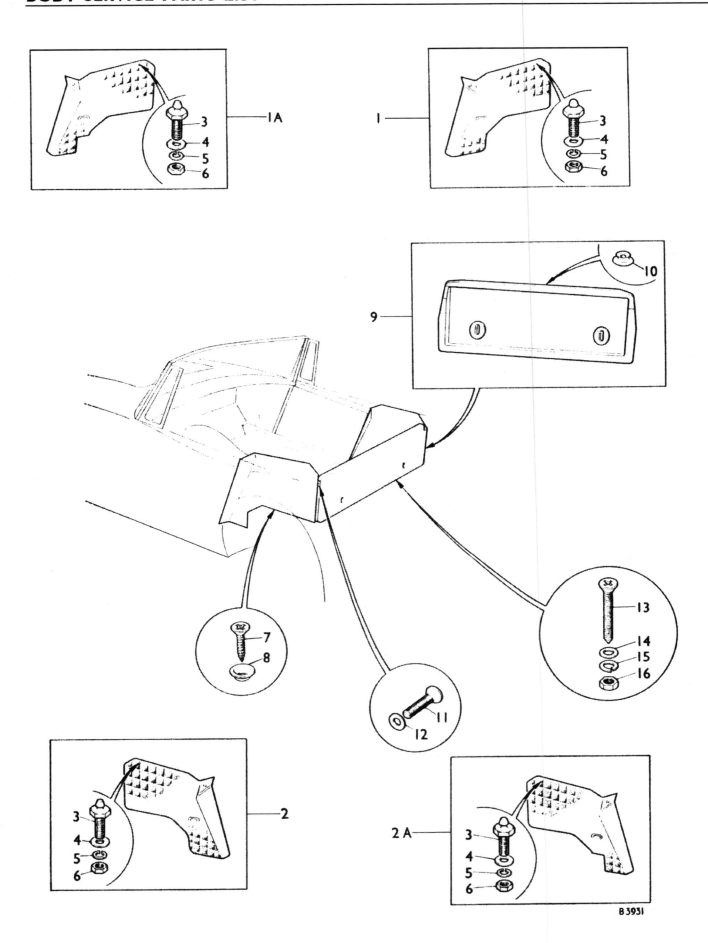

B 3931

	DESCRIPTION	Part No.	Illus. No.	Quantity	Stock recoms. DIST. Exp.	UK	D	Change Point	REMARKS

Trimming Details (BJ8)—*continued*

Liners, Door Seals—*continued*

Liner assembly—rear quarter

Description		Part No.	Illus. No.	UK	Change Point	REMARKS
Red	RH	†AHB 6288	1	1		
	LH	†AHB 6292	2	1		
Blue	RH	†AHB 6289	1	1	(C) H-BJ8-25315 to 26704	
	LH	†AHB 6293	2	1		
Black	RH	†AHB 6290	1	1		
	LH	†AHB 6294	2	1		
Grey	RH	†AHB 6291	1	1		
	LH	†AHB 6295	2	1		
Red	RH	†AHB 6994	1A	1		
	LH	†AHB 6998	2A	1		
Blue	RH	†AHB 6995	1A	1	(C) H-BJ8-26705 to 82775	
	LH	†AHB 6999	2A	1		
Black	RH	†AHB 6996	1A	1		
	LH	†AHB 7000	2A	1		
Grey	RH	†AHB 6997	1A	1		
	LH	†AHB 7001	2A	1		
Red	RH	†AHB 7179	1A	1		
	LH	†AHB 7183	2A	1		
Blue	RH	†AHB 7180	1A	1		
	LH	†AHB 7184	2A	1	(C) H-BJ8-82776 on	
Black	RH	†AHB 7181	1A	1		
	LH	†AHB 7185	2A	1		
Grey	RH	†AHB 7182	1A	1		
	LH	†AHB 7186	2A	1		
Peg—fastener—hood compartment cover		TFP 1006	3	2		
Washer—plain—peg		PWZ 103	4	2		
Washer—spring—peg		LWZ 203	5	2		
Nut—peg		FNZ 103	6	2		
Screw—liner		RTP 606	7	8		
Washer—screw		FWP 406	8	8		

Panel—hood protection

Description	Part No.	Illus. No.	UK	REMARKS
Red	AHB 6627	9	1	
Blue	AHB 6628	9	1	
Black	AHB 6629	9	1	
Grey	AHB 6630	9	1	
Stud—fastener	†ADB 4811	10	5	Correction; was AD 34811
Washer—cup	BHA 4453	13		
Screw—panel to wheelarch	CMZ 0422	11	4	
Washer—plain—screw	PWZ 204	12	4	
Screw—panel to bulkhead	CMZ 0424	13	3	
Washer—plain—screw	PWZ 404	14	3	
Washer—spring—screw	LWZ 204	15	3	
Nut—screw	FNZ 104	16	3	

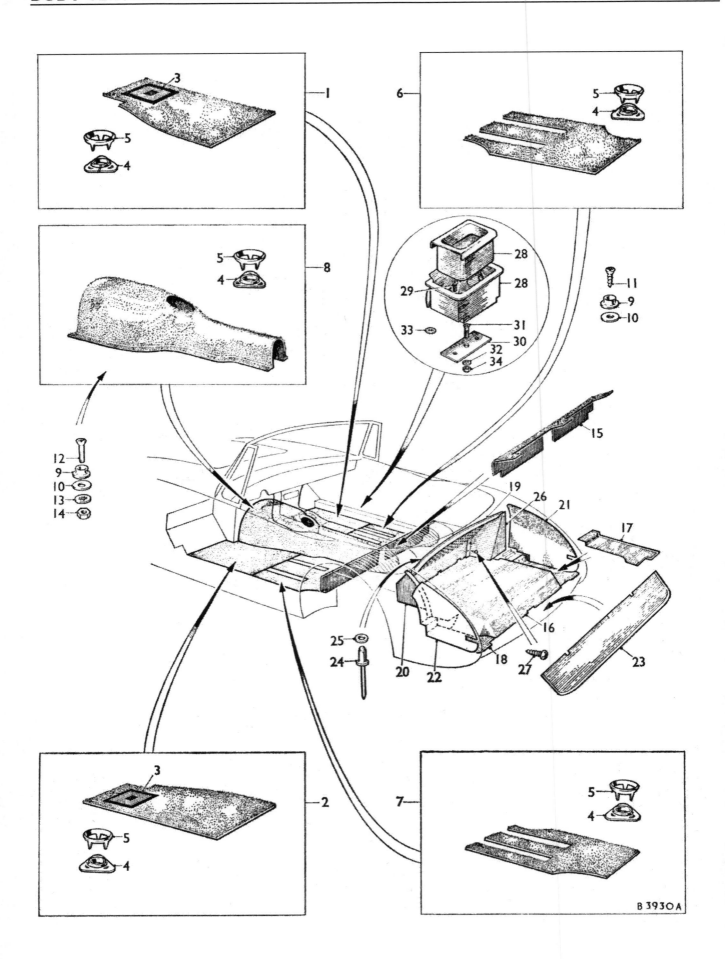

B 3930A

	DESCRIPTION	Part No.	Illus. No.	Quantity	Change Point	REMARKS

Trimming Details (BJ8)—*continued*

FLOOR FITTINGS

Carpet assembly—front

Red {	RH	AHB 9278	1	1	(C) H–BJ8–25315 to	
	LH	AHB 9302	2	1	(B) H–BJ8–78153	
	RH	AHB 7147	1	1	(B) H–BJ8–78154 on	
	LH	AHB 7149	2	1		
Blue {	RH	AHB 9279	1	1		
	LH	AHB 9303	2	1		
Black {	RH	AHB 9280	1	1		
	LH	AHB 9304	2	1		
Green {	RH	AHB 9281	1	1		
	LH	AHB 9305	2	1		
Pad—heel (rubber)		2H 6961	3	2		
Fastener		2H 8445	4	8		
Ring—spiked		14G 8736	5	8		

Carpet assembly—rear

Red {	RH	AHB 9310	6	1	(C) H–BJ8–25315 to	
	LH	AHB 9318	7	1	(B) H–BJ8–78153	
	RH	AHB 7151	6	1	(B) H–BJ8–78154 on	
	LH	AHB 7153	7	1		
Blue {	RH	AHB 9311	6	1		
	LH	AHB 9319	7	1		
Black {	RH	AHB 9312	6	1		
	LH	AHB 9320	7	1		
Green {	RH	AHB 9313	6	1		
	LH	AHB 9321	7	1		
Fastener		2H 8445	4	4		
Ring—spiked		14G 8736	5	4		

Carpet assembly—gearbox

Red		†AHB 6878	8	1	(C) H–BJ8–25315 to	
					(B) H–BJ8–78153	
Red		†AHB 7155	1	8	(B) H–BJ8–78154 on	
Blue		AHB 6879	8	1		
Black		AHB 6880	8	1		
Green		AHB 6881	8	1		
Fastener		2H 8445	4	12		
Ring—spiked		14G 8736	5	12		
Stud—fastener		ADB 4811	9	24		
Washer—stud		ADA 2765	10	24		
Screw—stud to floor		CTZ 605	11	16		
Screw—stud to gearbox cover		CMZ 0208	12	8		
Washer—shakeproof		AJD 7622	13	8		Not available; use LWZ 402
Washer—shakeproof		LWZ 402	13	8		
Nut		CNZ 102	14	8		

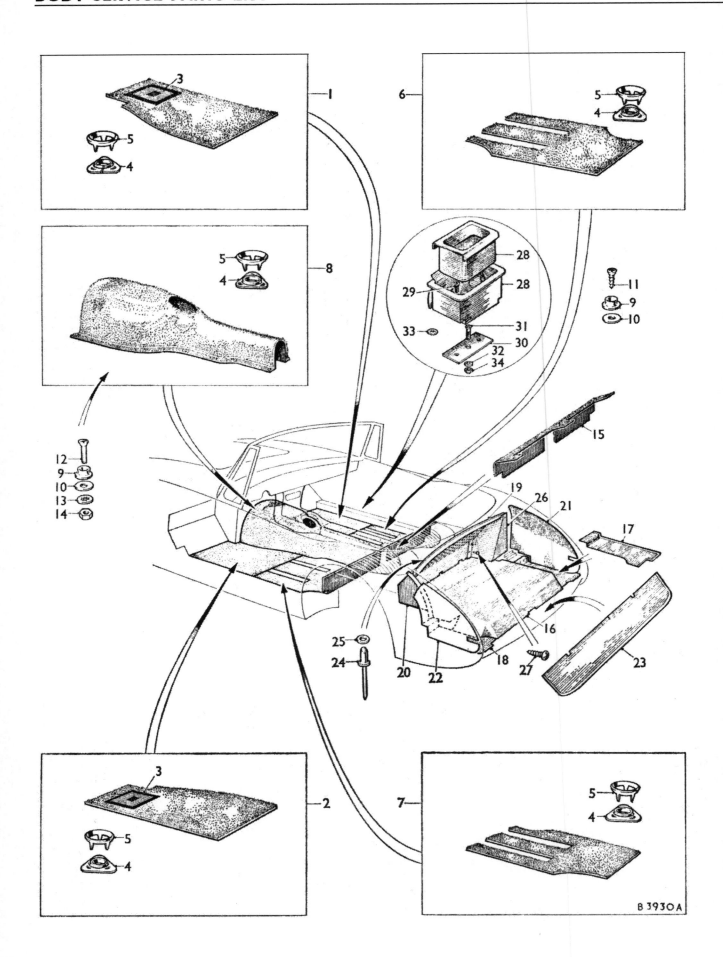

DESCRIPTION	Part No.	Illus. No.	Quantity	Change Point	REMARKS
Trimming Details (BJ8)—*continued*					
Floor Fittings—*continued*					
Carpet—heelboard Red	†14B·7830	15	1	⎤	W.S.E. use bulk material ADE 565
Blue	†AHB 8692	15	1	(C) H–BJ8–25315 to 26704	W.S.E. use bulk material AHB 8782
Black	†AHB 8693	15	1		W.S.E. use bulk material ADE 539
Green	†AHB 8844	15	1	⎦	W.S.E. use bulk material AHB 8783
Red	AHB 7028	15	1	(C) H–BJ8–26705 to (B) H–BJ8–78153	
Red	AHB 7144	15	1	(B) H–BJ8–78154 on	
Blue	AHB 7029	15	1		
Black	AHB 7030	15	1		
Green	AHB 7031	15	1		
Cover—boot Main floor	4B 3255	16	1		
Side floor—RH	4B 3248	17	1		
Side floor—LH	4B 3249	18	1		
Rear axle panel	4B 3253	19	1		
Wheelarch—LH	14B 7829	20	1		
Rear quarter—RH	AHB 8641	21	1		
Rear quarter—LH	AHB 8653	22	1		
Rear skirt	AHB 8665	23	1		
Rivet—rear axle panel cover	DMP 0835	24	6		
Washer—plain	PWZ 102	25	6		
Liner—boot—fuel pipe	14B 8708	26	1		
Screw—liner	PTP 604	27	6		
Ashtray	14B 2016	28	1		
Screw	CMZ 0208	29	2		
Plate—tapped ashtray	14B 5711	30	1		
Screw	CMZ 0208	31	1		
Washer—shakeproof	†AJD 7622	32	1		W.S.E. use LWZ 402
Washer—shakeproof	LWZ 402	32	1		
Nut	CNZ 102	33	1		
BULK MATERIALS					
Leathercloth—50″ (127cm.) wide Red	1BL 555		A/R		Part No. change; was 5D 8877
Blue	1BL 252		A/R		Part No. change; was 5D 8828. W.S.E. use 1AL 252
Blue	1AL 252		A/R		
Black	1BL 107		A/R		Part No. change; was 5D 8826. W.S.E. use 1KL 1113
Grey	1BL 452		A/R		Part No. change; was 5D 8513
Leathercloth—50″ (127cm.) wide Red	1KL 2558		A/R	⎤	Part No. change; was 27H 3396 W.S.E. use 1KL 1558 ⎤Used for console fascia and scuttle top
Red	1KL 1558		A/R		
Blue	1KL 2260		A/R		Part No. change; was 27H 3395
Black	1KL 2113		A/R		Part. No. change; was 27H 3393 W.S.E. use 1KL 1113
Black	1KL 1113		A/R		
Grey	1KL 2458		A/R		Part No. change; was 27H 3394
Leathercloth—50″ (127cm.) wide Red	1KL 3559		A/R	(C) H–BJ8–23155 on	Part No. change; was 27H 3392 ⎤Used for seat rolls, cushion borders and armrest
Blue	1KL 3259		A/R		Part No. change; was 27H 3391
Black	1KL 3114		A/R		Part No. change; was 27H 3389
Grey	1KL 3457		A/R	⎦	Part No. change; was 27H 3390
Carpet Black	ADE 539		A/R		
Red	†ADE 565		A/R	⎤(C) H–BJ8–25315 to	W.S.E. use 5D 4199
Red	5D 4199		A/R	⎦(B) H–BJ8–78153	
Red	†5D 9363		A/R	(B) H–BJ8–78154 on	
Blue	AHB 8782		A/R		
Green	AHB 8783		A/R		
Underfelt—carpet	AAA 743		A/R		

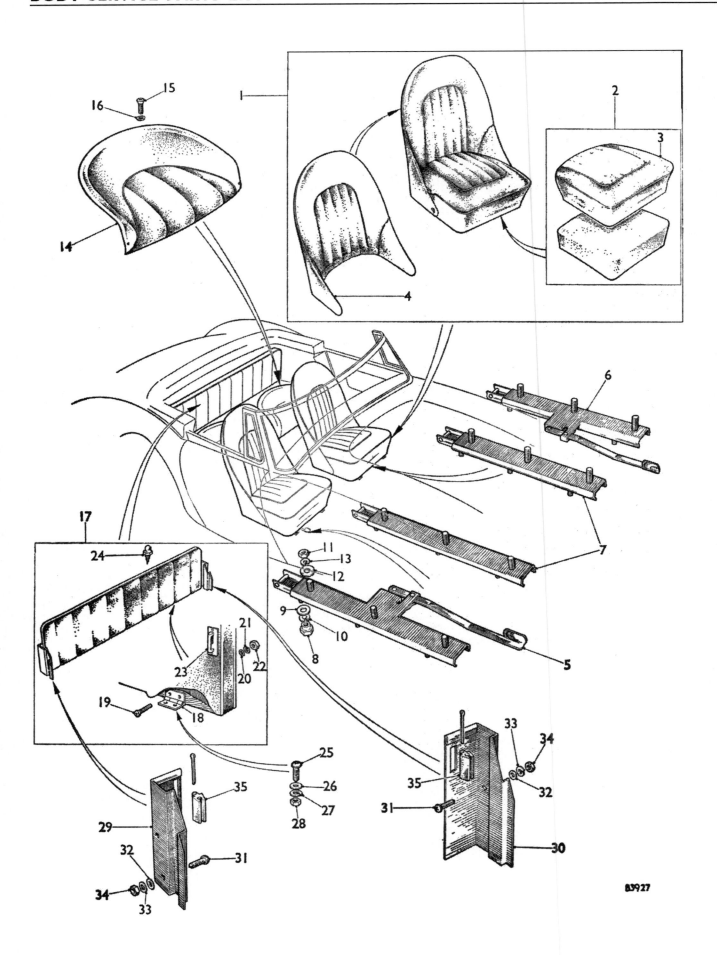

83927

	DESCRIPTION	Part No.	Illus. No.	Quantity	Change Point	REMARKS

SEATS AND FITTINGS

Pages

† BJ 7 ...   .   BO 2–BO 4

BJ7

	Page	Plate
† COVER—FRONT CUSHION AND SQUAB	BO 3	O 1
† CUSHION—FRONT SEAT...	BO 3	O 1
† PAN—REAR SEAT	BO 4	O 1
† SLIDE—FRONT SEAT	BO 4	O 1
† SQUAB—REAR SEAT	BO 4	O 1

SEATS AND FITTINGS (BJ7)

Seat assembly

Description		Part No.	Illus. No.	Quantity
Red with White piping	RH	†4B 4206	1	1
	LH	†4B 4207	1	1
Red with Black piping	RH	†AHB 5538	1	1
	LH	†AHB 5559	1	1
Blue with White piping	RH	†AHB 5539	1	1
	LH	†AHB 5560	1	1
Black with White piping	RH	†AHB 5540	1	1
	LH	†AHB 5561	1	1
Black with Red piping	RH	†AHB 9867	1	1
	LH	†AHB 9868	1	1
Black with Black piping	RH	†AKE 5267	1	1
	LH	†AKE 5268	1	1
Grey with Green piping	RH	†AHB 5542	1	1
	LH	†AHB 5563	1	1
Grey with Red piping	RH	†AHB 5543	1	1
	LH	†AHB 5564	1	1

Cushion assembly

Description		Part No.	Illus. No.	Quantity
Red with White piping	RH	†14B 1382	2	1
	LH	†14B 1383	2	1
Red with Black piping	RH	†AHB 5545	2	1
	LH	†AHB 5566	2	1
Blue with White piping	RH	†AHB 5546	2	1
	LH	†AHB 5567	2	1
Black with White piping	RH	†AHB 5547	2	1
	LH	†AHB 5568	2	1
Black with Red piping	RH	†AHB 9869	2	1
	LH	†AHB 9870	2	1
Black with Black piping	RH	†AKE 5269	2	1
	LH	†AKE 5270	2	1
Grey with Green piping	RH	†AHB 5549	2	1
	LH	†AHB 5570	2	1
Grey with Red piping	RH	†AHB 5550	2	1
	LH	†AHB 5571	2	1

Cover—cushion

Description		Part No.	Illus. No.	Quantity
Red with White piping	RH	†14B 1387	3	1
	LH	†14B 1388	3	1
Red with Black piping	RH	†AHB 5552	3	1
	LH	†AHB 5573	3	1
Blue with White piping	RH	†AHB 5553	3	1
	LH	†AHB 5574	3	1
Black with White piping	RH	†AHB 5554	3	1
	LH	†AHB 5575	3	1
Black with Red piping	RH	†AHB 9877	3	1
	LH	†AHB 9878	3	1
Black with Black piping	RH	†AKE 5271	3	1
	LH	†AKE 5272	3	1
Grey with Green piping	RH	†AHB 5556	3	1
	LH	†AHB 5577	3	1
Grey with Red piping	RH	†AHB 5557	3	1
	LH	†AHB 5578	3	1

Cover—squab

Description	Part No.	Illus. No.	Quantity
Red with White piping	†14B 1386	4	1
Red with Black piping	†AHB 5580	4	1
Blue with White piping	†AHB 5581	4	1
Black with White piping	†AHB 5582	4	1
Black with Red piping	†AHB 9871	4	1
Black with Black piping	†AKE 5273	4	1
Grey with Green piping	†AHB 5584	4	1
Grey with Red piping	†AHB 5585	4	1

† Revised Information.

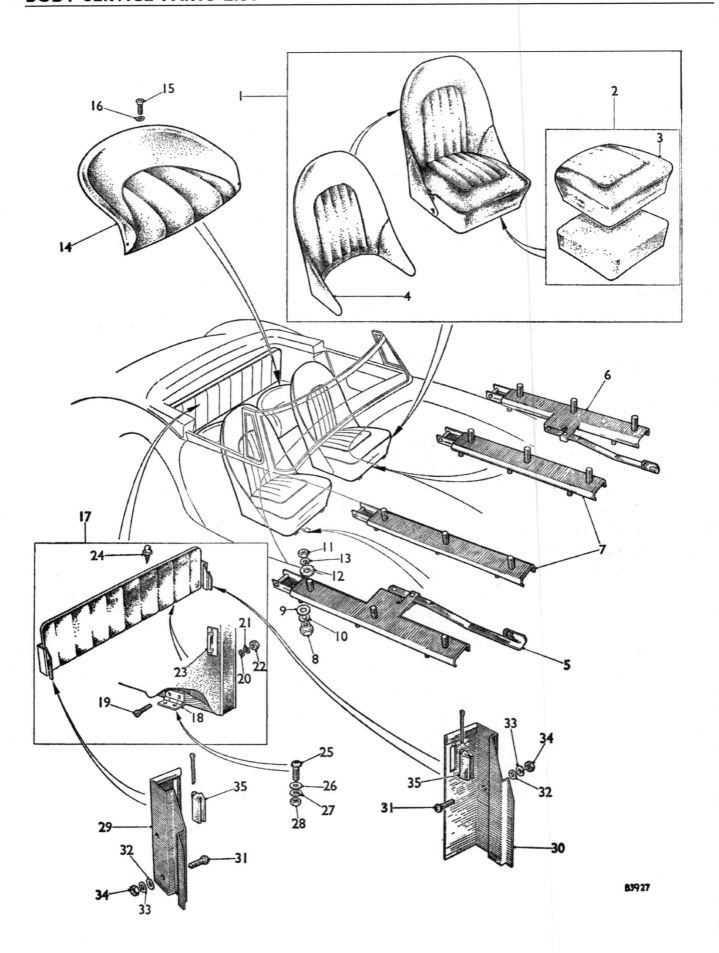

	DESCRIPTION	Part No.	Illus. No.	Quantity	Stock recoms. DIST. Exp.	UK	D	Change Point	REMARKS

Seats and Fittings (BJ7)—*continued*

Slide—seat

	DESCRIPTION	Part No.	Illus. No.	Qty	Exp.	UK	D	Change Point	REMARKS
	With lever—RH	14B 2774	5	1					
	With lever—LH	14B 2767	6	1					
	Plain	14B 2768	7	2					
Nut		14B 2877	8	12					
Washer—plain		PWZ 106	9	12					
Washer—spring		LWZ 206	10	12					
Nut		FNZ 104	11	12					
Washer—plain		PWZ 204	12	12					
Washer—spring		LWZ 204	13	12					
Pan—rear seat									
	Red with ivory white piping	4B 3200	14	2					
	Red with black piping	AHB 8862	14	2					
	Blue with ivory white piping	AHB 8548	14	2					
	Black with ivory white piping	AHB 8549	14	2					
	Black with red piping	AHB 9872	14	2					
	Black with black piping	AKE 5274	14	2					
	Grey with green piping	AHB 8550	14	2					
	Grey with red piping	AHB 8864	14	2					
Screw—seat pan to rear bulkhead		RJP 606	15	8					
Washer—cup—screw		FWP 406	16	8					
Squab assembly—rear									
	Red with ivory white piping	AHB 9688	17	1					
	Red with black piping	AHB 9689	17	1					
	Blue with ivory white piping	AHB 9690	17	1					
	Black with ivory white piping	AHB 9691	17	1					
	Black with red piping	AHB 9873	17	1					
	Black with black piping	AKE 5275	17	1					
	Grey with green piping	AHB 9692	17	1					
	Grey with red piping	AHB 9693	17	1					
Hinge		14B 3500	18	2					
Screw—hinge to squab		PMZ 0308	19	4					
Washer—plain		PWZ 103	20	4					
Washer—spring		LWZ 203	21	4					
Nut		FNZ 103	22	4					
Staple—breeching		2K 9579	23	2					
Peg—fastener—hood stowage compartment cover		TFP 810	24	2					
Screw—squab hinge to floor		PMZ 0308	25	4					
Washer—plain		PWZ 103	26	8					
Washer—spring		LWZ 203	27	4					
Nut		FNZ 103	28	4					
Bracket—squab fixing—RH		AHB 9554	29	1					
Bracket—squab fixing—LH		AHB 9555	30	1					
Screw—bracket to body		PMZ 0408	31	4					
Washer—plain		PWZ 104	32	4					
Washer—spring		LWZ 204	33	4					
Nut		FNZ 104	34	4					
Stop—squab (rubber)		2H 9215	35	2					

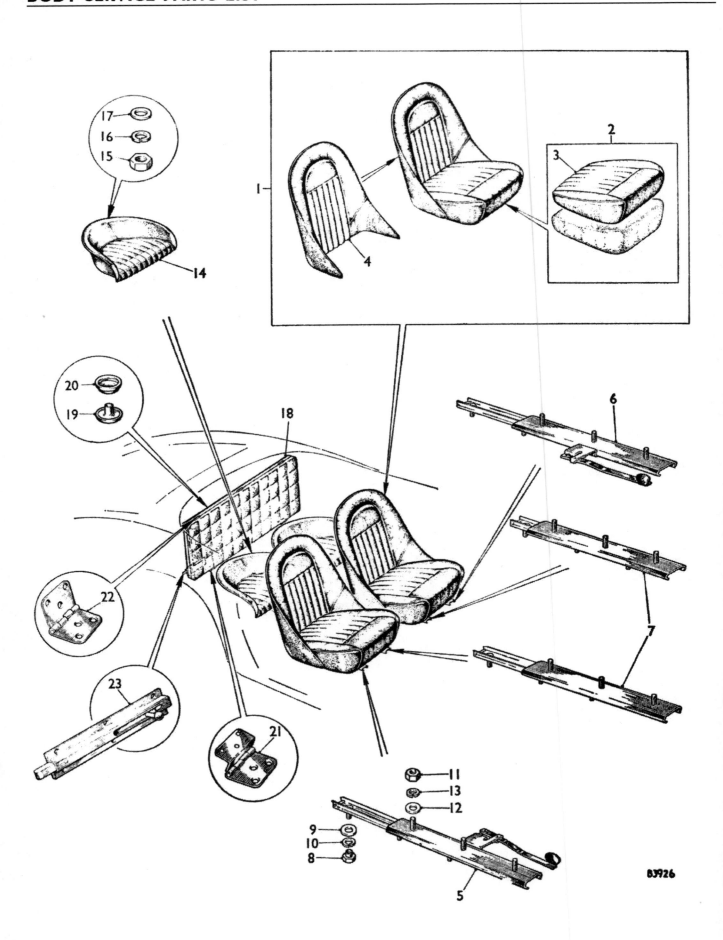

83926

	DESCRIPTION	Part No.	Illus. No.	Quantity	Change Point	REMARKS

SEATS AND FITTINGS

		Pages
† BJ 8 … … … … … … … …		BO 5–BO 7

BJ8

	Page	Plate
† COVER—FRONT CUSHION AND SQUAB … …	BO 6	O 2
† CUSHION—FRONT SEAT… … … … …	BO 6	O 2
† PAN—REAR SEAT … … … … …	BO 7	O 2
† SLIDE—FRONT SEAT … … … … …	BO 7	O 2
† SQUAB—REAR SEAT … … … … …	BO 7	O 2

SEATS AND FITTING (BJ8)

Description		Part No.	Illus. No.	Quantity	Remarks
Seat assembly					
Red	RH	AHB 6130	1	1	
	LH	AHB 6135	1	1	
Blue	RH	AHB 6131	1	1	
	LH	AHB 6136	1	1	
Black	RH	AHB 6132	1	1	
	LH	AHB 6137	1	1	
Grey	RH	AHB 6133	1	1	
	LH	AHB 6138	1	1	
Cushion assembly					
Red	RH	AHB 6145	2	1	
	LH	AHB 6186	2	1	
Blue	RH	AHB 6146	2	1	
	LH	AHB 6187	2	1	
Black	RH	AHB 6147	2	1	
	LH	AHB 6188	2	1	
Grey	RH	AHB 6148	2	1	
	LH	AHB 6189	2	1	
Cover—cushion					
Red		AHB 6150	3	2	
Blue		AHB 6151	3	2	
Black		AHB 6152	3	2	
Grey		AHB 6153	3	2	
Cover—squab					
Red		AHB 6155	4	2	
Blue		AHB 6156	4	2	
Black		AHB 6157	4	2	
Grey		AHB 6158	4	2	
Seat assembly					
Red	RH	AHB 6575	1	1	
	LH	AHB 6579	1	1	
Blue	RH	AHB 6576	1	1	
	LH	AHB 6580	1	1	
Black	RH	AHB 6577	1	1	
	LH	AHB 6581	1	1	
Grey	RH	AHB 6578	1	1	
	LH	AHB 6582	1	1	
Cushion assembly					
Red	RH	AHB 6584	2	1	
	LH	AHB 6745	2	1	
Blue	RH Leather	AHB 6585	2	1	Optional extra
	LH	AHB 6746	2	1	
Black	RH	AHB 6586	2	1	
	LH	AHB 6747	2	1	
Grey	RH	AHB 6587	2	1	
	LH	AHB 6748	2	1	
Cover—cushion					
Red		AHB 6594	3	2	
Blue		AHB 6595	3	2	
Black		AHB 6596	3	2	
Grey		AHB 6597	3	2	
Cover—squab					
Red		AHB 6589	4	2	
Blue		AHB 6590	4	2	
Black		AHB 6591	4	2	
Grey		AHB 6592	4	2	

† Revised Information.

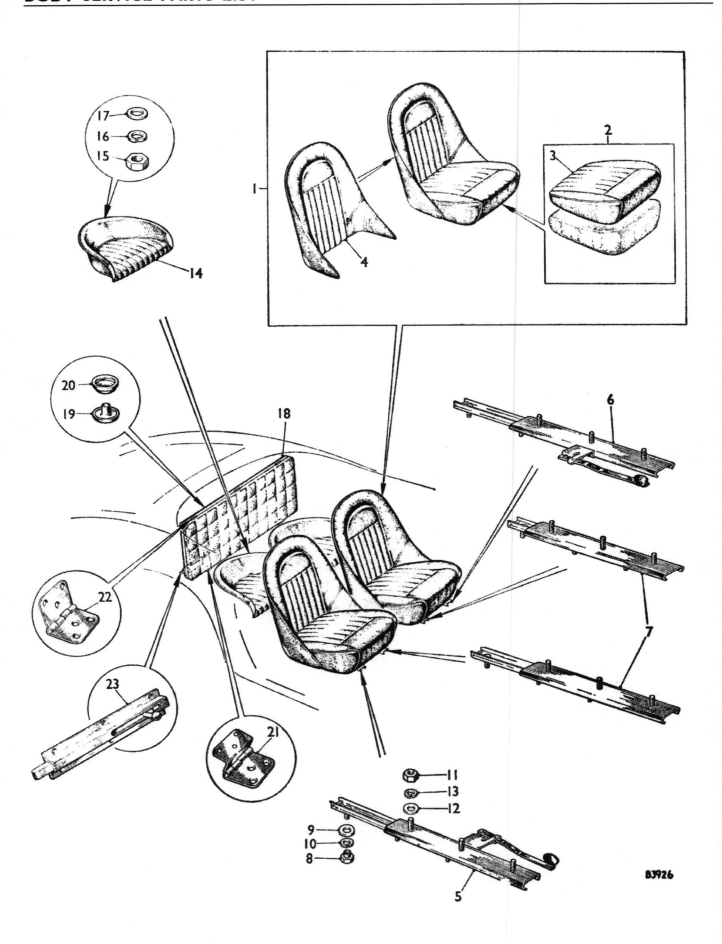

B3926

	DESCRIPTION	Part No.	Illus. No.	Quantity	Stock recoms. DIST. Exp.	UK	D	Change Point	REMARKS

Seats and Fittings (BJ8)—*continued*

Slide—seat

DESCRIPTION	Part No.	Illus. No.	Quantity				Change Point	REMARKS
With lever—RH	14B 2774	5	1					
With lever—LH	14B 2767	6	1					
Plain	14B 2768	7	2					
Nut	14B 2877	8	12					
Washer—plain	PWZ 106	9	12					
Washer—spring	LWZ 206	10	12					
Nut	FNZ 104	11	12					
Washer—plain	PWZ 204	12	12					
Washer—spring	LWZ 204	13	12					
Pan—rear seat								
Red	AHB 6140	14	2					
Blue	AHB 6141	14	2					
Black	AHB 6142	14	2					
Grey	AHB 6143	14	2					
Red ⎫	AHB 6200	14	2					
Blue ⎪ Leather	AHB 6201	14	2					Optional extra
Black ⎪	AHB 6202	14	2					
Grey ⎭	AHB 6203	14	2					
Nut—seat pan to floor	FNZ 103	15	8					
Washer—spring	LWZ 203	15	8					
Washer—plain	AJD 7202	17	8					
Squab—rear								
Red	AHB 6095	18	1					
Blue	AHB 6096	18	1					
Black	AHB 6097	18	1					
Grey	AHB 6098	18	1					
Red ⎫	AHB 6798	18	1					
Blue ⎪ Leather	AHB 6799	18	1					Optional extra
Black ⎪	AHB 6800	18	1					
Grey ⎭	AHB 6801	18	1					
Button—strap	4B 6821	19	2					
Socket—strap	7H 9866	20	2					
Hinge—squab to hood protection panel	AHB 6091	21	2					
Hinge—squab to extension board	AHB 6092	22	3					
Bolt—slide	AHB 6093	23	2					

† Revised Information.

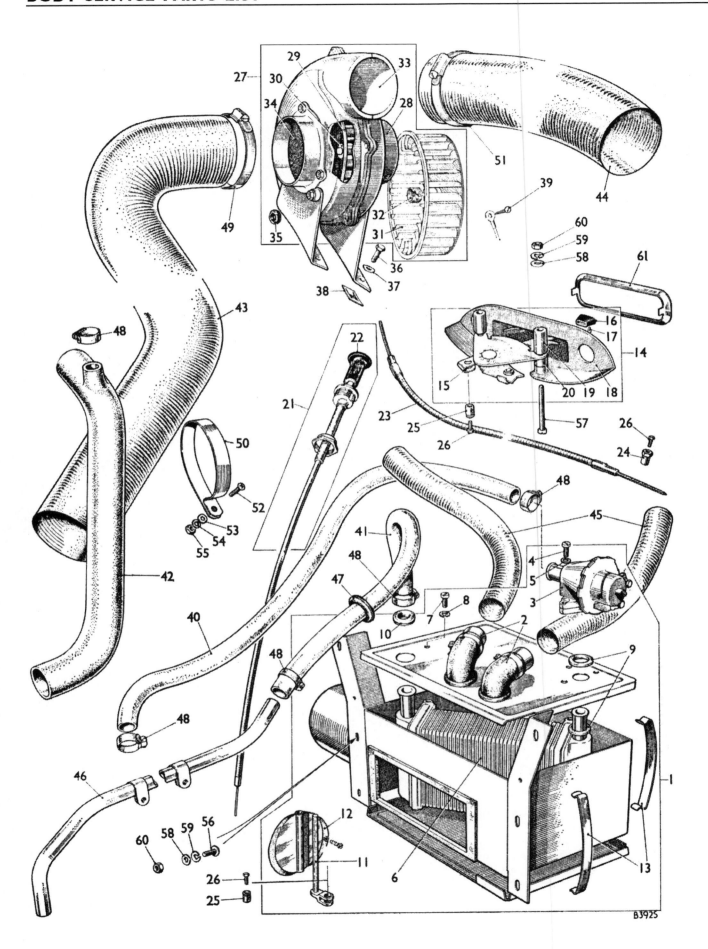

	DESCRIPTION	Part No.	Illus. No.	Quantity	Stock recoms. DIST. Exp.	UK	D	Change Point	REMARKS

HEATER AND VENTILATION DETAILS

		Page	Plate
AIR INTAKE—VENTILATOR … … … …		BP 4	P 2
BEZEL—HEATER CONTROL LEVER … … …		BP 3	P 1
BLOWER—HEATER … … … … …		BP 2	P 1
CONTROL—LEVER—HEATER … … … …		BP 2	P 1
CONTROL—PUSH-PULL—HEATER … … …		BP 2	P 1
CONTROL—PUSH-PULL—VENTILATOR … …		BP 4	P 2
HEATER UNIT … … … … … …		BP 2	P 1
HOSE—AIR—VENTILATOR … … … …		BP 4	P 2
HOSE—HEATER … … … … … …		BP 3	P 1

HEATER AND VENTILATION DETAILS

HEATER (OPTIONAL EXTRA)

DESCRIPTION	Part No.	Illus. No.	Quantity	Exp.	UK	D	Change Point	REMARKS
Heater kit	NSP		1					For accessory kit see the Approved Accessories Salesman's Guide
Heater unit assembly	14B 6599	1	1					
Elbow	14G 3499	2	2					
Valve—water	27H 1171	3	1	★	★			
Screw—valve	AJD 3204Z	4	2					
Washer—spring	LWZ 303	5	4					
Radiator and seals	27H 1173	6	1					
Screw—radiator	AJD 1012	7	2					
Washer—spring	LWZ 303	8	2					
Ring—seal—radiator and valve	27H 1248	9	2					
Grommet	17H 1591	10	1					
Arm and spindle	27H 1176	11	1					
Valve—air inlet	27H 1177	12	1					
Clip—spring	27H 1174	13	3					
Control assembly—lever	14B 6600	14	1					
Lever	13H 78	15	1					
Knob—lever	13H 76	16	1					
Screw—knob	53K 1302	17	1					
Panel—lever control	13H 77	18	1					
Spacer—long	24B 632	19	2					
Spacer—short	24B 633	20	2					
Control assembly—push-pull	14B 7780	21	1					
Knob RHD	17H 1494	22	1					
Cable—heater control	14B 7776	23	1	★	★		(C) H–BJ7–17551 to 25314	
Control assembly—push-pull	14B 7781	21	1					
Knob LHD	17H 1494	22	1					
Cable—heater control	14B 7777	23	1	★				
Control assembly—push-pull	14B 7780	21	1					
Knob	17H 1494	22	1				(C) H–BJ8–25315 on	
Cable—heater control	14B 7777	23	1	★	★			
Clamp—cable	14G 6451	24	1					
Trunnion—cable	14B 7810	25	3					
Screw—clamp and trunnion	53K 155	26	4					
Blower assembly	14B 6598	27	1					
Motor	7H 6836	28	1					
Rotor (metal)	17H 1574	29	1					Alternative to 17H 8108
Nut—collet	27H 602	30	1					
Rotor (plastic)	17H 8108	31	1					Alternative to 17H 1574
Ring—compression	17H 6836	32	1					
Casing	17H 819	33	1					
Mesh—intake	17H 1597	34	1					
Grommet	†27H 1232	35	4					Part No. change; was 27H 1179
Bolt—blower to wheelarch	ABZ 0407	36	4					
Washer—plain	6K 9433	37	4					
Nut—spring	6K 9817	38	4					
Screw—earth—blower to wheelarch	PTZ 1004	39	1					

† Revised Information.

Issue 1   **BP 1 & BP 2**

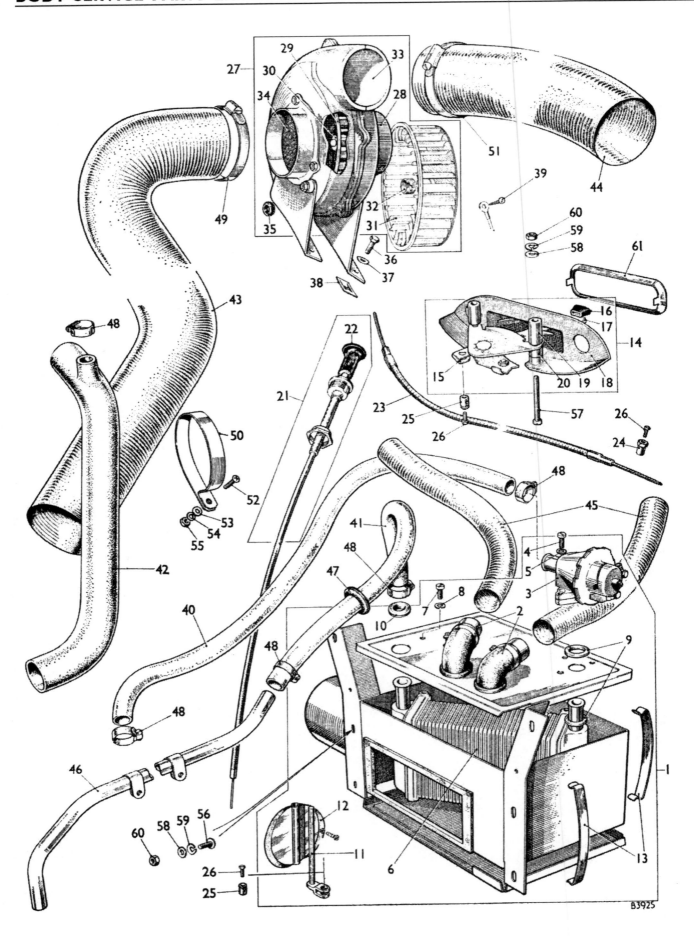

B3925

				DESCRIPTION	Part No.	Illus. No.	Quantity	Stock recoms. DIST. Exp.	UK	D	Change Point	REMARKS

Heater and Ventilation Details—*continued*
Heater—*continued*

Hoses

Description	Part No.	Illus. No.	Qty	Exp	UK	Remarks
Heater to control tap (25″ [63·50cm.])	37H 537	40	A/R	★	★	] Available in multiples of feet
Heater to water pipe	14B 7550	41	1	★	★	
Radiator to pump	AHB 8971	42	1	★	★	
Inlet to blower	14B 9821	43	1			
Blower to heater	14B 6601	44	1			
Heater to demister (11½″ [29·21cm.])	14B 6602	45	1			
Heater to demister (13½″ [34·29cm.])	14B 6603	45	1			
Pipe—water—heater hose to radiator hose	AHB 9249	46	1			
Grommet—hose through dash	14B 9820	47	2			

Clips

Description	Part No.	Illus. No.	Qty	Change Point	Remarks
Water hose	HCS 0507	48	5		
Hose to blower	HCS 3036	49	1		
Hose to wheelarch	AHH 5714	50	1		
Hose to blower and heater	HCS 2632	51	2		
Screw—clip to wheelarch	PMZ 0310	52	1		
Washer—plain	PWZ 103	53	1		
Washer—spring	LWZ 203	54	1		
Nut	FNZ 103	55	1		
Screw—heater to air duct panel	PMZ 0308	56	6		
Screw—control panel to fascia panel	PMZ 0328	57	2		
Washer—plain	PWZ 103	58	8		
Washer—spring	LWZ 203	59	8		
Nut	FNZ 103	60	4		
Bezel—control panel aperture	AHB 6788	61	1	†(C) H-BJ8-25315 on	
Door—heater outlet					See page BP4

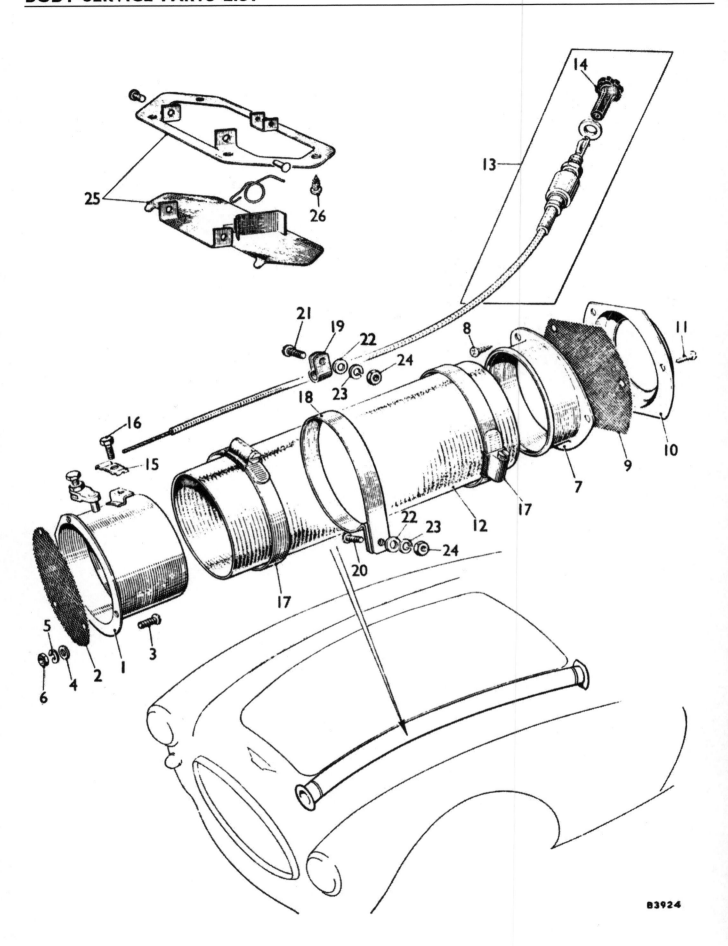

B3924

	DESCRIPTION	Part No.	Illus. No.	Quantity	Stock recoms. DIST. Exp.	UK	D	Change Point	REMARKS

Heater and Ventilation Details—*continued*

VENTILATION DETAILS

DESCRIPTION		Part No.	Illus. No.	Quantity	Change Point
Intake—air		14B 7711	1	1	
Gauze—intake		4G 6575	2	1	
Screw—intake to body		PMZ 0308	3	3	
Washer—plain		PWZ 103	4	2	
Washer—spring		LWZ 203	5	3	
Nut		FNZ 103	6	3	
Flange—air intake		14B 7712	7	1	
Screw—flange to body		PTZ 1003	8	3	
Gauze		14B 8780	9	1	
Bezel		14B 8781	10	1	
Screw—gauze and bezel to air duct panel		PTZ 603	11	3	
Hose—air		14B 2749	12	1	
Control assembly—push-pull	RHD	14B 7782	13	1	
Knob		17H 1493	14	1	†(C) H-BJ7-17551 to 25314
Control assembly—push-pull	LHD	14B 7779	13	1	
Knob		17H 1493	14	1	
Control assembly—push-pull		14B 7782	13	1	†(C) H-BJ8- 25315 on
Knob		17H 1493	14	1	
Clamp—control cable		14G 6451	15	1	
Screw—clamp		53K 155	16	1	
Clips					
Hose to intake and flange		HCS 3036	17	2	
Hose to wheelarch		AHH 5714	18	1	
Control cable to bonnet opening support		PCR 0307	19	1	
Screw—clip to wheelarch		PMZ 0310	20	1	
Screw—clip to bonnet opening support		CMZ 0308	21	1	
Washer—plain		PWZ 103	22	2	
Washer—spring		LWZ 203	23	2	
Nut		FNZ 103	24	2	
Door—outlet—ventilation and heater		13H 59	25	2	
Screw—door to air duct panel		PTZ 603	26	8	

	DESCRIPTION	Part No.	Illus. No.	Quantity	Stock recoms. DIST. Exp.	UK	D	Change Point	REMARKS

PAINTS

PAINTS

Black (Code BK1)
Healey Blue (Code BU2)
Colorado Red (Code RD2)
Ivory White (Code WT3)
Florida Green (Code GN1)
British Racing Green (Code GN25)
British Racing Green—dark (Code GN29)
†Golden Beige Metallic (Code BG19)

For Part Nos. container sizes, primers, undercoats, and thinners, etc. refer to B.M.C. Service Paint Scheme Book

© **Copyright Austin Motor Company Limited 1969
and Brooklands Books Limited 2014**

This book is published by Brooklands Books Limited and based upon text and
illustrations protected by copyright and published in 1969 by
Austin Motor Company Limited and may not be reproduced
transmitted or copied by any means without the prior written permission
of British Motor Corporation Limited and Brooklands Books Limited.

Brooklands Books Ltd., PO Box 904, Amersham, Bucks,
HP6 9JA, England   www.brooklandsbooks.com

Part No. AKD 3524

© Copyright Austin Motor Company Limited 1969
British Motor Corporation Limited 1966
and Brooklands Books Limited 2014

This book is published by Brooklands Books Limited and based upon text and
illustrations protected by copyright and first published in 1969 by
Austin Motor Company Limited and in 1966 by
British Motor Corporation Limited and may not be reproduced
transmitted or copied by any means without the prior written permission
of British Motor Corporation Limited and Brooklands Books Limited.

Brooklands Books Ltd., PO Box 904, Amersham, Bucks,
HP6 9JA, England   www.brooklandsbooks.com

Part No. AKD 3523, AKD 3524 and Extract from Part No. AKD 5036

ISBN: 9781783180387   AH3BPC   7W4/3-62

OFFICIAL TECHNICAL BOOKS

Brooklands Technical Books has been formed to supply owners, restorers and professional repairers with official factory literature.

Model	Original Part No.	ISBN
Workshop Manuals		
Austin-Healey 100 BN1 & BN2	97H997D	9780907073925
Austin-Healey 100/6 & 3000	AKD1179	9780948207471
(100/6 - BN4, BN6, 3000 MK. 1, 2, 3 - BN7, BT7, BJ7 & BJ8)		
Austin-Healey Sprite Mk. 1 Frogeye	AKD4884	9781855201262
Austin-Healey Sprite Mk. 2, Mk. 3 & Mk. 4 and	AKD4021	9781855202818
MG Midget Mk. 1, Mk. 2 & Mk. 3		
Parts Catalogues / Service Parts Lists		
Austin-Healey 100 BN1 & BN2	050 Edition 3	9781783180363
Austin-Healey 100/6 BN4	AKD1423	9781783180493
Austin-Healey 100/6 BN6	AKD855 Ed.2	9781783180486
Austin-Healey 3000 Mk. 1 and Mk. 2 (BN7 & BT7)	AKD1151 Ed.5	9781783180370
Mk. 1 BN7 & BT7 Car no. 101 to 13750,		
Mk. 2 BN7 Car no. 13751 to 18888,		
Mk. 2 BT7 Car no. 13751 to 19853		
Austin-Healey 3000 Mk. 2 and Mk. 3 (BJ7 & BJ8)	AKD 3523 & AKD 3524	9781783180387
BJ7 Mk. 2 Car no. 17551 to 25314 and		
BJ8 Mk. 3 Car no. 25315 to 43026		
Austin-Healey Sprite Mk. 1 & Mk. 2 and	AKD 3566 & AKD 3567	9781783180509
MG Midget Mk. 1		
Austin-Healey Sprite Mk. 3 & Mk. 4 and	AKD 3513 & AKD 3514	9781783180554
MG Midget Mk. 2 & Mk. 3 (Mechanical & Body Edition 1969)		
Austin-Healey Sprite Mk. 3 & Mk. 4 and	AKM 0036	9780948207419
MG Midget Mk. 2 & Mk. 3 (Feb 1977 Edition)		
Handbooks		
Austin-Healey 100	97H996E	9781869826352
Austin-Healey 100/6	97H996H	9781870642903
Austin-Healey 3000 Mk 1 & 2	AKD3915A	9781869826369
Austin-Healey 3000 Mk 3	AKD4094B	9781869826376
Austin-Healey Sprite Mk 1 'Frogeye'	97H1583A	9780948207945
Also Available		
Austin-Healey 100/6 & 3000 Mk. 1, 2 & 3 Owners Workshop Manual		9781783180455
Austin-Healey Sprite Mk. 1, 2, 3 & 4		
MG Midget 1, 2, 3 & 1500 1958-1980		
Owners Workshop Manual Glovebox Edition		9781855201255
Austin-Healey Sprite Mk. 1, 2, 3 & 4		
MG Midget 1, 2, 3 & 1500 1958-1980 Owners Workshop Manual		9781783180332
Carburetters		
SU Carburetters Tuning Tips & Techniques		9781855202559
Restoration Guide		
Restoring Sprite & Midgets		9781855205987
Road Test Series		
Austin-Healey 100 & 100/6 Gold Portfolio 1952-1959		9781855200487
Austin-Healey 3000 Road Test Portfolio		9791783180394
Austin-Healey Frogeye Sprite Road Test Portfolio 1958-1961		9781783180530
Austin-Healey Sprite Gold Portfolio 1958-1971		9781855203716

(**www.brooklandsbooks.com**)

Printed in Great Britain
by Amazon

46566341R00176